540

GCSE CHEMI

LONGMAN REFERENCE GUIDES

LONGMAN REFERENCE GUIDES

Series editors: Geoff Black and Stuart Wall

TITLES AVAILABLE
Biology
CDT
Chemistry
English
French
Geography
Mathematics
Physics
Science
World History

CHEMISTRY

LONGMAN REFERENCE GUIDES

Mark McElroy
John Sadler

Longman

Longman Group UK Limited,
Longman House, Burnt Mill, Harlow,
Essex CM20 2JE, England
and Associated Companies throughout the world.

First published 1990

British Library Cataloguing in Publication Data

Sadler, John, 1938–
Chemistry.
1. England. Secondary Schools. Curriculum subjects: Chemistry G.C.S.E. examinations. Techniques
I. Title II. McElroy, Mark
540'.76

ISBN 0-582-05790-6

Designed and produced by the Pen & Ink Book Company Ltd, Huntingdon, Cambridgeshire

Set in 9/10pt Century Old Style

Printed and bound in Great Britain

HOW TO USE THIS BOOK

Throughout your GCSE course you will be coming across terms, ideas and definitions that are unfamiliar to you. The Longman Reference Guides provide a quick, easy-to-use source of information, fact and opinion. Each main term is listed alphabetically and, where appropriate, cross-referenced to related terms.

- Where a term or phrase appears in **different type** you can look up a separate entry under that heading elsewhere in the book.
- Where a term or phrase appears in **different type** and is set between two arrowhead symbols ◀ ▶, it is particularly recommended that you turn to the entry for that heading.

AUTHORS' PREFACE

This book aims to highlight the importance of both chemists and chemicals to our world. Chemistry is a technical subject, and this book should help you to understand the language of the subject. The book covers the topics in all the GCSE Groups' various syllabuses, as well as giving valuable insight into other areas that students will find interesting.

One of the features of the book is the labelling of chemicals with hazard symbols, as a quick and easy guide to their potential danger. You should use this book as a starting-point for further investigation, and we hope it will inspire you to become more involved with chemistry.

We are indebted to Geoff Black and Stuart Wall, who encouraged us to write this text, and to Emily Sadler, herself a GCSE student, for reading the text and making valuable suggestions for its improvement.

HAZARD SYMBOLS

The following hazard signs are shown against various chemicals throughout this book.

Corrosive

These chemicals must be handled with care. They destroy living tissues.

Explosive

These substances may explode if ignited in air or exposed to heat.

Harmful

These chemicals are less of a health risk than poisonous substances, but they must be handled with care.

Highly flammable

These are solids, liquids or gases that easily catch fire.

Irritant

These substances are not corrosive but they can cause irritation of the skin.

Oxidizing

These substances create a fire risk.

Radioactive

Radioactive chemicals should be treated in the same way as poisonous substances.

Toxic

These substances are a serious health risk, and can cause death.

ACETIC ACID

Acetic acid is probably the best-known acid. Its **systematic** name is **ethanoic acid**.

ACIDIC OXIDES

Acidic oxides are oxides which neutralise alkalis or bases or which have a pH to damp indicator paper of less than 7. The elements which form these oxides are to be found in the non-metallic elements on the right-hand side of the periodic table. Common acidic oxides are SO_2, SO_3, NO_2, CO_2. However, not all non-metallic elements form oxides which are acidic – some form neutral oxides, for example, hydrogen whose oxide is water.

◀ Oxides ▶

ACID RAIN

Natural rainwater has a pH of about 5.6 – normal rain is acid! So rain with a pH of less than 5.6 is classed as acid rain. Acid rain is not new, it was first observed over a hundred years ago. However, the damage caused by acid rain is more obvious now than before.

The main causes of acid rain are the **acidic oxides** of **sulphur** and **nitrogen** produced by industrial combustion processes. Two different burning or combustion processes form these acidic oxides:

When coal is burnt: the sulphur-containing compounds in the coal combine with oxygen from the air to produce gaseous **sulphur dioxide**, SO_2. This gas is passed into the atmosphere and mixes with the air by wind and diffusion. In the air sulphur dioxide is oxidised to sulphur trioxide, SO_3, which reacts with rain to form very dilute **sulphuric acid**, H_2SO_4.

sulphur dioxide	+ oxygen	→	sulphur trioxide
$SO_2(g)$	+ $\frac{1}{2}O_2(g)$	→	$SO_3(g)$
water	+ sulphur trioxide	→	dilute sulphuric acid
$H_2O(l)$	+ $SO_3(g)$	→	$H_2SO_4(aq)$

High-temperature burning: this process causes the nitrogen and oxygen in the air supplied to the fuel to combine to form oxides of nitrogen. These are symbolised as NO_x but are really a mixture of NO and NO_2.

nitrogen	+ oxygen	→	nitrogen (II) oxide
$N_2(g)$	+ $O_2(g)$	→	$2NO(g)$
nitrogen	+ oxygen	→	nitrogen (IV) oxide
$N_2(g)$	+ $2O_2(g)$	→	$2NO_2(g)$

These two oxides of nitrogen react with water to produce very dilute **nitric acid**, $HNO_3(aq)$.

Sources of acid rain

There are two main sources of these pollutant acidic oxides - large industrial furnaces burning coal, and all motor vehicles burning liquid fuels. Coal-fired power stations are the greatest single source of sulphur dioxide and a great source of nitrogen oxides. Motor cars produce most of the nitrogen oxides that pollute the air.

Effects of acid rain

The chemical effects are predictable from the properties of **acids**. The effects will be seen on:

- Any stone structure made from forms of calcium carbonate such as marble, limestone and Portland stone and also stone containing limestone, e.g. sandstone, which is sand held together with a 'cement' of calcium carbonate.
- Steel constructions such as bridges, piers and exposed steel-reinforced concrete.

The biological effects are largely the result of aluminium compounds being released into the soil. In forests, trees die, and when these compounds enter lakes water life is killed.

Control of acid rain

There are several ways of reducing acid rain:

- conversion to energy sources that do not depend on combustion, for example, nuclear fuels or tidal, solar or wave power
- the removal of the pollutants in waste gases that cause the problem.
- Neutralisation of acids in flue-gases by a process that allows neutralised products to escape into the air.

Prevention of acid rain in practice

From power stations: a simple chemical principle tells us that acidic oxides can be neutralised by reaction with alkalis or bases. One of the commonest bases is limestone, a form of calcium carbonate, $CaCO_3$. So, by reacting waste power station gases with powdered limestone, acidic pollutants can be neutralised to form a waste solid salt. This is done in **lime-scrubbers.** It is necessary to either dump the solid waste or make use of it. Limestone reacts with sulphur oxides to form calcium sulphate, $CaSO_4$, commonly called gypsum.

calcium carbonate	+	sulphur dioxide	+	oxygen	→	calcium sulphate	+	carbon dioxide
$CaCO_3(s)$	+	$SO_2(g)$	+	$\frac{1}{2}O_2(g)$	→	$CaSO_4(s)$	+	$CO_2(g)$

Gypsum is the main constituent of plaster and plasterboard. There is a ready market for it. This would be a good example of turning a nuisance into a benefit. However, only the purest limestone makes 'plaster-quality' gypsum. This process would require massive quarrying operations in environmentally sensitive parts of the country and would produce carbon dioxide (a greenhouse gas) in place of the sulphur dioxide being removed!

From motor-vehicle engines: nitrogen oxides from motor vehicles must be treated differently. They must be removed before they come out of the exhaust pipe. This can be done using a catalytic converter.

ACIDS

Acids form one of the most important and useful types of compounds known to us. Because of their sour taste, they were among the first chemicals to be easily recognised. However, it is obviously unsafe to use taste to identify an acid, as many chemicals are toxic.

Acids are most easily identified by their effect on natural colouring matter or on synthetic dyes. Most of the colours extracted from vegetables, fruits, roots and flowers will change colour when an acid is added to them. Colour changes such as these were the earliest safe test for acids. We call these dyes **indicators.** Universal indicator is a mixture of synthetic dyes which, with pH, change colour through the colours of the rainbow.

The molecules of acids contain hydrogen atoms. However, not every molecule which contains hydrogen atoms is an acid. For example, water molecules contain hydrogen atoms but water is a neutral compound. Table A.1 lists some of the common acids.

Name of acid	*Formula*	*Strength*	*Type*
hydrochloric	HCl	strong	mineral
sulphuric	H_2SO_4	strong	mineral
nitric	HNO_3	strong	mineral
phosphoric	H_3PO_4	strong	mineral
ethanoic	CH_3COOH	weak	organic

Table A.1

What makes acids acidic?

Acidic properties are the result of a chemical reaction between the pure acid and water. In the absence of water, acids do not show acidic properties. For example, the reaction of gaseous hydrogen chloride with water produces a mixture of hydrated hydrogen ions and chloride ions.

hydrogen chloride	+ water	→	hydrated hydrogen ion	+ chloride ion
$HCl(g)$	+ $H_2O(l)$	→	$H_3O^+(aq)$	+ $Cl^-(aq)$

The hydrated hydrogen ion is also sometimes called the oxonium ion.

The hydrated hydrogen ion formed in this reaction is the active ion in every one of the chemical reactions of acids – it

- changes the colour of indicators
- reacts with metals to form hydrogen
- reacts with carbonates and hydrogencarbonates to form carbon dioxide and water.
- reacts with oxide and hydroxide ions in bases to form water.

With **metals**, e.g. magnesium

a) $Mg(s) + 2HCl(aq) \rightarrow MgCl_2(aq) + H_2(g)$
b) $Mg(s) + 2H^+(aq) \rightarrow Mg^{2+}(aq) + H_2(g)$

With **carbonates**, e.g. calcium carbonate.

a) $CaCO_3(s) + 2HCl(aq) \rightarrow CaCl_2(aq) + H_2O(l) + CO_2(g)$
b) $CO_3^{2-}(s) + 2H^+(aq) \rightarrow H_2O(l) + CO_2(g)$

With **metal oxide bases**, e.g. copper (II) oxide.

a) $CuO(s) + H_2SO_4(aq) \rightarrow CuSO_4(aq) + H_2O(l)$
b) $O^{2-}(s) + 2H^+(aq) \rightarrow H_2O(l)$

Equation b), called an ionic equation, shows that the reaction involves the hydrated hydrogen ion. Equation a) shows the use of normal formulae but does not display the role of the hydrogen ion.

The strength and concentration of acids

- The *strength* of an acid is proportional to the concentration of hydrogen ions present in the solution.
- The *concentration* of an acid is proportional to the mass or the number of moles of the acid dissolved in a litre of solution. The more acid dissolved the greater is the concentration.

A lot of confusion exists about the meaning of the terms 'strong' and 'weak' when they are used to describe acids. This is because these terms have a different meaning in everyday use. For example, we speak of a 'strong' drink when we mean a 'concentrated' drink. Chemists use the terms 'strong' and 'weak' or 'concentrated' and 'dilute' in a very different way. For a chemist, ethanoic acid (acetic acid) can be concentrated but it will always be a weak acid whereas hydrochloric acid will always be a strong acid. Why is this? Hydrogen ions are formed when molecules of the acid react with water molecules. The more this reaction occurs the stronger is the acid. An acid like ethanoic acid (acetic acid) may have many moles of ethanoic acid molecules dissolved in one litre of solution but very few hydrogen ions will form from them. We can illustrate this in the following way for two acid solutions each having the same concentration of 0.1 moles per litre. After mixing and reaction has occurred we will have:

In 0.1 M ethanoic acid solution

ethanoic acid	+ water	↔	hydrated hydrogen ion	+ ethanoate ion		
$CH_3CO_2H(l)$	+ $H_2O(l)$	↔	$H_3O^+(aq)$	+ $CH_3CO_2^-(aq)$		weak acid
99% unreacted molecules			1% reacted to form ions			pH 3

In 0.1 M hydrochloric acid solution

hydrogen chloride	+ water	→	hydrated hydrogen ion	+ chloride ion	
HCl(g)	+ $H_2O(l)$	→	$H_3O^+(aq)$	+ $Cl^-(aq)$	strong acid
no unreacted molecules			100% reacted to form ions		pH 1

The hydrochloric acid will contain 100 times more hydrogen ions than the ethanoic acid. This gives it a pH of two units lower (see **pH**) making, it a much stronger acid. Note, however, that both acid solutions have the same concentration.

Hazards of acids

The reactions of acids can be both hazardous and useful. For example, acids will dissolve most metals, all carbonates and hydrogencarbonates and most metallic oxides. Yet whilst these reactions can be put to use, accidental contact between acids and these substances will cause damage and destruction. Every container of acid should carry the hazard label for irritant or harmful substance. Strong acids will usually carry the 'corrosive' symbol.

Safe handling of acids

This needs care. Eye protection must be worn. Carrying bottles of acid must be done with care. Acid spills must be neutralised with a safe alkali, such as sodium hydrogencarbonate, and washed away with water. Acid in the eyes and on the skin *must be washed with lots of plain water immediately* and a medical check should be made to ensure no lasting damage has been caused.

◀ Acid rain ▶

ADDITION POLYMERISATION

Addition polymerisation is one of the many types of chemical **reactions.** In addition polymerisation many small molecules join together into fewer very long molecules and the *only* product is the polymer itself. For example, ethene is polymerised in this way to poly(ethene). Compare the **condensation polymerisation** method for making other common polymers.

	high temperature and pressure	
$nC_2H_4(g)$	$\rightarrow$	$-\!\![C_2H_4]_n\!\!-$
	initiator	
many thousands of ethene molecules		a single molecule poly(ethene)

A characteristic of the molecules of substances that polymerise by addition is that they contain carbon-carbon double bonds

Structures of some molecules which polymerise by addition are:

```
H     H        H     Cl       F     F       H     H
 \   /          \   /          \   /         \   /
  C = C          C = C          C = C         C = C
 /     \        /     \        /     \       /     \
H       H      H       H      F       F     H       CN
```

ethene — chloroethene (vinyl chloride) — tetrafluoroethene — acrylonitrite

◄ Bonds ►

ADDITION REACTIONS

Addition occurs when two substances react to form a single product. An addition reaction is not the same as an addition polymerisation. An important example of this type of reaction is the addition of bromine to ethene: if ethene is bubbled through, or shaken with bromine dissolved in 1,1,1,-trichloroethane, a colour change from pale brown to colourless is seen. This change is caused by the **addition** of bromine to ethene.

bromine + ethene → 1,2-dibromoethane

```
             H   H                 H
              \ /                  |
Br             C             Br — C — H
|      +       ‖                   |
Br             C      →      Br — C — H
              / \                  |
             H   H                 H
```

The same colour change is seen with an aqueous solution of bromine.

ADHESIVES

Adhesives are polymers. They can be natural such as animal glue and plant resins or synthetic as are epoxy resins. Some adhesives consist of a polymer in a solvent. When applied, the solvent evaporates and the adhesive is left to do its job: the solvent has helped to make the application easier. Other adhesives, such as Araldite, consist of two pastes that require mixing. One of the pastes is the initiator. When mixed the initiator starts the polymerisation process which 'sets' the adhesive.

AGRICULTURAL CHEMICALS

These consist of **fertilisers**, lime, pesticides, soil conditioners and trace element supplements. A large chemical industry exists to fill the need for these chemicals. Some are used to maintain or increase food supplies, the others to protect food from damage by pests.

AIR

The air we live in and breathe is a mixture of gases. It consists mainly of nitrogen, 78%. This may seem rather surprising since neither animals nor plants can make use of this gas. Oxygen occupies about 21% and argon about 1% of the total by volume. There is a very small but vital proportion of carbon dioxide. Although this gas is only about 0.04% of the air it is the source of all plant life. The proportion of carbon dioxide is also now known to have a critical effect on the average temperature of the Earth. It is a 'Greenhouse gas'. Industrial activity over the past hundred years has increased the proportion of carbon dioxide from 0.029% to present values of 0.035%. Because of the activity of volcanoes, plants and animals plus the industrial and everyday activities of humans, there are also small but significant amounts of methane, sulphur oxides, nitrogen oxides, carbon monoxide, ozone and hydrocarbons in the air. The effects of these 'pollutants' is discussed in other parts of the book.

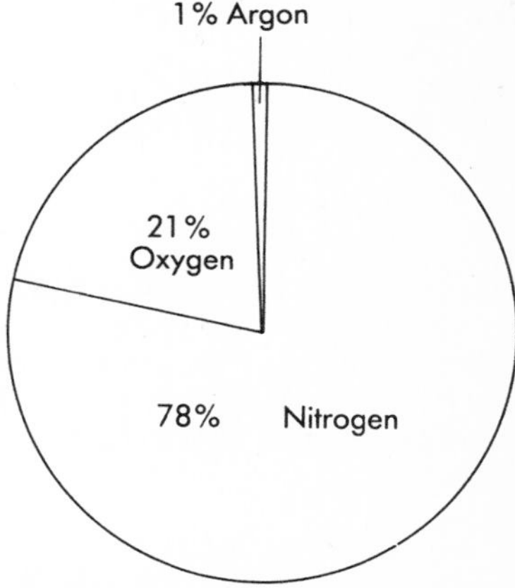

Fig. A.1 The volume composition of air

Extraction of gases from the air

The main gases in air are useful elements and are extracted for industrial and medical use. The process of extraction is by cooling, to remove water vapour and carbon dioxide, followed by alternately compressing and expanding the air until it becomes a liquid at about −200°C. The separate component elements are then obtained by **fractional distillation**. At −200°C, liquid air is at a temperature lower than the boiling points of its three main components. It is warmed in a fractionating column. The nitrogen, b.p. −196°C, and argon, b.p. −190°C evaporate first as their boiling points are lower than liquid oxygen (the more negative the temperature the lower the boiling point). Liquid oxygen, boiling point −183°C, is left at the bottom of the column. Nitrogen gas from the top of the column is either reliquefied or compressed into cylinders of gas for further use. Argon is drawn off near the top of the column and compressed into cylinders for use.

Table A.2 shows the boiling points of the gases extracted from air by this process. Note the larger the negative value of the boiling point, the lower the temperature. This is easier to see if boiling points are given in Kelvin (Celsius plus 273).

Gas	*B.p. in °C*	*B.p. in K*
xenon	−108	165
krypton	−153	120
oxygen	−183	90
argon	−186	87
nitrogen	−196	77
neon	−246	27
helium	−269	4

Table A.2

USES OF AIR

In addition to being a source of pure nitrogen, oxygen and argon, air is used in many industrial processes as a cheap source of the oxygen and nitrogen that it contains.

For its oxygen

In processes such as the smelting of iron in a blast furnace or the oxidation of sulphur dioxide in the **contact process**, the presence of other gases in the air does not affect the chemical reactions occurring. In these circumstances, there is no need to carry out a costly separation of the oxygen before use.

The major use of oxygen in air is for combustion of fuels to generate electricity.

For its nitrogen

In the **Haber process** for the production of ammonia, air is used as a source of nitrogen. Here again, the gas is not separated before use, but the oxygen must be removed by chemical reaction during the process.

ALCOHOL ABUSE

Ethanol (alcohol) is a drug. The effects of alcohol on the body are well known but are often taken too lightly. The body's reaction to alcohol can range from relaxation and loss of inhibition through loss of coordination and slow reactions to permanent liver and brain damage and addiction. Alcohol related accidents at work or on the roads cause many injuries and deaths.

The reducing reaction of ethanol is the basis of one type of **breathalyser** used for detecting ethanol in the body.

ALCOHOL

Alcohols are organic compounds containing an hydroxyl group.

They form an **homologous series** of organic compounds. The formula of every alcohol can be worked out from a general formula, $C_nH_{2n+1}OH$, where n is a whole number. If n=1 the formula is CH_3OH, methanol. The next two are also shown below.

```
     H              H   H               H   H   H
     |              |   |               |   |   |
  H- C -OH       H- C - C - OH       H- C - C - C -OH
     |              |   |               |   |   |
     H              H   H               H   H   H
```

Methanol (n=1) Ethanol (n=2) Propanol (n=3)

The fourth member is called butanol and later members are named more logically from Greek numbers so we have *pent*anol, *hex*anol, *hept*anol, *oct*anol etc.

The presence of the −OH group gives all the alcohols similar chemical properties. For example, they all react with acids to form **esters** and all can be dehydrated to **alkenes**. **Ethanol**, C_2H_5OH, is the best known alcohol. It is present in beers, wines, and spirits. It is the main ingredient of methylated spirit – 'meths'. Industrial ethanol is mainly used as a solvent – for example, the fragrances in perfumes are dissolved in nearly pure ethanol. Varnishes, polishes, cosmetics and printing inks all use ethanol in their preparation.

ALKALI METALS – GROUP 1 METALS

The alkali metals are the elements of group 1 of the **periodic table**. They are the most reactive metals known. They derive their name from the fact that their oxides and hydroxides are **alkalis**.

Alkali metals are quite unlike the construction metals we know well in our daily lives. They are soft enough to cut with a knife; melt at low temperatures; react vigorously with water and oxidise rapidly in air at room temperature. **Lithium**, **sodium** and **potassium** have densities of less than $1 g/cm^3$ and so float on water as they react with it.

The alkali metals form a family or group of elements with very similar properties. Their properties change in a uniform way from one element to the next down the group – we call this a trend.

PHYSICAL PROPERTIES

Physical similarities and trends within this group are shown in the Table A.3 below.

Metal	*M.p. in °C*	*Malleability*	*Flame-colour*
lithium	181	like hard toffee	red
sodium	98	like plasticine	yellow
potassium	63	like cold butter	lilac

Table A.3

CHEMICAL PROPERTIES

Similarities

In their chemical properties, the alkali metals also show similarities and trends. They all react with **oxygen** in the air, **water** and **chlorine.** The similarity of their reactions enables us to write equations for these reactions in which the symbol M is used for any of the alkali metals. So, for example, they will all react according to the equations, as shown in Table A.4.

Reactions	*Properties of the products*
with air: $4M(s) + O_2(g) \rightarrow 2M_2O(s)$	the oxides are alkalis like sodium oxide
with water: $2M(s) + 2H_2O(1) \rightarrow 2MOH(aq) + H_2(g)$	the hydroxides are alkalis like sodium hydroxide
with chlorine: $2M(s) + Cl_2(g) \rightarrow 2MCl(s)$	the chlorides are salts like sodium chloride

Table A.4

To work out the equation for the reaction of any one of the alkali metals with air, water or chlorine, simply insert the symbol for the metal in place of the symbol M in the above equations. For example, the equation for the reaction of Rubidium, Rb, with water will be

$$2Rb(s) + 2H_2O(l) \rightarrow 2RbOH(aq) + H_2(g)$$

It would not be advisable to try this reaction in a laboratory for it is likely to be quite violent! However, the equation does show what products to expect – an alkaline compound, rubidium hydroxide, and hydrogen gas. Even the vigour of the reaction can be predicted from a knowledge of the reactivities of the family as a whole.

The least reactive metal in the group is **lithium** – at the top. Reactivity increases down the group and the most reactive alkali metal is at the bottom – **caesium. Francium** would be expected to be even more reactive than **caesium** but, as a synthetic element, it has not been made in sufficient quantities to give visible proof of this.

Differences

A simple illustration of the reactivity difference between the top three metals is seen in their reaction with water. Lithium floats, does not melt and reacts steadily but reasonably safely. Sodium also floats, melts to a silvery globule and rapidly disappears with a faint bang. Potassium floats and melts like sodium but the hydrogen given off catches fire. The reaction is very fast and ends with a small but noisy explosion. It will not be surprising to discover that the reactions of lower members of the group are dangerous to carry out!

Electron structures

The electron arrangement of the atoms of these elements is shown in Table A.5.

Element	*Electron arrangement*
Li	2 1
Na	2 8 1
K	2 8 8 1

Table A.5

The atom of each element has one electron in its outer shell of electrons. This is the reason why these elements are in *group one*.
The atoms form ions by loss of the single outer electron, giving ions with one positive charge Li^+, Na^+ and K^+.
Group 1 metal ions, combine with halide ions, X^-, to form salts with the general formula MX, e.g. NaCl and KBr.

◀ Charges on ions, groups of the periodic table ▶

ALKALINE EARTH METALS – GROUP 2 METALS

The metals of group 2 of the periodic table are known as the alkaline earth metals. They are the metals most commonly found combined in the rocks of the earth. Magnesium forms about 2% and calcium about 4% of the earth's crust.

Group 2 metals are silvery grey.

Comparison with group 1 metals

Group 2 metals are:

- harder and cannot be cut with a knife
- slower to tarnish on contact with air
- slower to react with water and other reagents
- denser than group 1 metals and also denser than water
- changes in properties down the group are similar, e.g.
  - they become softer – they become denser
  - reactivity increases so the most reactive member of the group is the radioactive element – radium.

Calcium and magnesium form compounds which are widespread in the rocks of the planet. They are the two elements of the group commonly studied. Like metals of group 1, they form alkaline compounds when they react with water. Using M as the symbol for any group 2 metal:

metal	+ water	→	metal hydroxide (alkali)	+ hydrogen
M(s)	+ $2H_2O(l)$	→	$M(OH)_2(s)$	+ $H_2(g)$

Their oxides are also basic and react with water to form alkalis.

basic oxide	+ water	→	alkaline hydroxide
MO(s)	+ $H_2O(l)$	→	$M(OH)_2(s)$

Electron structures

The electron arrangements of group 2 elements are shown in Table A.6. The atoms of each element have 2 electrons in their outer electron shell. The atoms form ions by loss of both outer electrons, giving ions with two positive charges, e.g. Mg^{2+} and Ca^{2+}.
Group 2 metal ions combine with two halide ions (X^-) to form salts of general formula MX_2, e.g. $MgCl_2$ and $CaBr_2$.

Element	*Electron arrangement*
Be	2 2
Mg	2 8 2
Ca	2 8 8 2

Table A.6

◄ Charges on ions ►

ALKALIS

Alkalis are water soluble **bases.** The commonest ones are **slaked lime,** $Ca(OH)_2$, **sodium hydroxide** NaOH, and **ammonia** NH_3.

REACTIONS

Alkalis react with **acids** in the same way that all bases do – they neutralise them to form a **salt** and **water:**

calcium hydroxide	+	hydrochloric acid	→	calcium chloride	+	water
$Ca(OH)_2(s)$	+	2HCl(aq)	→	$CaCl_2(aq)$	+	$2H_2O(l)$
sodium hydroxide	+	hydrochloric acid	→	sodium chloride	+	water
NaOH(aq)	+	HCl(aq)	→	NaCl(aq)	+	$H_2O(l)$

ammonia solution		hydrochloric acid		ammonium chloride	water
	+		$\rightarrow$		+
$NH_3(g) + H_2O(l)$	+	$HCl(aq)$	$\rightarrow$	NH_4Cl	+ $H_2O(l)$

The active part of every alkali is the hydroxide ion, OH^- which reacts with hydrogen ions, H^+ to form water. In the reaction of sodium hydroxide and hydrochloric acid shown above, the ionic equation for the *reaction* is:

$OH^-(aq)$	+ $H^+(aq)$	$\rightarrow$	$H_2O(l)$	spectator ions
alkali	acid		water	$Na^+(aq)$ + $Cl^-(aq)$

But on evaporation, $Na^+(aq) + Cl^-(aq) \rightarrow NaCl(s)$

The sodium and chloride ions are **spectator ions** and do not *react.* They are present in the solution as freely moving ions. If the water is evaporated away, then these ions will join up into a lattice and salt crystals will form. This is the principle for the preparation of **salts** from acids and alkalis.

STRONG AND WEAK ALKALIS

Like acids, alkalis can be strong or weak. The explanation of this is also similar to the explanation for **strong** and **weak acids**. The ion responsible for alkalinity is the hydroxide ion, OH^-. Any solution that contains hydroxide ions will be alkaline.

- If an alkali solution contains a very small concentration of hydroxide ions it will be a weak alkali.
- If it contains a high concentration of hydroxide ions it will be a strong alkali.

However, the hydroxide ion concentrations may not be the same as the alkali concentrations. For example, in a very concentrated solution of ammonia, the concentration of hydroxide ions is *low* – ammonia solution is a weak alkali. However, even in a dilute solution of sodium hydroxide, the hydroxide ion concentration is *high* – sodium hydroxide solution is a strong alkali.

$$NH_3(aq) + H_2O(l) \leftrightarrow NH_4^+(aq) + OH^-(aq)$$

99% molecules — 1% hydroxide ions after reaction

In the example above, 99% of the original 100% of ammonia molecules have not reacted with water. The 1% that have reacted have produced hydroxide ions which give the solution its weak alkalinity.

In the case of sodium hydroxide, the sodium hydroxide dissolves and releases hydroxide ions.

$$NaOH(s) + (aq) \rightarrow Na^+(aq) + OH^-(aq)$$

100% hydroxide ions after dissolving

((aq) stands for water. There is no reaction here – just dissolving, so the water does not take part in the reactions and its formula need not be used)

For equal concentrations, say one molar, the sodium hydroxide is 100 times more alkaline than the ammonia solution.

ALKANES

Alkanes are members of a **homologous series** of organic hydrocarbons. The general formula of the series is C_nH_{2n+2}. The names end in −ane which indicates that they are alkanes. Alkanes are saturated hydrocarbons because all their bonds are single bonds.

```
    H              H  H               H  H  H
    |              |  |               |  |  |
 H— C —H        H— C— C— H         H— C— C— C— H
    |              |  |               |  |  |
    H              H  H               H  H  H
```

Alkanes are not very reactive compounds, however they burn in air to produce carbon dioxide, water and heat energy. For this reason they are important as **fuels**. Methane is usally found as Natural gas together with **crude oil**. The other alkanes are present in crude oil, which is a complex mixture of hydrocarbons. They are extracted by **fractional distillation**.

Methane – the main constituent of natural gas – is an environmentally 'clean' fuel. It produces only carbon dioxide and water as it burns. Also, methane has the advantage over other fossil fuels of producing less of the 'greenhouse gas' carbon dioxide for each unit of energy produced on burning. Natural gas also contains a very small proportion of sulphur compounds and so does not contribute greatly to 'acid rain' pollution.

$$CH_4(g) + 2O_2(g) \rightarrow CO_2(g) + 2H_2O(l) + \text{heat}$$

A possible danger arises when methane is used as a fuel. This is the risk of incomplete combustion which leads to the formation of **carbon monoxide**.

$$C_2H_4(g) + 1.5\ O_2(g) \rightarrow CO(g) + 2H_2O(l)$$

Carbon monoxide forms when there is not enough oxygen for carbon dioxide formation. It is a toxic gas. The likely conditions for it to be produced occur when:

- air is prevented from getting to the gas flame; this may be caused by blocked gas boiler air-intakes
- rooms in the home are sealed against draughts preventing air getting in to complete the combustion of the gas

Other alkanes are well known for their special uses. Liquid **propane** is 'Calor gas' and liquid **butane** is used as a camping stove fuel as well as a fuel for blowlamps, gas lighters and some types of self-heating hair curlers.

ALKENES

Alkenes are a homologous series of unsaturated hydrocarbons with a general formula of C_nH_{2n}. Their molecules contain one double bond between two carbon atoms. They are made by **'cracking'** crude oil or the less valuable petroleum fractions.

The most important alkene is **ethene**, C_2H_4. Ethene is the first member of the homologous series.

Other members of this series have names corresponding to those of the alkanes but with the ending **−ene**, for example prop*ene* and but*ene*.

```
H     H       H       H - H            H       H    H    H
 \   /         \      |   |             \      |    |    |
  C = C          C = C - C - H            C = C - C - C - H
 /   \         /          |             /           |    |
H     H       H           H            H            H    H
```

ethene propene butene

The carbon – carbon double bond in alkenes

This bond contains four electrons, two from each carbon atom in the bond see Fig. A.2.

Testing for alkenes

The carbon – carbon double bond will react quickly with **bromine**. Bromine water (a pale brown solution of bromine in water) will become colourless if shaken with an alkene. This is the easiest test for alkenes.

```
H                    H
   X    X      X •
 •  C  •  C
  X •  X       X
H        •   •  H
```

Fig. A.2 An ethene molecule

Uses

The carbon – carbon double bond in all alkenes is very reactive. This makes alkenes useful starting materials for making other substances. Alkenes are also easily polymerised to make, for example, poly(ethene) and poly (propene).

ALLOTROPES

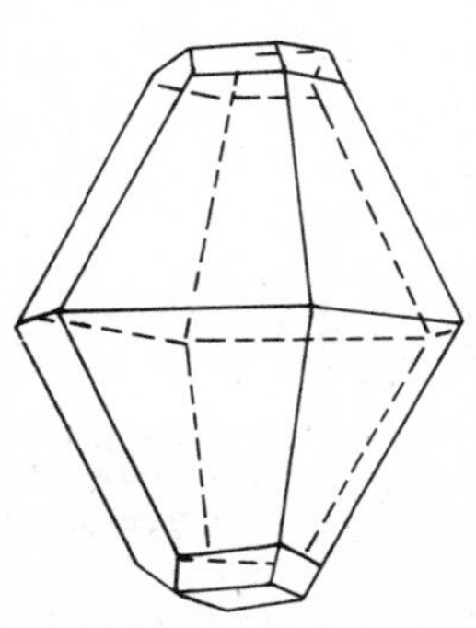

Rhombic sulphur crystal

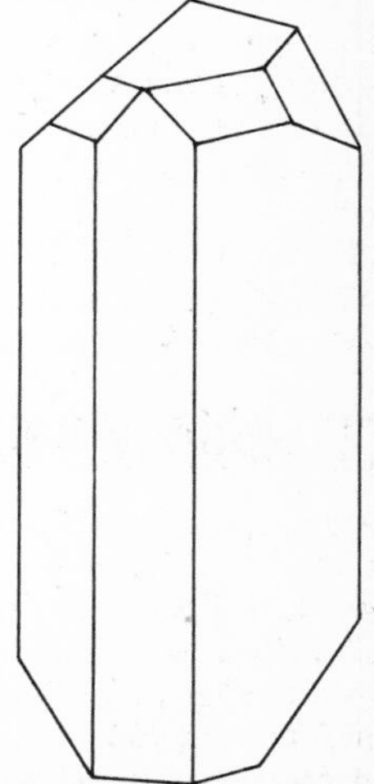

Monoclinic sulphur crystal

Fig. A.3 Allotropes of sulphur

Some elements can exist in different forms. These different forms of the same element are called *allotropes*.

The two crystalline forms of **carbon** are diamond and graphite; the two crystalline forms of *sulphur* are rhombic (alpha) and monoclinic (beta) sulphur. (See Fig. A.3).

Allotropes have the same chemical properties but different physical properties. For example, rhombic sulphur has a higher density and a lower melting point than monoclinic sulphur. The two allotropes **oxygen**, O_2, and **ozone** O_3, are different *molecular* forms of the element oxygen.

ALLOYS

Alloys are mixtures of metals (although carbon and silicon are sometimes included). The constituent metals are mixed in molten form and cast. Alloys can be 'tailored' to meet the properties required by the engineering industry. Soft metals can be hardened, weak metals can be strengthened, reactive metals can be made corrosion resistant. Even the colour of an alloy can be affected by alloying. Table A.7 shows several common alloys and indicates some useful property changes that can be produced by alloying.

Alloy	*Composition*	*Property*	*Uses*
brasses	copper, 66–70% zinc, 30–34%	harder and cheaper than copper, resists corrosion	ornaments, screws, rivets, cartridges, watertaps
bronze	copper, 90% tin, 10%	hard, strong can be cast into intricate shapes, corrosion-resistant	castings
coinage bronze	copper, 95% tin, 3.5% zinc, 1.5%	hard, strong and corrosion-resistant	coinage, penny and twopenny pieces
cupro-nickel	copper, 75% nickel, 25%	strong, corrosion-resistant, easy to shape cold without annealing	'silver' coins
duralumin	aluminium, 95% copper, 4% magnesium, 1%	higher strength/weight ratio than steel or aluminium, low density	aircraft framework
solder	lead, 67% tin, 33%	low melting point, stronger than tin or lead	joints in electrical work, plumbing and tin-can making
steel	iron, 99% carbon, 0–1%	strong, cheap, easily shaped and welded	bridges, ships, vehicles, rails, gears

Alloy	*Composition*	*Property*	*Uses*
stainless steel	iron, 73% chromium, 18% nickel, 8% carbon, 1%	very resistant to rusting, strong and hard wearing	cutlery, kitchen utensils, chemical plant
type metal	lead, 74% antimony, 16% tin, 10%	easily cast but hardened by the antimony to keep its shape in use	printer's type

Table A.7

ALPHA PARTICLES

These are helium nuclei, He^{2+}, usually written ^4_2He, given off during one type of radioactive decay. An alpha particle contains 2 neutrons and 2 protons – it weighs 4 atomic mass units. An **atom** which gives off an alpha particle will therefore lose mass by 4 atomic mass units. The loss of two protons also causes the atomic number to decrease by two units. The result is a daughter element two positions back in the periodic table and 4 mass units lighter. For example:

$$^{238}_{92}U \rightarrow {}^{234}_{90}Th + {}^4_2He$$

Alpha particles are the largest of the two radioactive particles produced during radioactive decay. They are stopped by quite thin sheets of plastic, aluminium and even skin. However, because they are so heavy, they cause much tissue damage if they do get inside the body. For this reason any radioactive material that gives off alpha particles is especially dangerous if it is swallowed or inhaled. Radon gas which seeps out of granite rock is an 'alpha emitter'. It enters buildings in areas of the country where the underground rock is granite. Radon gas is now thought to be responsible for a large part of the background radiation we are all exposed to in our daily lives.

ALUMINA, Al_2O_3

Alumina is **aluminium oxide.** It is rarely found in a pure state in nature. Alumina is the only **ore** from which aluminium metal is presently extracted on a large scale. Alumina is extracted in a pure form from **bauxite** which is a common but impure form of alumina. Alumina has a rare property among metal oxides; it dissolves in strong alkalis. The **Bayer process** for purifying alumina from bauxite relies upon this property.

Aluminium is the most abundant metal, and the third most abundant element, in the **Earth's crust.**

Sir Humphry Davy was the first to separate aluminium from its oxide – by electrolysis – in 1807. Davy called the metal 'alumium'. He did not obtain the pure metal, however, but an iron-aluminium alloy. It was not until 1825 that Hans Oersted obtained aluminium metal.

No mass production by electrolysis was possible until there was large-scale electricity generation in 1886. In the years between 1808 and 1886, aluminium was obtained first by reducing aluminium chloride with potassium (1827) and later (1855) more cheaply by using sodium.

alkali metal	+	aluminium chloride	→	alkali metal chloride	+	aluminium
3K	+	$AlCl_3$	→	3KCl	+	Al
3Na	+	$AlCl_3$	→	3NaCl	+	Al

The **sodium** and **potassium** for these processes was made by **electrolysis**, so aluminium was once a very expensive metal. Napoleon III of France had aluminium cutlery specially made to impress important foreign visitors. This was made using potassium and was as expensive as gold! At the Paris exhibition of 1855, aluminium ingots made with sodium as the reducing agent were first displayed. They were then about half the price of gold. By 1859 the price was two hundred times lower than in 1855. This drastic reduction in price continued with the invention of the electrolytic method in 1886. That method is still in use today.

ALUMINA SMELTING

This is the name given to the process of reduction of the ore; it is carried out by **electrolysis**. It is a very expensive method of reduction because it uses a form of energy made by the combustion of **coal** which is always inefficient.

Alumina melts at 2040 °C, a temperature far too high for successful electrolysis. There are no materials that will resist that temperature and be economical to use. It was, therefore, many years after the first discovery of aluminium that an economic method was found to extract it. In 1886 two scientists, C. Hall in the U.S.A. and P. Heroult in France independently invented the process still in use today. The main feature of their process was the use of a special substance called **cryolite**, to dissolve the alumina. This could be used at the much lower temperature of about 1000°C and made the more economical electrolysis process possible. The electrolysis cells used are shown in the diagram, Fig. A.4.

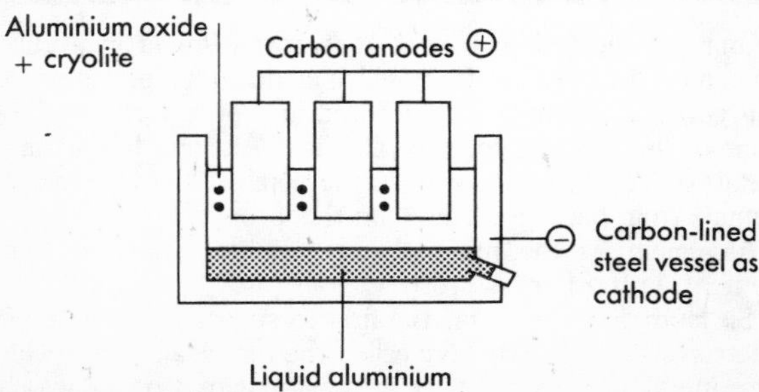

Fig. A.4 Alumina smelting – electrolysis cell

The cell itself is made of carbon blocks, covered outside by steel plate. The anodes and cathodes are made of carbon. The electrolyte is a 5% solution of alumina in molten cryolite (Na_3AlF_6). Electrolysis decomposes the alumina into aluminium and oxygen. The aluminium is deposited on the pool of metal at the bottom of the cell. The oxygen reacts with the carbon anodes forming carbon dioxide.

At anode:	oxide ions	minus	electrons		oxygen gas
	$6O^{2-}(l)$	$-$	$12e^-$	$\rightarrow$	$3O_2(g)$

followed by

carbon anode	+	oxygen gas	$\rightarrow$	carbon dioxide
$3C(s)$	+	$3O_2(g)$	$\rightarrow$	$3CO_2(g)$

At cathode:	aluminium ions	plus	electrons		molten aluminium
	$4Al^{3+}(l)$	+	$12e^-$	$\rightarrow$	$4Al(l)$

From time to time, the carbon anodes must be renewed because they have burnt away. The molten aluminium is 'sucked out' of the cell about once-a-day. The process produces large quantities of waste gas and dust.
The waste gas contains:

- carbon monoxide
- carbon dioxide
- sulphur dioxide
- fluorides.

The gases are scrubbed to remove the toxic components.
The dust contains:

- fluoride particles
- carbon
- alumina

They are removed by **electrostatic precipitators** and recycled.

PROPERTIES AND USES OF ALUMINIUM

Properties

- it is a shiny metal
- it has a low density (about one-third that of iron)
- it is an excellent conductor of heat and electricity
- it is non-magnetic
- it is a fairly cheap metal – about twice the cost of zinc and lead but seven times the cost of iron. When first produced it was as costly as gold, nowadays it is ten thousand times cheaper!
- it is very resistant to corrosion

Uses

The tarnish-free shine on aluminium allows it to be used for making mirrors and lamp reflectors. It is also used to make heat-proof suits for firemen; the shiny surface reflects away the intense heat of a fire.

Aluminium is excellent for making pans because it is a good heat conductor, carrying heat quickly from source to food. However, in the home it should not be confused with stainless steel which is much more widely used in making kitchen utensils and equipment. In fact, aluminium is not as strong as steel of the same thickness and so aluminium pans are thicker than stainless steel pans of the same strength. Aluminium pans are therefore not usually lighter than steel pans.

Aluminium's excellent electrical conductivity makes it an ideal metal for overhead electricity lines (but not for electric kettles!). Its low density allows longer distances between pylons than would be possible with the much denser alternative – **copper**.

The table of density, electrical conductivity and price (Table A.8) illustrates the economics of the choice.

Metal	*Relative density*	*Relative conductivity*	*Relative cost (1989)*
copper	3.3	1.6	1.00
aluminium	1.0	1.0	0.80

Table A.8 Copper and aluminium – economics of choice

The figures show that copper is three times denser than aluminium (that is, for equal volumes, copper has three times the weight) but is only one and a half times better at conducting electricity. So, weight for weight, aluminium is twice as good an electrical conductor. Because it is also cheaper it is not surprising that it is used in overhead electrical cables. In fact, aluminium is not strong enough to support *itself* in long lengths, so the cable has a steel core for strength and an aluminium outer layer for conducting.

It can be used to make compass mountings in aircraft and ships because of its non-magnetic property.

Aluminium alloys are a major material for making aircraft bodies. The fuel needed to fly an aeroplane increases as the weight increases. The lighter the body, the less fuel and the more passengers the plane can carry.

Aluminium has a weakness. It corrodes badly in alkalis and seawater. These dissolve away the protective oxide coating (see below). Care must be taken not to bring alkaline substances into contact with it. Aluminium cooker parts will be damaged by contact with oven cleaners – which are usually alkaline because alkalis dissolve grease and fat (see **soap**). Aluminium is also unsuitable for use in marine environments because it is attacked by salt water.

ALUMINIUM FROM RECYCLED SCRAP

A large proportion of the aluminium produced now is from recycled scrap. In

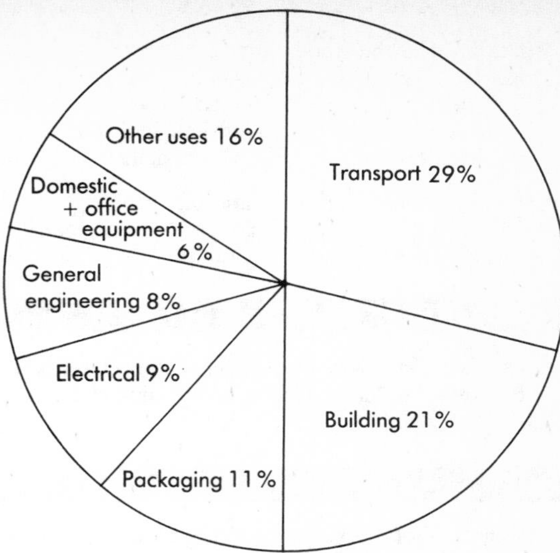

Fig. A.5 Major uses of aluminium (1987: Europe)

Britain the proportion is about 25 – 30%. In some countries it is greater. Most scrap is produced in the factory making the aluminium articles. The rest is used-scrap. The amount of used-scrap recycled depends on efficient or easy collection. Milk-bottle tops are not economical to collect but drinks cans made entirely of aluminium are and a campaign is starting in Britain to encourage their collection. The energy used in recycling scrap aluminium is only 5% of that used in making it in the first place. In the U.S.A., where recycling is more established than in Britain, about 75% of aluminium drinks cans are recycled.

Why doesn't aluminium corrode like iron?

The surface of aluminium is covered by a very thin oxide coating which protects the metal from chemical reaction with many corrosive substances. The metal does not corrode in water like iron because the oxide film is a perfect cover over the metal preventing air or water from penetrating. The oxide coating on iron flakes off easily, exposing more metal to the rusting process until all the metal has corroded.

The oxide film can be thickened by a process known as **anodising**. This is often carried out on aluminium which is to be used outdoors. The protection is increased and the appearance improved. Anodised aluminium will also absorb dyes and so can be coloured to make it more attractive. Much look-alike brass is gold-dyed anodised aluminium.

ALUMINIUM HYDROXIDE, $Al(OH)_3$

Aluminium hydroxide, like the oxide, is **amphoteric**. It is a white solid which does not dissolve in water. One of its common uses is as an ingredient in '**antacids**'. It will neutralise excess stomach acid, hydrochloric acid, and relieve the pain of acid-indigestion. Aluminium hydroxide is not soluble in water so does not form a strong alkali thereby making it quite safe to swallow.

aluminium hydroxide	+	hydrochloric acid	→	aluminium chloride	+	water
$Al(OH)_3(s)$	+	$3HCl(aq)$	→	$AlCl_3(aq)$	+	$3H_2O(l)$

ALUMINIUM OXIDE, Al_2O_3

Aluminium oxide, like aluminium hydroxide, is **amphoteric**. It is the main component of **Bauxite**. The crystalline solid contains aluminium ions, Al^{3+}, and oxide ions, O^{2-}.

AMALGAMS

An amalgam is a mixture of **mercury** and another **metal**. Amalgams are alloys of mercury. For instance, sodium amalgam, written Na/Hg, is formed at the cathode during the electrolysis of brine using a mercury cathode. Amalgams are metals diluted with mercury – an unreactive metal. So, for example, sodium amalgam reacts with water more slowly than pure sodium, producing hydrogen and sodium hydroxide solution. It is this low reactivity that enables sodium amalgram to react safely with water.

sodium amalgam	+	water	→	sodium hydroxide	+	hydrogen	+	mercury
2Na/Hg	+	$2H_2O(l)$	→	$2NaOH(aq)$	+	$H_2(g)$	+	$2Hg(l)$

The mercury can be recycled. Sodium hydroxide made by this method is very pure.

A lead amalgam, Pb/Hg, is used to make tetraethyl lead for use in the **antiknock** additive of leaded petrol.

Dental amalgam is a mixture of a dental alloy of silver and tin mixed in equal weights with mercury. The amalgam is malleable for a short time and can be packed into a tooth cavity. It becomes solid enough to carve to shape after a few minutes and eventually it sets. It is hard enough to resist the chewing and grinding action of teeth on food, non-toxic and resistant to acids in food.

A curiosity is ammonium amalgam. It was the discovery of this that led to salts of ammonia being named ammon*ium*, because of the similarity with metal amalgams such as sod*ium* amalgam.

AMINO ACIDS

Amino acids are the 'building blocks' of **proteins**. To make amino acids, plants must take up nitrogen from **nitrogenous fertilisers** in the soil. The amino acids are then built up into **polymers** called proteins. An amino acid has both an amino group, $-NH_2$, and an acid group, $-COOH$, in its molecule.

AMMONIA

Ammonia is a common gas given off from rotting animal manure. It has a very obvious pungent smell and so must have been recognised for thousands of years. The salt we now know as ammonium chloride was called the salt of Ammon (a God) by the Egyptians, hence its old name; sal-ammoniac (salt of Ammon). Arabic alchemists used hartshorn – a salt made from the horns of a hart (a male deer old enough to have grown antlers). Ammonia solution made from hartshorn was, until recently, called 'spirits of hartshorn'. Ammonia was first made in a reasonably pure form by **Joseph Priestley**.

Nitrogen fixation

It is an unfortunate fact that the nitrogen in the air cannot easily be used to make nitrogen compounds. Before Haber invented his process, industry relied upon three sources of nitrogen compounds:

- The mineral nitrates e.g. sodium nitrate found in Chile and called 'Chile saltpetre'.
- Natural manures from which ammonium compounds could be extracted or which could be used directly as fertilisers in agriculture e.g. guano (hardened bird droppings from islands off the coast of Peru where seams hundreds of feet thick had been deposited over centuries).
- Ammonia and its compounds made as a by- product of the manufacture of coal-gas.

When these sources became insufficient to meet the world's demands, the time was right for the discovery of a method of synthesising them. The process is often called 'fixation' since it takes nitrogen from the air and concentrates or 'fixes' it into a compound. Plants can only use nitrogen that has been 'fixed'.

The synthetic ammonia industry began in Germany in 1912. The process now used all over the world was invented by Fritz Haber in 1908. Ammonia was needed to make dyes, explosives and fertilisers. At that time there were shortages of natural compounds to make these products and intensive research was being carried out to find a synthetic (man-made) compound that could be used in their manufacture. Haber's research showed the exact conditions of temperature, pressure and catalyst needed to make ammonia economically using nitrogen in the air and hydrogen – a process called **synthesis.** Haber, helped by Carl Bosch, made the laboratory process into a large-scale industrial process.

Even in 1909 there was a concern to conserve energy and Haber introduced an energy saving feature called a '**heat exchanger**' which worked by recycling the heat from the gaseous products back to the reacting gases.

Ammonia gas-uses in industry

Ammonia is used to make nitric acid, fertilisers, urea and explosives.

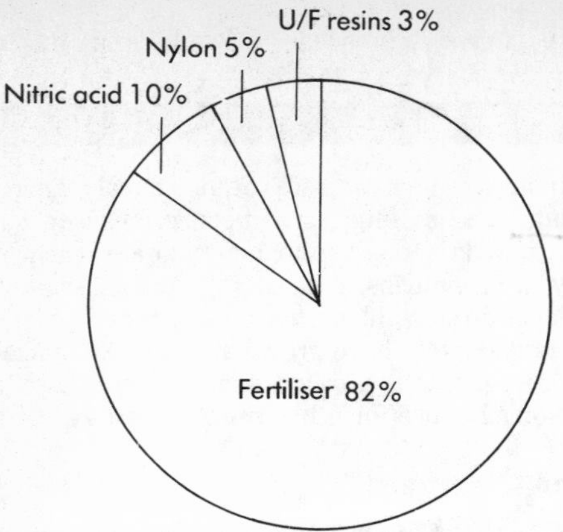

Fig. A.6 Uses of ammonia gas in industry

World production of ammonia has increased rapidly since the 1950s as is shown by the graph below. (See Fig. A.7)

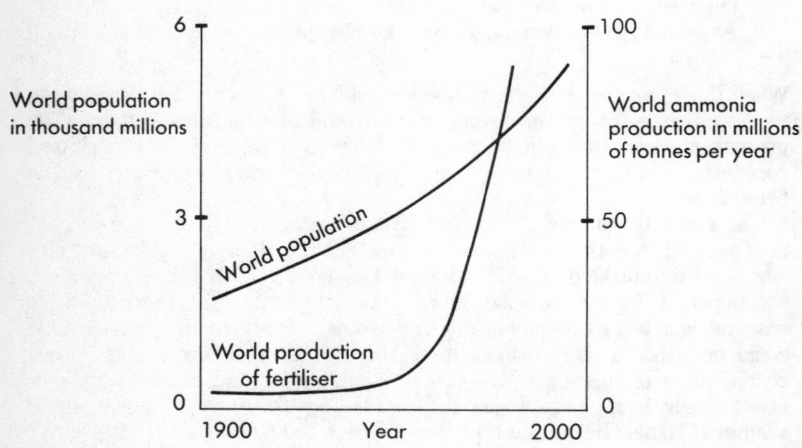

Fig. A.7 World ammonia production and world population figures

The curve showing growth in the manufacture of ammonia is the same shape as the growth curve of the world population. The more people there are then the more fertiliser is needed to grow food for them and so the more ammonia is manufactured.

Everyday uses

The alkalinity of ammonia solution makes it a useful cleaner for greasy surfaces such as cookers or windows. Any alkali will react with grease converting it into soap and allowing it to be wiped away. Ammonia is a weak alkali which can be used without damaging the skin as strong alkalis do.

Ammonia gas is a heart stimulant; it also unblocks the air passages in a blocked-up nose. For this reason *smelling salts*, ammonium carbonate crystals, are used both to bring people round from unconsciousness and to make breathing easier for people who have a cold or catarrh.

In the laboratory

Ammonia is made in the laboratory from one of its salts. Ammonium salts are formed from the neutralisation of ammonia with an acid. If an alkali is added to any ammonium salt the process is reversed and the ammonia is released.

any ammonium salt	+	any metal oxide or hydroxide	→	ammonia	+	a metal salt	+	water
e.g.								
ammonium chloride	+	sodium hydroxide	→	ammonia	+	sodium chloride	+	water
$NH_4Cl(s)$	+	$NaOH(aq)$	→	$NH_3(g)$	+	$NaCl(aq)$	+	$H_2O(l)$

The reaction is faster if heated. The ammonia formed is first passed through calcium oxide which dries it. It is then collected in a gas syringe or by upward delivery into an inverted gas jar – ammonia is less dense than air. Any attempt to collect ammonia in an upturned tube full of water is bound to fail because ammonia is very soluble.

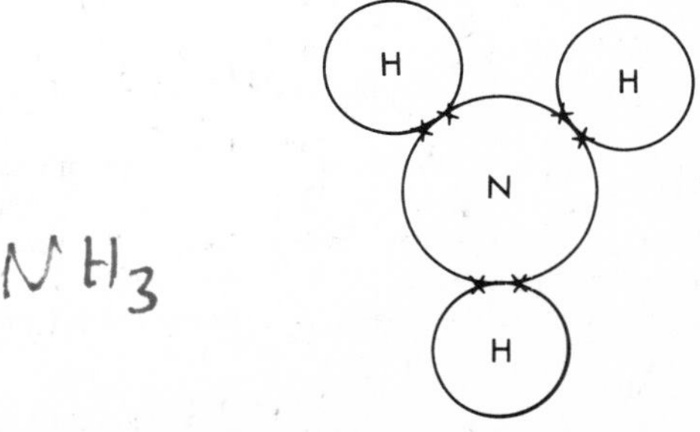

Fig. A.8 Structure of an ammonia molecule

Properties

- Ammonia is a colourless, pungent smelling, alkaline gas.
- It is very soluble in water. In fact one teaspoonful of water (about $5cm^3$) will dissolve $2000cm^3$ of ammonia gas at room temperature!
- The relative molecular mass of ammonia molecules is 17 – about half that of the molecules in air. This means that ammonia is less dense than air and also that its molecules diffuse quickly in air. The smell of ammonia gets about quickly!

Tests for ammonia

Ammonia is the only common alkaline gas. It is therefore very easy to detect and identify. It will turn damp indicator paper blue. If damp **universal indicator** paper is used the pH of ammonia will be about 12, indicating that ammonia is a weak alkali.

ammonia	+	water	↔	ammonium ions	+	hydroxide ions
$NH_3(g)$	+	$H_2O(l)$	↔	$NH_4^+(aq)$	+	$OH^-(aq)$

Ammonia also reacts with **hydrogen chloride** gas. It can be detected by bringing the open mouth of a bottle of concentrated hydrochloric acid close to the source of any unidentified gas. If a bluey-white smoke is seen then ammonia is present.

ammonia	+	hydrogen chloride	→	ammonium chloride smoke
$NH_3(g)$	+	$HCl(g)$	→	$NH_4Cl(s)$

◄ Caustic soda, Gases, Hydrogen chloride ►

AMMONIUM CHLORIDE, NH_4Cl

Commonly known as 'sal ammoniac'. It is used in the laboratory to make ammonia by warming it with an alkali. It is formed when ammonia gas reacts with hydrogen chloride.

Heating ammonium chloride causes it to *dissociate* into hydrogen chloride and ammonia gases. Because these are colourless gases, the solid disappears. As the gas mixture cools the solid reappears. A small amount of ammonium chloride heated in a tube will therefore seem to sublime on to the cooler upper part of the tube. The process is not true sublimation but **thermal dissociation. dissociation.**

white solid	heat ↔ cool	mixture of colourless gases
$NH_4Cl(s)$		$NH_3(g) + HCl(g)$

AMMONIUM NITRATE, NH_4NO_3

Ammonium nitrate is the commonest nitrogenous fertiliser. It is made by neutralising ammonia with nitric acid. It contains 35 percent nitrogen. It is also a powerful oxidising agent and an explosive substance. In Oppau, Germany, in 1921, 5,000 tonnes of it had formed a hard mass; it is **hygroscopic** and its damp crystals had stuck together in storage (caked). An attempt was made to loosen it by the use of small explosive charges. Disastrously, the whole lot exploded, killing more than 1000 people! Fertiliser quality ammonium nitrate is now coated with powdered chalk to prevent the crystals sticking together and thereby becoming dangerous in this way.

◀ **Percentage composition** ▶

AMMONIUM SULPHATE, $(NH_4)_5O_4$

Once the commonest nitrogenous fertiliser, it is now much less used than ammonium nitrate. It is made by neutralising ammonia with sulphuric acid. It contains 21 per cent nitrogen.

AMPHOTERIC OXIDES

As a general rule oxides and hydroxides of metals are bases and oxides of non-metals are acids. However, there are several exceptions to this rule. Aluminium and zinc oxides and hydroxides, for example, behave like both **acids** ***and*** **bases** – though not at the same time!

An amphoteric oxide or hydroxide is one that will neutralise an acid but will also neutralise a base. In each case a salt and water is formed. For example:

base		acid		salt-aluminium sulphate		water
$Al_2O_3(s)$	+	$3H_2SO_4(aq)$	$\rightarrow$	$Al_2(SO_4)_3(aq)$	+	$3H_2O(l)$
acid		base		salt-sodium aluminate		water
$Al_2O_3(s)$	+	$2NaOH(aq)$	$\rightarrow$	$2NaAlO_2(aq)$	+	$H_2O(l)$

Zinc oxide, ZnO, is also amphoteric. It reacts in a similar way to **aluminium oxide** with alkalis. The sodium zincate formed has the formula, Na_2ZnO_2. The hydroxides react in a similar way to the oxides, simply producing more water.

Applications

The **basic** nature of aluminium hydroxide allows it to neutralise stomach acid, as in **antacids**.

The **acidic** nature of aluminium oxide allows it to be separated from other metal oxides in the **Bayer process**.

ANALYSIS

Analysis is a process which tells us the 'what' and 'how much' about the elements present in a compound or mixture. There are two main types of chemical analysis; 'qualitative analysis' and 'quantitative analysis'.

QUALITATIVE ANALYSIS

This process is carried out to discover '**what**' is present. We may analyse a food and discover that it contains the elements carbon, hydrogen, oxygen and nitrogen. Or we may analyse a sample of petrol to find out which hydrocarbons are present in it. In both cases we have carried out a qualitative analysis.

QUANTITATIVE ANALYSIS

This process is carried out after the results of the qualitative analysis are known to discover '**how much**' of the elements or compounds are present. For example, if a sample of copper oxide is weighed, reduced to copper by heating in hydrogen and reweighed, the masses of copper and oxygen can be found. The results of this quantitative analysis can be used to find the formula of the copper oxide.

◀ Cations and anions, chromatography, food analysis, formulae ▶

ANHYDROUS

Anhydrous means literally 'without water'. It is a term used to describe solids which normally have **water of crystallisation** e.g. $CuSO_4 . 5H_2O$ but which have been **dehydrated**.

hydrated copper (II) sulphate	heat →	**anhydrous** copper (II) sulphate	+	steam
$CuSO_4\ 5H_2O(s)$	heat →	$CuSO_4(s)$	+	$5H_2O(g)$

Liquids, which are free from water are sometimes referred to as anhydrous to emphasise their dryness, e.g. anhydrous ethanol is pure ethanol, anhydrous ammonia is liquefied ammonia not an aqueous solution.

ANIONS

These are negatively charged **ions**. They are called anions because they are attracted to the **anode** (positive electrode) if the substance is electrolysed. Some examples are:-

O^{2-}, oxide; Cl^-, chloride; Br^-, bromide; I^-, iodide; Oh^-, hydroxide; No_3^-, nitrate; and SO_4^{2-}, sulphate.

Non-metal ions tend to be anions.

Anion tests – qualitative analysis for anions

Table A.9 gives the main anion tests.

Anion to be detected	*Test solution added*	*Result expected if anion is present*
hydroxide	indicator	high pH – blue or blue/green
chloride	silver nitrate solution*	white precipitate turning grey
sulphate	barium chloride solution*	white precipitate
carbonate	dilute acid – nitric always works	fizzing, CO_2 formed

Table A.9

* Note: it is best to add dilute nitric acid before adding these test reagents. If *carbonate* is present a 'false' indication will be given if nitric acid has not been added. Carbonates will give white precipitates with both these reagents and it will appear as if a chloride or a sulphate is present. Adding the acid removes the carbonate anions by converting them to carbon dioxide.

ANODISING

This is the process of artificially thickening the oxide coating on aluminium. It is done by electrolysis of dilute sulphuric acid using the aluminium as the anode. Oxygen formed at the anode reacts with aluminium converting the oxide layer from less than one millionth of an inch to several thousand times this thickness. The anodised layer makes the aluminium more resistant to corrosion. The layer is also harder than aluminium and protects it from scratching. Anodised aluminium has the unusual property of absorbing coloured dyes. The metal can therefore be permanently coloured without using paint.

ANTACIDS

Antacids are anti-acids. They are bases which reduce the acidity of the stomach contents. Too much acidity is often the cause of stomach pain. The bases or alkalis used in antacids are not harmful to the stomach. They are usually taken in a **solid** or **emulsion** form.

The ingredients vary between brands but antacids usually consist of one or more of the following: calcium carbonate (chalk), magnesium carbonate, sodium hydrogencarbonate, aluminium hydroxide and magnesium hydroxide.

Comparison of antacid activity

An antacid has two measurable properties

- how much stomach acid it neutralises
- how fast it neutralises the excess acid

The amount of acid neutralised depends on the moles of base in the tablets and also on which bases are present. For example, one mole of aluminium hydroxide neutralises three times as much acid as one mole of sodium hydrogencarbonate.

$Al(OH)_3(s)$ + $3HCl(aq)$ → $AlCl_3(aq)$ + $3H_2O(l)$
3 moles of acid
1 mole base

1 mole of acid
$NaHCO_3(s)$ + $HCl(aq)$ → $NaCl(aq)$ + $CO_2(g)$ + $H_2O(l)$

The speed of neutralisation depends largely on the surface area of the base. Temperature inside the stomach cannot be increased. The surface area is increased to speed up the process by either chewing the tablet or by using an emulsion which acts even more rapidly.

ANTIFREEZE

Antifreeze is **ethane** –1,2– diol. (ethyleneglycol).

```
   OH  OH
   |   |
H—C——C—H
   |   |
   H   H
```

It is added in proportions of up to 25% to the cooling water in a car's radiator. Its purpose is to lower the freezing point of the coolant to prevent freezing in winter. Without it, the expansion of freezing water would damage the car engine.

ANTIKNOCK

Antiknock is a lead compound which helps petrol to burn more efficiently and to prevent car engines 'knocking'. It was discovered by an American chemist **Thomas Midgley**. Antiknock, when introduced into petrol, saved fuel. Fears that it might cause lead poisoning were expressed from its introduction in 1928. At the time, however, these fears were exaggerated and, when people didn't 'die like flies' on contact with the new petrol, the complaints were forgotten.

Antiknock is a mixture of a lead compound (tetraethyl lead) and dibromoethane. Dibromoethane is added to prevent the lead compound in 'antiknock' from building up inside the engine. It converts the used lead into a gas which comes out of the exhaust rather than remaining as a solid deposit inside the engine. Dibromoethane is made with **bromine**.

Since 1989, unleaded petrol has become popular and more widely used as motorists have been made aware of the toxic effects of lead in the environment. Lead is especially dangerous for infants and young children because of its damaging effect on the brain. Unleaded petrol is more expensive to produce than leaded petrol, but it is currently cheaper to buy because a lower fuel tax has been levied on it. The widespread use of unleaded petrol will allow car makers to fit catalytic converters which will further reduce pollution from vehicle exhausts. However, this is likely to mean that more fuel will be consumed for the same mileage travelled. In changing to unleaded fuels for cars we are reducing the emission of a 'toxic' air pollutant and are putting in its place a 'greenhouse' pollutant – the kind of choice we will be faced with increasingly in the future.

◀ Catalytic converters ▶

ANTISEPTICS

Antiseptics are chemicals used to kill or check the growth of bacteria on the human body. Phenol (carbolic acid) was the first antiseptic to be used in medicine when Joseph Lister used it in surgical operations in 1865. With its use the number of deaths amongst surgical cases was reduced considerably. Improved antiseptics now in use are TCP and Dettol, both of which are derived from phenol. The relative effectiveness of antiseptics in killing *Salmonella typhosa* is shown in Table A.10.

Antiseptic	*Relative effectiveness*
phenol	1
TCP	23
DDT	280

Table A.10 Relative effectiveness of antiseptics

ARGON, Ar

Argon was the first of the family of noble gases to be extracted from air. It was discovered in 1894. By removing all the oxygen, nitrogen and carbon dioxide from air, Sir Wiliam Ramsay was able to isolate a gas which was twenty times denser than hydrogen. This new gas was named argon from the Greek word 'argos' meaning 'inert'. Argon has no chemical reactivity.

Argon is the commonest noble gas. It makes up 0.9% of the atmosphere. It can be extracted from the air by liquefaction followed by **fractional distillation.** It is used as a gas in electric light bulbs and also where a non-reactive atmosphere is required e.g. in 'argon arc-welding' to avoid reaction between the melted metal and oxygen in the air.

ASPHALT

This is a **bitumen** and grit mixture used to produce a smooth covering for roads and paths. The grit is usually limestone or granite.

ATOMIC MASS UNIT, m_u (amu)

The masses of protons, neutrons and electrons are too small to express conveniently in grams. The amu is a convenient unit for comparing the masses of **nucleons**. The masses of a proton and a neutron are each 1 amu. An electron weighs about 1/2000 amu.

◀ Sub-atomic particles ▶

ATOMIC NUMBER, Z

The number of **protons** in the nucleus of an atom is its atomic number. The atoms of different elements have different numbers of protons in the nucleus. Knowing the number of protons in an atom identifies the atom. In neutral atoms (but not in **ions**) the number of **electrons** is also the same as the atomic number.

The atomic number of an atom is usually shown at the bottom left of the symbol. For example, aluminium has an atomic number 13 and this is shown as $_{13}Al$.

ATOMS

Atoms are the smallest particles of an element able to take part in a chemical reaction. Atoms are composed of **protons, neutrons** and **electrons.** The hydrogen atom, H, is an exception – it contains no neutrons.

All atoms of the same element have identical numbers of protons but may have different numbers of neutons. Atoms with the same number of protons but different numbers of neutrons are **isotopes** of the element. For example, all hydrogen atoms have one proton in the nucleus. There are three isotopes of hydrogen having zero, one and two neutrons in addition to the proton. These isotopes are called **hydrogen, deuterium** and **tritium** respectively.

Atoms of different elements have different numbers of protons in the nucleus.

AUTOCATALYST

◀ Catalytic converters ▶

AVOGADRO'S CONSTANT

Avogadro's constant is the number of particles in one mole of substance.

- It is the number of atoms in a mole of atoms
  For example, a mole of copper atoms, 64grams of Cu, contains 6×10^{23} atoms
- It is the number of molecules in a mole of molecules
  A mole of hydrogen molecules, 2 grams of H_2, contains 6×10^{23} molecules.

AVOGADRO'S LAW

This states that equal volumes of gases contain equal numbers of molecules (or moles of molecules) when measured at the same temperature and pressure.

The law is based on many careful measurements taken from a wide variety of gases. It can be stated the other way round as equal numbers of molecules (or moles of molecules) of all gases occupy equal volumes.

Measurement shows that 1 mole of any gas has a volume of $24dm^3$ at room temperature (25°C) and 1 atmosphere pressure (normal air pressure). $24dm^3$ is therefore called the **molar volume** of any gas at room temperature and normal atmospheric pressure.

This law applies only to gases but is very useful because a measurement of the moles of any gas can be obtained simply by measuring its volume.

BAKELITE

Bakelite was the first synthetic plastic to be made. It is a dark coloured **thermosetting plastic** first discovered by Leo Baekeland, a Belgian chemist, in 1909. It is a **condensation polymer** of phenol and formaldehyde. Bakelite becomes a **cross-linked polymer** in the process of moulding. Once formed it cannot be melted. This makes it ideal for making heat-resistant articles. Electrical plugs and fittings, and the handles of saucepans are made of bakelite. It has been replaced in many applications by similar polymers, e.g., urea-formaldehyde and melamine-formaldehyde which are white and can be coloured.

BARIUM CHLORIDE, $BaCl_2$

A solution of this salt is used to detect the presence of sulphates – sulphate ions – in unknown compounds. Sulphate ions react with barium chloride to form an insoluble white precipitate of barium sulphate.

barium chloride solution		any sulphate		barium sulphate precipitate		chloride ions
$BaCl_2(aq)$	+	$SO_4^{2-}(aq)$	→	$BaSO_4(s)$	+	$2Cl^-(aq)$

This is the standard test for sulphates.
Soluble barium compounds are very poisonous.

BARIUM SULPHATE, $BaSO_4$

Barium sulphate is a white solid. It is insoluble in water. It is used in medical diagnosis as a stomach filler to improve the visibility of stomach ulcers under X-rays. Even though barium compounds are toxic, the insolubility of barium sulphate makes it safe to use.

BASES

A base is a substance which will react with and neutralise an acid to form a salt. When metals react with oxygen the oxides formed are bases. Some metal oxides react with water and form metal hydroxides which are also bases. Most bases are oxides or hydroxides of metals. Ammonia, however, is a base though it is not a metal oxide.
Common bases are:

- Alkali metal oxides and hydroxides such as lithium oxide, Li_2O, and sodium hydroxide, NaOH
- Alkaline earth oxides and hydroxides such as magnesium oxide, MgO and calcium hydroxide, $Ca(OH)_2$
- Oxides of transition elements such as copper CuO and iron Fe_2O_3

base	+	acid	→	salt	+	water
CuO(s)	+	H_2SO_4(aq)	→	$CuSO_4$(aq)	+	H_2O(l)

Uses

Bases are used to make useful salts from acids by neutralisation. Many of the salts which do not occur naturally are made in this way. They are also used to neutralise waste acids from chemical processes. Calcium hydroxide suspension, known as 'milk of lime' from its appearance, is widely used for this purpose in industry. Acid waste would otherwise pollute rivers and sewage processes.

BATTERY

A battery is the common name for an electrical cell or a group of cells. It produces direct electrical current by chemical reaction inside the cell.
◀ **Cells – electrical, Direct current** ▶

BAUXITE

Bauxite is the common ore containing aluminium oxide. It is the only economic source of aluminium oxide. Aluminium oxide is extracted from bauxite by the **Bayer process.** Bauxite is not found in the UK. It is imported from Australia, Brazil, Jamaica and the USA.

BAYER PROCESS

The Bayer process is used to purify **aluminium oxide.** Powdered **bauxite** contains aluminium oxide, iron oxide and silicon dioxide. Of these, only the aluminium oxide is soluble in hot alkali. The Bayer process consists of reacting powdered bauxite with hot sodium hydroxide solution. Alumina dissolves but the oxides of iron and silicon are unaffected. These two oxides can be filtered off and are waste products. They are currently dumped in plastic-lined ponds to prevent rain-soluble alkali from entering ground water and maybe even drinking water supplies.

The dissolved alumina forms a concentrated solution and the alumina it contains can be precipitated by adding pure crystals of hydrated alumina around which the alumina from the solution crystallises. Before smelting the hydrated aluminium oxide is dehydratede to pure alumina, Al_2O_3.

◀ **Siting of chemical plant** ▶

BECQUEREL, HENRI (1852–1908)

Henri Becquerel discovered **radioactivity** by chance in 1896. He was studying substances which gave off light when exposed to sunlight. Becquerel thought some of them might be giving off X-rays. One such substance was a uranium salt which glowed in the dark and would affect a photographic plate through its wrapper. One day, when the sun was not shining and he could not experiment with his materials, he placed some crystals of the uranium salt on a paper-wrapped photographic plate in a cupboard. Developing the plate later, he found that the photographic plate had been affected. He had accidentally discovered that the radiation from the uranium compounds was not caused by exposure to sunlight. He had discovered **radioactivity**. He had also inadvertently disproved Dalton's theory that the atom was the smallest particle of matter!

BENEDICT'S SOLUTION

This solution is used to test for **reducing sugars**. If an unknown substance is warmed with Benedict's solution and a cloudy green, orange or brown mixture is produced, the unknown substance is a reducing sugar. The precipitate formed is orange/brown. The mixture often appears green if small amounts of sugars are present. It is often used for detecting the **glucose** or **maltose** formed by the **hydrolysis** of **starch**.

BETA PARTICLES

Beta (β) particles are electrons emitted by the nucleus of a radioactive atom. They are able to penetrate thin pieces of paper, plastic and aluminium. Beta particles are one of three types of radiation given off by the disintegrating nuclei of decaying radioactive elements such as carbon-14 nuclei. It is an electron formed by the disintegration of a neutron into a proton and a beta-particle.

neutron	→	proton	+	electron (particle)
(no charge)		(1+ charge)		(1− charge)
mass 1 amu		mass 1 amu		mass negligible

1 amu is an **atomic mass unit** – a unit used to express the masses of nucleons.

In this process a neutron has been converted into a proton. The radioactive nucleus has gained a proton and lost a neutron. The mass of the nucleus remains the same (electrons have negligible mass) but the atomic number of the nucleus increases by one unit.

To ensure that the **mass numbers** and the **atomic numbers** balance in nuclear **equations,** the electron is given a mass number of zero and an atomic number of −1. Its symbol is ${}^{0}_{-1}e$.

BIODEGRADABLE

The term biodegradable is usually used when referring to man-made products which can be broken down by microorganisms in the soil. Very few plastics are biodegradable. The problem of disposal of plastic litter is perhaps best solved by:

- Making a greater effort to decompose plastic waste and reuse the decomposition products as fuels or in the manufacture of more plastics.
- Sorting and recycling plastics in the same way that metals are recycled.

In principle, almost any chemical product can be biodegraded. It is theoretically possible to breed or 'genetically engineer' microbes to feed on even the most unreactive or toxic of substances. Microbes can be purchased that will degrade **crude oil,** toxic phenol and many other troublesome chemical pollutants and wastes. When first manufactured synthetic detergents were not biodegradable – the modern product is. **Detergent** manufacturers made a deliberate change in the structure of the detergent molecule to make them biodegradable.

BIOMASS

Biomass is a term used to describe plant material and waste organic material which is not used as food. It includes:
– forest and crop waste
– sewage and farm manure
– unwanted plant or animal products

Biomass is seen as an alternative fuel source to take over from the fossil fuels which are rapidly being used up. The biomass materials mentioned can be:

- used directly as fuels, e.g. wood or straw
- decomposed by heat to produce fuel gases and fuel oils
- fermented to give **ethanol** or biogas which usually leaves a residue that can be used as a fertiliser.

BITUMEN

Bitumen is a black solid left after the most useful fractions have been distilled from **crude oil.** It is thermoplastic – it softens on heating and solidifies again on cooling. A mixture of bitumen and rock is called **asphalt** and is used to surface roads. The bitumen acts as the 'glue' and as a waterproofing agent. It is also used as a waterproofing agent in roofing felt and paints.

BLAST FURNACE

A blast furnace is any furnace used for **smelting** metals heated by a fuel burning in a blast of air. The commonest blast furnaces are those used for the production of **iron** and **zinc**. The 'blast' is usually preheated air, 1200 °C in the iron-making furnace, blown in at the bottom of the furnace through pipes called tuyeres (pronounced 'tweers'). Typical ironmaking blast furnaces are about 150 ft high and lined with a heat- resistant alumina-silica (heat resistant oxides) brick. (See Fig. B.1.)

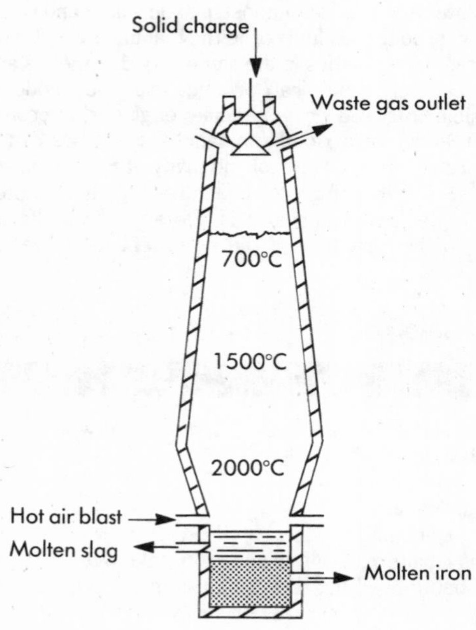

Fig. B.1 A blast furnace

BLEACH

Bleaching is the process of whitening of coloured substances or materials. Bleaching is a chemical reaction in which the coloured substance may be either oxidised or reduced to a white (colourless) product. Domestic bleach, in spite of its name, is more often used as a **disinfectant** than a bleach. (See Table B.1.)

Bleach	*Date first used*	*Bleaching reaction*	*Materials bleached*	*Special properties*
sulphur dioxide	unknown but ancient	reduction: sulphur dioxide + dye → reduced dye (white)	newspaper and fabrics	cheap, but bleached articles soon yellow in the air if not dyed
hypochlorite chlorine in alkali	1788	oxidation: hypochlorite + dye → oxidised dye (white)	fabrics, paper and tissues	cheap, very effective, very corrosive
hydrogen peroxide	1878	oxidation: peroxide + dye → oxidised dye (white)	delicate fabrics & hair	least corrosive solution

Table B.1 Bleaches and their uses

BOILER SCALE

This is **calcium carbonate**. It is chemically the same as **kettle-fur**. It is deposited on the hot surfaces of boilers in the home and industry when temporary hard water is being heated. It can cause loss of heating efficiency in boilers or blockages in the pipes carrying hot water.

BOILING

Molecules in **liquids** are in incessant, random motion – they never stop moving about in all possible directions. As more heat energy is added, this random motion becomes more and more vigorous. At any temperature, some of the molecules move fast enough to be able to escape from the liquid into the vapour. At higher temperatures more of the molecules escape. So, as the temperature increases, the number of molecules in the vapour increases. This increases the **pressure** of the vapour. When the pressure of the vapour reaches the pressure of the atmosphere (in a container open to the air) the liquid temperature will not rise further. The **boiling point** has been reached.

If heating is continued, all that happens is that more and more molecules escape into the surrounding air and the liquid evaporates away. The faster heat is applied at this stage, the faster the boiling liquid will evaporate – but the temperature will not change! All the added **energy** is used in increasing the number of molecules escaping into the more energetic vapour state. The *average* energy of the molecules in the liquid remains the same so the temperature stays constant.

◀ Boiling point ▶

BOILING POINT

When a liquid is heated it reached a point where its temperature does not rise further. The liquid is then boiling and that temperature is its boiling point (b.p.).

At the boiling point, the pressure of the vapour produced by the boiling liquid is equal to the external pressure.

- So boiling water at 100°C has a vapour pressure equal to the normal pressure of the atmosphere (Fig. B.2)
- If the external pressure is lowered by putting the water in a vacuum – the boiling point is lower than 100°C because the pressure of water vapour reaches the vacuum pressure with very little rise in temperature.
- If the pressure is increased, the boiling point is higher. This fact is used in pressure cooking. Temperatures up to 120°C cook food more quickly than boiling in an open pan.

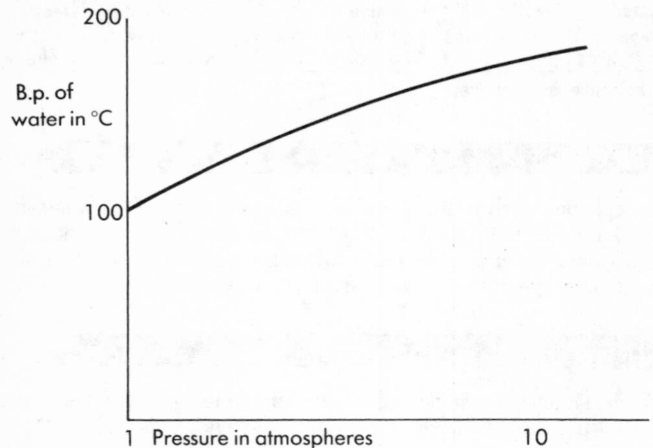

Fig. B.2 Graph of b.p. against pressure

Boiling points are often given in degrees Celsius, °C. However, they are also frequently given in absolute degrees, K, called Kelvin (not degrees) Kelvin). The b.p. of water at normal atmospheric pressure is 100°C which is 373K.

The boiling point of a substance gives information about its structure:

- Substances with low boiling points (roughly less than 500°C) are composed of molecules rather than ions. They have molecular structures. e.g., sulphur, b.p.444°C
- Substances with boiling points greater than 500°C are composed of ions; they have ionic **giant structures**. e.g., NaCl, b.p.1413 °C

BONDS

All chemical substances (**elements** and **compounds**) contain **atoms** or **ions** held together by bonds. These bonds can be of two different types – covalent or ionic.

- Molecular structures contain **covalent bonds**
- Giant ionic structures contain **ionic bonds**.

Bond-breaking and bond-making

When a chemical reaction occurs, the bonds present in the reactants are broken, the atoms rearrange themselves and new bonds are formed to make the products.

Bond breaking requires an input of energy.

Bond making gives out energy.

- If the energy taken in to break bonds equals that given out in making the new bonds, the temperature will be the same before and after the reaction.
- If the energy taken in to break the bonds is more than that given out in making new bonds, the products will be colder than the reactants. The reaction is then an **endothermic reaction**.
- If the energy taken in to break the bonds is less than the energy given out in making new bonds, the products will be hotter than the reactants. The reaction is then an **exothermic reaction**.

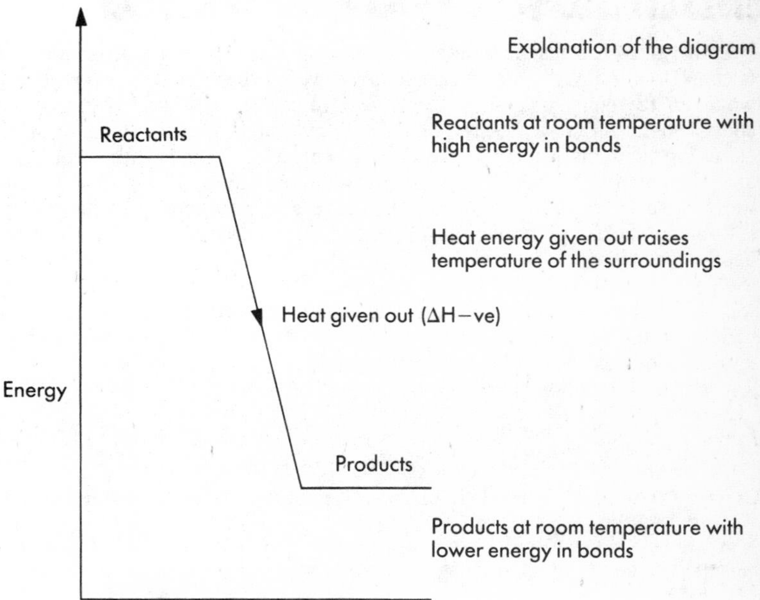

Fig. B.3 An energy level diagram for an exothermic reaction

A similar energy level diagram for an endothermic reaction will show the energy in the bonds of the products to be higher than that in the reactants.

BRASS

Brass is an **alloy**. It is a solid mixture of the metals **copper** and **zinc**. It is used both for its attractive appearance and cheapness. Brass is often used as a substitute for copper but it is stronger, harder, more easily shaped and being less dense than copper it is lighter for the same size. Zinc is about one third the cost of copper hence brass is cheaper than copper. A range of brasses is made containing from 5% – 50% zinc, see Table B.2.

Brass	*Composition*		*Use*
	Copper/%	*Zinc/%*	
gilding metal	95	5	jewellery
cartridge brass	70	30	ammunition cartridges
yellow brass	66	34	screws and tubes

Table B.2 Types of brass

BREATHALYSER

Breathalysers are instruments for measuring the concentration of **ethanol** (alcohol) in the breath. From the ethanol level in the breath it is possible to work out the concentration in the blood. Any motor vehicle driver who has above 80 milligrams of ethanol per 100 cm^3 of blood, the legal limit, is comitting a criminal offence in the U.K. Older forms of the breathalyser made use of ethanol's chemical reaction as a **reducing agent**. The glass tube into which suspect motorists were asked to blow contained small, evenly-packed crystals of acidic potassium dichromate. When breath containing ethanol vapour was blown through the tube, the ethanol changed the orange colour of the potassium dichromate crystals to green. The more ethanol in the breath, the longer the length of green crystals was at the end of the test. Near the middle of the tube's length was a 'legal limit' mark. If the colour change extended beyond this mark the test was failed.
The chemical reaction is:

orange crystals	+	alcoholic breath	→	green crystals	+	other products of the reaction
$Cr_2O_7^{2-}(s)$	+	ethanol	→	$Cr^{3+}(s)$	+	water and ethanoic acid

BREWING

Brewing is the process that produces ale, beer and lager. It is recorded that the slaves who built the pyramids of Egypt were given beer to drink. In the Middle Ages, when water in Britain could not be relied upon to be pure, ale was drunk in its place. The basis of brewing ale, beer and lager as well as wine is **fermentation**. The difference between the products lies in their alcoholic concentration and flavour; see Table B.3 which shows the products from different fermented plant materials.

Fermented material	*Name of product*	*Percentage alcohol in product*
malted barley after distillation	whisky	about 50% ethanol
grape juice	wine	8% – 13% ethanol
	fortified wines – sherry and port	about 20% ethanol
	brandy	about 40% ethanol
malted barley	beer	3% – 4% ethanol
	low-alcohol beer	< 1.2% ethanol
	alcohol-free beer	0.05% ethanol

Table B.3 Products of fermentation

BRINE

Brine is a concentrated solution of **sodium chloride**, NaCl, (salt) in water. Saturated brine contains about 25% by weight of salt in water.

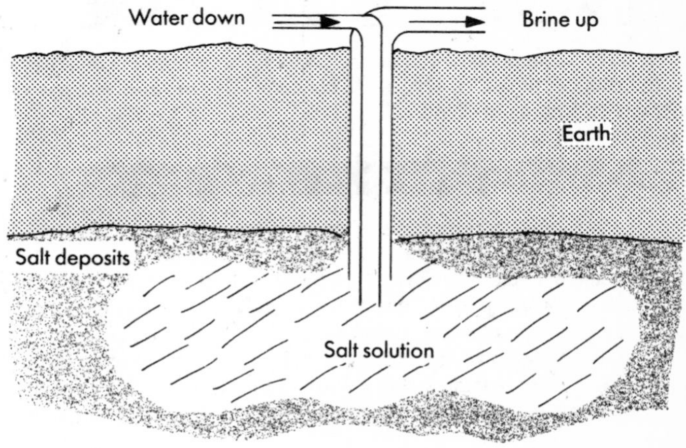

Fig. B.4 Solution mining

Sodium chloride is extracted as brine by a process known as 'solution mining'. In the UK, this involves pumping water down a hole bored into the salt layers below the Cheshire plain. The solution which returns to the surface is brine. This is then used in the nearby chemical industry for the production of the products shown in Fig. B.5.

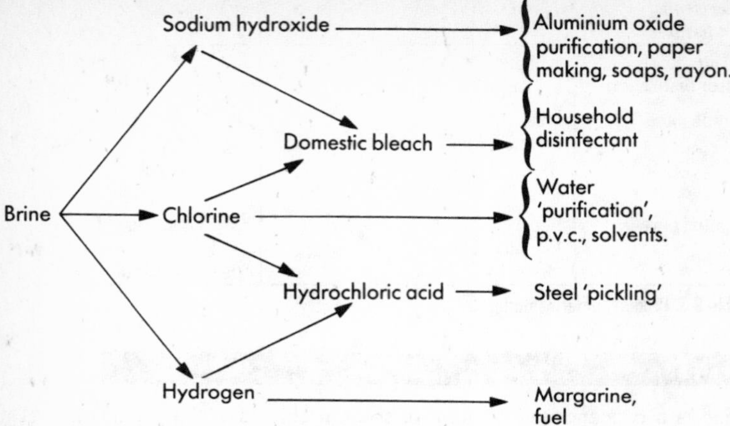

Fig. B.5 Uses of brine

BROMIDES

Bromides are compounds containing **bromine**. Metal bromides e.g., potassium bromide, are **salts**. Hydrogen bromide, HBr, is an acidic gas similar in properties to hydrogen chloride.

BROMINE, Br_2

Bromine is the only non-metallic element that remains liquid at room temperature. It was discovered by Balard in 1824. It is a brown, unpleasant-smelling liquid that derives its name from the Greek word; *bromos* meaning 'stench'. Bromine is extremely toxic, and great care must be taken to avoid a container of the element smashing as it vaporises quickly when spilt. One of the chief uses of bromine has been in the manufacture of **antiknock** – a petrol additive. The increasing sales of petrol without this additive – 'unleaded petrol' – will reduce the future importance of bromine as a chemical raw material.

EXTRACTION

Bromine is extracted from **sea-water**. It is a halogen. The main principle of the method is easily understood with a simple knowledge of the reactivity of the **halogens**. This tells us that chlorine will displace bromine from bromides. The sea contains quite a high concentration of bromide ions so if the conditions are right – a pH of 3.5 – bromide can be converted to bromine by reaction with chlorine. Sulphuric acid is added to produce the low pH.

chlorine gas	+	bromide solution	pH 3.5 →	bromine solution	+	chloride solution
$Cl_2(g)$	+	$2Br^-(aq)$	pH 3.5 →	$Br_2(aq)$	+	$2Cl^-(aq)$

The bromine can be driven out of the solution by blowing air through the mixture. Bromine is finally condensed to a liquid and distributed to 'users'.

bromine solution	air blast →	bromine vapour	+	waste sea-water
bromine vapour	condenser →	liquid bromine		

The extraction process used plentiful and cheap raw materials – sea-water, chlorine and sulphuric acid. These are either made in nearby factories or on-site. A **contact process** for sulphuric acid manufacture is easily incorporated into the plant for bromine extraction giving cheaper acid. The acidity of the used water becomes neutralised and diluted as it re-enters the sea.

Reactions

Bromine reacts with the elements and compounds that chlorine reacts with, but less vigorously. Bromine will displace iodine from iodides.

bromine		any iodide		a bromide		iodine
$Br_2(aq)$	+	$2NaI(aq)$	→	$2NaBr(aq)$	+	$I_2(aq)$

BROWNIAN MOTION

When tiny particles of a solid, suspended in liquid or gas, are observed under a microscope, they can be seen to be moving around in a 'random dance'. This activity was first brought to the attention of scientists by a botanist, Robert Brown. The explanation was given by Albert Einstein. He calculated that the motion was caused by air or water molecules bombarding the solid particles from every possible direction. **Molecules** are not visible even under a microscope. Suspended particles can be seen because they are thousands of times bigger than molecules. So, only the *motion* of these particles is visible under a microscope, not the molecules that are the *cause of the motion*. (See Fig. B.6.)

Observing Brownian motion is indirect evidence of the existence of the much smaller particles we call molecules. Direct evidence would be the sight of the molecules of liquid or gas. In Brownian motion we see only the effects of the moving molecules, which make up gases and liquids, as they collide with the suspended solid particles.

◀ Kinetic theory of gases ▶

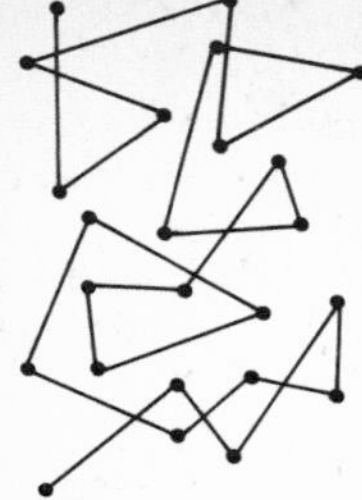

Positions of a dust particle at intervals of a few seconds. The air molecules causing this random motion cannot be seen.

Fig. B.6 Brownian motion

BUNSEN, ROBERT (1811–1899)

Robert Bunsen is, perhaps, best known as the inventor of the carbon-zinc battery and the perfecter of the burner that carries his name. Bunsen studied the colours chemicals produced when introduced into the flame of his burner. He discovered that elements present in very small quantities could be identified by these colours. During his researches he discovered the elements **caesium** and **rubidium** which he named after their flame colours.

BURETTE

A burette is a graduated glass tube with a tap at the bottom. It is used for dispensing liquids. In use it is held vertically in a clamp. It will measure, accurately, the volume of liquid run out through the tap. Its main use is in **titration** where any volume up to 50.00 cm^3 can be measured to the nearest 0.05 cm^3.

A burette should never be filled with alkali, which will attack the glass and lead to measuring errors.

BURNING

Burning occurs when a substance reacts with air and produces a flame and heat. Burning is the common name for **combustion**. For example, natural gas, methane, burns in air:

methane	+	air	→	carbon dioxide	+	water vapour	+	heat
$CH_4(g)$	+	$2O_2(g)$	→	$CO_2(g)$	+	$2H_2O(g)$	+	heat

Some substances will burn in gases which contain no oxygen. For example, hydrogen will burn in chlorine to form hydrogen chloride. In fact a substance will burn in any gas that it reacts with. Anything which burns in air will burn much more strongly in pure oxygen because pure oxygen is five times more concentrated than the oxygen in air.

BUTANE, C_4H_{10}

Butane is the fourth member of the family of saturated hydrocarbons called **alkanes**. The molecule contains four carbon atoms and ten hydrogen atoms. Butane is extracted from crude oil by **fractional distillation**. Butane has two **isomers**. The 'normal' isomer has the structure:

$$\begin{array}{ccccccccc} & & H & & H & & H & & H & & \\ & & | & & | & & | & & | & & \\ H & - & C & - & C & - & C & - & C & - & H \\ & & | & & | & & | & & | & & \\ & & H & & H & & H & & H & & \end{array}$$

but- *fourth*
-ane *alkane*

BUTENE, C_4H_8

Butene must not be confused with butane. Butene is a four carbon atom **alkene** – an unsaturated hydrocarbon.

$$\begin{array}{ccccccccc} & & H & & H & & H & & H & & \\ & & | & & | & & | & & | & & \\ H & - & C & - & C & - & C & = & C & - & H \\ & & | & & | & & & & & & \\ & & H & & H & & & & & & \end{array}$$

but- *fourth*
-ene *alkene*

BY-PRODUCT

A by-product is a chemical formed in the process of making something else. It is the less important product of a chemical reaction. By-products reduce waste. The chemical industry has many by-products. It is important to the profitability of most industrial chemical processes to be able to use or sell by-products. Examples are:

- **Sulphuric acid** made from waste sulphur dioxide produced in the smelting of zinc ores by CSL, Bristol
- **Cement** made by using ICI using clay waste washed from limestone quarried in Derbyshire.

CAESIUM, Cs

Caesium was discovered in 1860 by **Robert Bunsen.** He derived its name from the Latin word for blue, *caesius*; after its flame colour.

Caesium is an **alkali metal** – a member of **group 1** of the **periodic table.**

Properties

It is the most reactive naturally ocurring metal known. It reacts with water, oxygen and chlorine violently and explosively. Its atoms readily lose one electron to form Cs^+ ions, so its compounds have similar formulae to those of sodium, lithium and potassium, e.g. CsCl, CsOH, Cs_2O etc. The melting points of the alkali metals become lower down the group, and caesium melts at 29°C; it would melt in the hand but the experience would be far from advisable!

CALCIUM, Ca

Calcium was first made by **Humphry Davy** in 1808. He named it from the Latin; *calx* meaning 'lime'.

Calcium is an **alkaline earth metal** – a member of **group 2** of the **periodic table.**

REACTIONS

Its main reactions are with **air** and with **water.** To keep it out of contact with air it is kept under oil. It is a hard, silvery metal but is usually covered with a grey film caused by its reaction with air.

In water

It sinks and reacts safely at a steady rate. It gives off hydrogen gas which is easily collected in the apparatus shown below. The product is a milky suspension of **calcium hydroxide** in its **saturated solution.**

calcium	+	water	→	calcium hydroxide	+	hydrogen
Ca(s)	+	$2H_2O(l)$	→	$Ca(OH)_2(s)$	+	$H_2(g)$

When filtered, this mixture produces a filtrate which is **lime water.** This is easily proved by blowing into the filtrate through a straw. The milkiness produced is a **calcium carbonate** suspension like that obtained when using lime water to test for carbon dioxide.

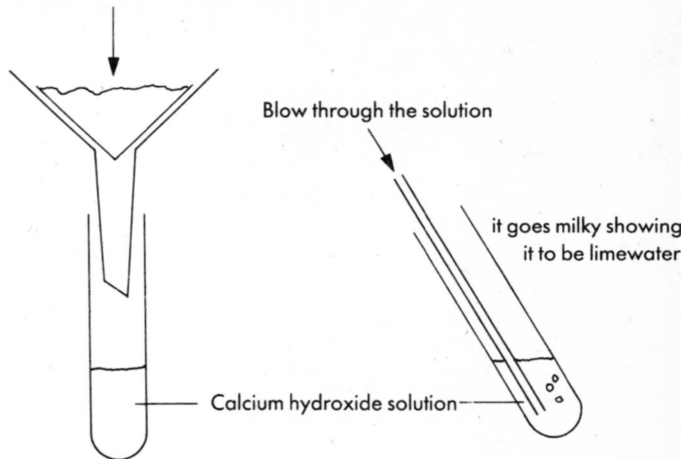

Fig. C.1 a) Filtration of calcium hydroxide solution b) Testing the calcium hydroxide solution

lime-water		carbon dioxide		calcium carbonate		water
$Ca(OH)_2(aq)$	+	$CO_2(g)$	→	$CaCO_3(s)$	+	$H_2O(l)$

In air

Calcium burns brightly in air with a red flame. The oxide is formed.

calcium	+	oxygen	→	calcium oxide	+	heat
$2Ca(s)$	+	$O_2(g)$	→	$2CaO(s)$		

Calcium oxide is called **quicklime.** It reacts very strongly with water giving out much heat, whilst swelling and crumbling to a powder. This reaction converts the quicklime (here 'quick' means 'active') into **slaked lime** ('slaked' means 'to have the thirst for water satisfied').

quick-lime	+	water	→	slaked lime	+	heat
$CaO(s)$	+	$H_2O(l)$	→	$Ca(OH)_2(s)$		

This process is a **hydration** reaction and so slaked lime is often called *hydrated lime.*

CALCIUM CARBONATE, $CaCO_3$

Calcium carbonate is best known as **limestone** or chalk. It is common in nature. The Pennines are largely limestone and the South Downs mainly chalk. Marble, a hard crystalline form of limestone which takes a high polish, is used as an ornamental stone in building.

REACTIONS

Calcium carbonate is a white solid, insoluble in pure water. It will dissolve in acids, acid rain and in water which contains dissolved carbon dioxide – a dilute solution of carbonic acid.

water	+	carbon dioxide	+	limestone or chalk	→	calcium hydrogencarbonate solution
$H_2O(l)$	+	$CO_2(g)$	+	$CaCO_3(s)$	→	$Ca(HCO_3)_2(aq)$

This reaction is of great importance in chemistry since it explains the formation of **kettle fur, boiler scale, stalagmites** and **stalactites**, the action of petrifying wells and the presence of hard water in the limestone and chalk areas of the country (see Fig. C.2).

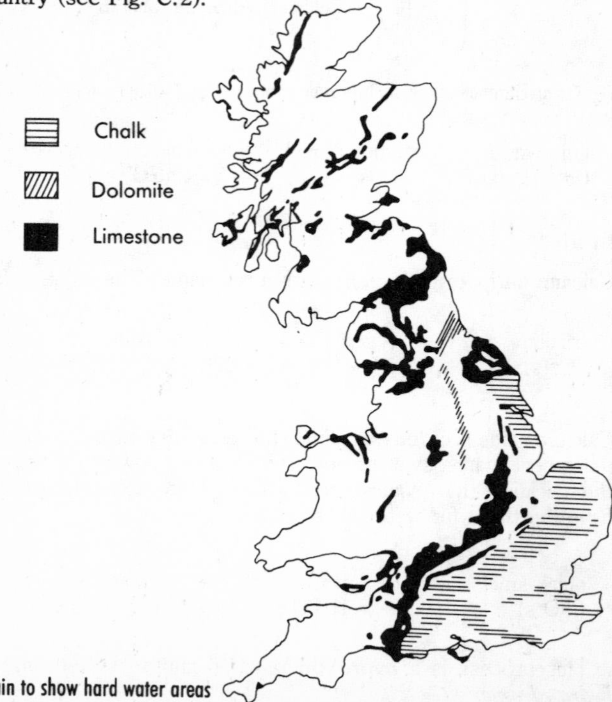

Fig. C.2 Map of Britain to show hard water areas

Everyday uses

Purified calcium carbonate is used in indigestion tablets. Most other uses of calcium carbonate do not require the pure compounds and limestone is used.

Laboratory uses

The reaction of marble chips with hydrochloric acid forms the basis of a common laboratory investigation. By using marble chippings of different sizes and acid of different concentrations it is possible to investigate the effects of particle size and acid concentration on the **rate of reaction**.

calcium carbonate	+	hydrochloric acid	→	calcium chloride	+	water	+	carbon dioxide
$CaCO_3(s)$	+	$2HCl(aq)$	→	$CaCl_2(aq)$	+	$H_2O(l)$	+	$CO_2(g)$

The rate or speed of the reaction can be measured by timing the collection of carbon dioxide gas in a gas syringe.

◀ Limestone ▶

CALCIUM HYDROGENCARBONATE, $Ca(HCO_3)_2$

Calcium hydrogencarbonate is formed in nature when limestone or chalk rocks are attacked by solutions of carbon dioxide, for instance, rain water in contact with soil. Solid calcium hydrogencarbonate cannot be obtained. If the solution is allowed to evaporate, it decomposes to calcium carbonate. This process produces **stalactites, stalagmites** and petrified plants.

calcium hydrogencarbonate solution	→	kettle-fur boiler-scale stalactite and stalagmite	+	water	+	carbon dioxide
$Ca(HCO_3)_2(aq)$	→	$CaCO_3(s)$	+	$H_2O(l)$	+	$CO_2(g)$

The same process occurs when the solution is heated. This produces **kettle-fur** and **boiler-scale** in kettles and boilers.

CALCIUM HYDROXIDE, $Ca(OH)_2$

Calcium hydroxide is commonly called **slaked lime** or hydrated lime. It is made by hydrating **quicklime (calcium oxide)**.

calcium oxide	+	water	→	calcium hydroxide		
$CaO(s)$	+	$H_2O(l)$	→	$Ca(OH)_2(s)$	+	heat

This is a strongly **exothermic reaction**.

Industrial uses

- Solid hydrated lime is applied to acidic agricultural land. It neutralises the excess acidity and brings the pH of the soil into the range 6 – 8, which is preferred by plants. Clay soils are also improved by 'liming', their structure becomes 'granular' and they drain better.

- Calcium hydroxide is industry's cheapest alkali and is used to neutralise waste acids.
- It is also commonly used to precipitate heavy-metals from chemical plant wastes – for example in the metal processing industry. All heavy metal hydroxides, e.g. hydroxides of copper, cadmium, lead and chromium, are insoluble and can be filtered out of liquid industrial waste before it enters the sewage or river system.

Laboratory uses

A solution of calcium hydroxide is called 'lime-water'. It is used to identify **carbon dioxide** gas.

lime water	+ carbon dioxide	→	calcium carbonate milkyness	+	water
$Ca(OH)_2(aq)$	+ $CO_2(g)$	→	$CaCO_3(s)$	+	$H_2O(l)$

CALCIUM OXIDE, CaO

Calcium oxide, or **quicklime**, is made by decomposing limestone at a high temperature (900°C).

limestone	→	quicklime	+	carbon dioxide
$CaCO_3(s)$	→	$CaO(s)$	+	$CO_2(g)$

This process can be done in the laboratory by fixing a small marble chip in a loop of stiff wire and positioning it in the hottest part of a bunsen burner flame for ten minutes.

On a larger scale, the thermal decomposition of limestone is carried out in a **lime-kiln**. The product is usually hydrated before being sold to the chemical and agricultural industries.

Uses

- Calcium oxide is used in the steel industry where it serves the same purpose as **limestone** in the **blast furnace** – it reacts with acidic impurities in steel converting them into slag. For other uses see **Calcium hydroxide**.

CALCIUM PHOSPHATE, $Ca(PO_4)_3$

- Calcium phosphate is a major component of animal bones.
- It is found as a rock, called rock-phosphate, which is imported into Britain.
- Most of the world's supply of phosphatic **fertiliser** is made from rock-phosphate.
- Calcium phosphate is not very soluble in water. However, if it is reacted with concentrated sulphuric acid, it is made into a water-soluble form known as **calcium superphosphate**.

CALCIUM SUPERPHOSPHATE

This is more soluble than calcium phosphate. It is in this form that phosphate fertiliser is usually sold because it is a quick-acting fertiliser. It is manufactured by heating calcium phosphate with 70% sulphuric acid.

CARBOHYDRATES

A carbohydrate is a compound of carbon, hydrogen and oxygen only, in which the proportion of hydrogen to oxygen is two to one – i.e. the same ratio as in water.

Common carbohydrates are glucose, $C_6H_{12}O_6$, sucrose $C_{12}H_{22}O_{11}$, and starch, $(C_6H_{10}O_5)_n$. Each is seen to have a hydrogen to oxygen ratio of 2:1. We can give the general formula as $C_nH_{2m}O_m$ where the number n may be the same as, or different from the number m.

Carbohydrates are essential components of a balanced diet.

CARBON

Carbon is a non-metallic element at the top of group four of the **periodic table.** In the form of charcoal it has been known from prehistoric times. Its name is derived from the Latin *carbo*; meaning 'charcoal'.

It exists as two **allotropes** – **graphite** and **diamond.** The difference in physical properties between these two forms of the same element is very striking. Table C.1 shows these differences in detail.

Properties of diamond	*Properties of graphite*
hardest known natural substance (Mohs' scale = 10)	relatively soft substance (Mohs' scale = 3)
does not conduct electricity	conducts electricity
good conductor of heat (explains why diamonds feel cold)	poor conductor of heat
density 3.5 g/cm^3	density 2.2 g/cm^3
colourless, transparent solid	dark grey solid

Table C.1 Comparing diamond with graphite

Structure

Both diamond and graphite are **macromolecular structures** (see Figs. C.3 and C.4).

Uses

Carbon is the cheapest **reducing agent** used for metal extraction. It will reduce the oxides of all metals below it in the **reactivity series.** It has been used for at least 5000 years to produce iron from iron oxide. Charcoal was the

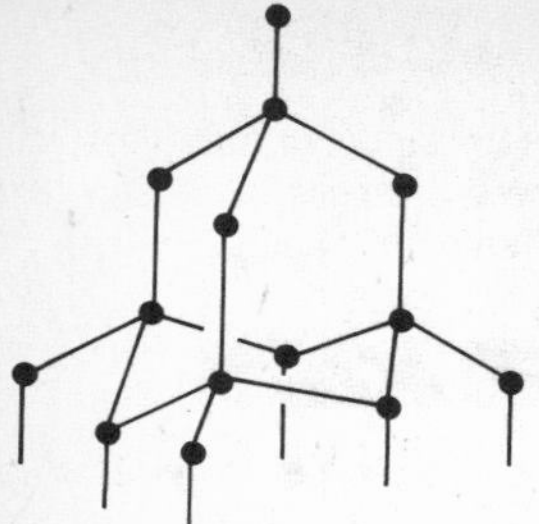

Fig. C.3 Diamond

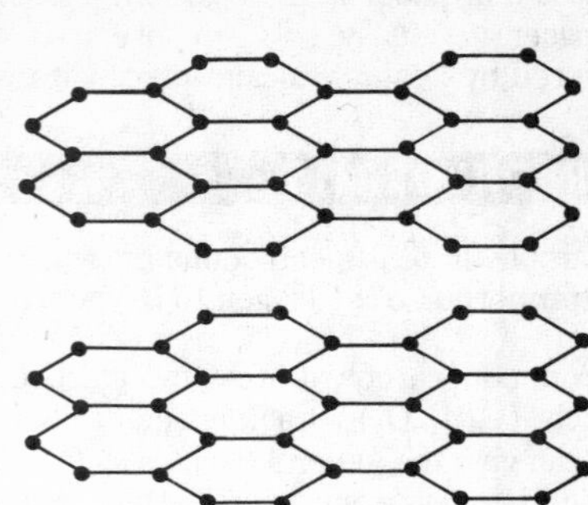

Fig. C.4 Graphite

reducing agent used, until 1709, since when the industry has used **coke**.
◀ **Charcoal** ▶

CARBON COMPOUNDS

Carbon is not a common element in non-living matter. However, it forms *more compounds* than all the other elements put together; more than two million carbon compounds are known.

Compounds of carbon are mainly present in, or formed from, plants and animals. They are called organic compounds. They include:

- nutrients such as **carbohydrates, proteins** and **fats**.
- waste products of the life processes such as **ethanol, methane** and **carbon dioxide**
- natural polymers such as silk, wool and cotton
- products of slow decay such as **crude oil** and **coal**

CARBON CYCLE

The carbon cycle shows the circulation of combined carbon between living organisms, the earth and the atmosphere.

A study of the carbon cycle (see Fig. C.5) will help us to understand the fact that the amount of carbon on earth remains constant whilst it flows through a cycle of chemical compounds and reactions. The world's carbon supply is locked up in the animals, plants and rocks of the land and oceans, in fossil fuels and in the atmosphere.

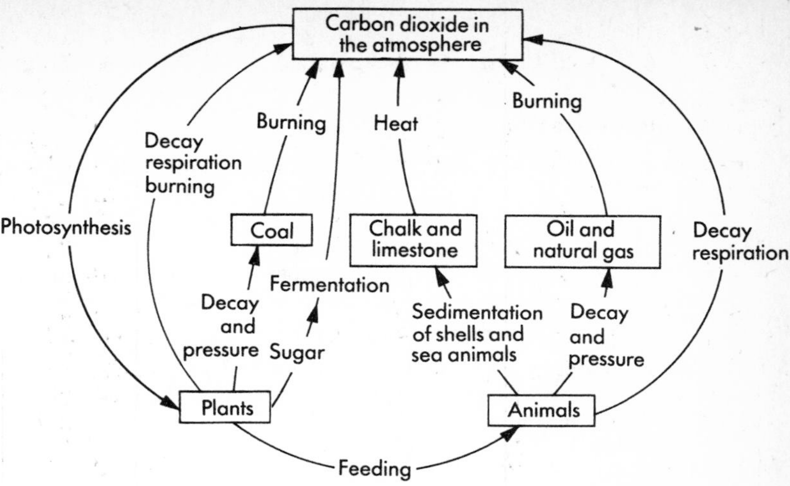

Fig. C.5 Carbon cycle

CARBON DIOXIDE, CO_2

Carbon dioxide gas is colourless, has no smell and is denser than air.

Reactions

It does not burn and will not allow other substances to burn in it.

When dissolved in water it forms a weakly acidic solution sometimes called carbonic acid.

Solid carbon dioxide is known as 'dry-ice'. It **sublimes** at temperatures above −78 °C producing gas without melting – hence is always 'dry'.

Carbon dioxide in the air

The processes of formation and removal of carbon dioxide from the air are shown in the **carbon cycle.** These processes normally keep the percentage of carbon dioxide in the air fairly constant. However, since large amounts of fossil fuels began to be used in the last century, the percentage has increased from about 0.029% in 1850 to 0.035% now. Carbon dioxide is a 'greenhouse gas' and it has been claimed that the increased concentration in the air is the cause of an increase in the average world temperature over the past century.

Preparation

All carbonates and hydrogencarbonates react with dilute acids to form carbon dioxide. A convenient method of obtaining a supply of the gas in the laboratory is to react dilute hydrochloric acid with marble chips.

calcium carbonate		hydrochloric acid		calcium chloride		water		carbon dioxide
$CaCO_3(s)$	+	$2HCl(aq)$	→	$CaCl_2(aq)$	+	$H_2O(l)$	+	$CO_2(g)$

Test for carbon dioxide

Carbon dioxide is the only gas which turns calcium hydroxide solution (limewater) milky.

carbon dioxide	+	lime water	→	calcium carbonate	+	water
$CO_2(g)$	+	$Ca(OH)_2(aq)$	→	$CaCO_3(s)$	+	$H_2O(l)$

The milkiness is a suspension of calcium carbonate. This will dissolve if an excess of the gas is passed through the suspension, forming **calcium hydrogencarbonate** solution.

Structure

Because it is a gas at room temperature carbon dioxide is a molecular compound. The molecule contains a carbon atom bonded to two oxygen atoms by double bonds. (See Fig. C.6.)

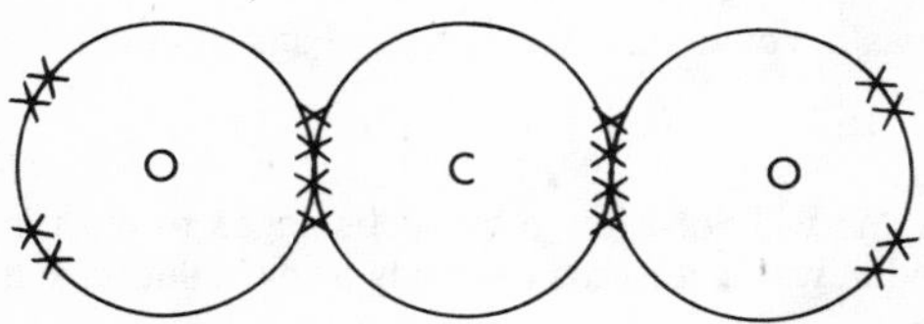

Fig. C.6 A carbon dioxide molecule

Uses

- It will put out fires so many fire extinguishers are filled with liquid carbon dioxide. Its high density allows it to smother a fire, keeping out air. In use it leaves no residue and is not toxic.
- Drinks such as lemonade, cola, beer, some natural spring waters, soda-water and champagne owe their fizziness to carbon dioxide dissolved under pressure
- It is a coolant in some nuclear reactors
- It is used in the manufacture of urea (a fertiliser), sodium hydrogencarbonate and sodium carbonate.

◀ Fire extinguishers ▶

CARBONIC ACID, H_2CO_3

This is the common name for a solution of carbon dioxide in water. It is a weak acid, pH about 4.

water	+	carbon dioxide	→	carbonic acid
$H_2O(l)$	+	$CO_2(g)$	→	$H_2CO_3(aq)$

Carbon dioxide dissolved in water under pressure is called soda water. It is a carbonic acid solution.

CARBON MONOXIDE, CO

Carbon monoxide is a colourless gas. It has no smell but is very toxic.

Reactions

It reacts with the haemoglobin in the blood to form carboxyhaemoglobin. This compound will not transport oxygen in the way that haemoglobin does, and so vital parts of the body can be starved of oxygen resulting in unconsciousness and eventually death.

Formation

It forms during the burning of carbon-containing fuels if they are not supplied with enough oxygen to form carbon dioxide. This can happen in sealed combustion chambers such as a motor vehicle engine or in homes where there is too little ventilation. For example, a natural gas fuelled hot-water heater, in a bathroom which has been sealed to prevent draughts, can produce carbon monoxide if the flame does not receive its oxygen supply from outside.

methane	+	adequate oxygen	→	carbon dioxide	+	water
$CH_4(g)$	+	$2O_2(g)$	→	$CO_2(g)$	+	$2H_2O(l)$
methane	+	insufficient oxygen	→	carbon monoxide	+	water
$CH_4(g)$	+	$1\frac{1}{2}\ O_2(g)$	→	$CO(g)$	+	$2H_2O(l)$

Carbon monoxide, when formed in motor vehicle engines, is a serious air pollutant in heavy traffic areas. It can be reduced by fitting a **catalytic converter** to the engine.

Carbon monoxide does not build up in the atmosphere as carbon dioxide does. It is readily biodegraded in the soil.

CARBOXYLIC ACIDS

Carboxylic acids are organic acids derived from **alkanes**. Ethanoic acid, derived from ethane, is commonly known as acetic acid. Like all carboxylic acids it contains a $-CO_2H$ group.

$$H-\overset{\displaystyle H}{\underset{\displaystyle H}{\overset{|}{\underset{|}{C}}}}-C\begin{matrix}\nearrow O \\ \searrow OH\end{matrix}$$

Ethanoic acid (**acetic acid**) – this acid in dilute solution is **vinegar.**

The carboxylic acids form a **homologous series** – a family of acids with the same general formula $C_nH_{2n+1}CO_2H$ and very similar properties.

CAST IRON

Most of the iron produced in a **blast furnace** is converted into steel. Some, however, is cast as soon as it comes from the furnace into 'pigs' of solid iron. This iron is called cast-iron or pig-iron. It contains 3–5% **carbon** absorbed from the carbon used in its production. Cast iron is brittle and so cannot be 'worked' by hammering. It is, however, hard, corrosion-resistant and cheaper than steel. It can be used wherever strength is not required as in underground pipes or car engine castings.

CATALYST

A catalyst is a substance which speeds-up a chemical reaction yet is left chemically unchanged at the end of the process. There is often confusion about the definition of a catalyst. Firstly, a catalyst reacts with the substances involved in the chemical reaction. Once reacted, it helps these substances to combine more quickly than they would without it. When all the reactants have been used up, the catalyst is reformed. It is still there at the end and can be used again – it is chemically unchanged.

Secondly, for reasons beyond the scope of this book, catalysts cannot slow-down reactions, only make them go faster. A so-called 'negative catalyst' is always used up as it acts and therefore does not fit the definition.

Uses

Catalysts are important in industrial chemistry because they allow higher production and therefore greater economy in processes such as the **Haber process** and the **contact process.** In fact, very many chemical processes make use of catalysts. Even expensive metal catalysts such as platinum can be used economically. For example, quite soon cars in the U.K. will have to be fitted with a platinum catalyst. These catalysts will last for many years and will contain very small amounts of platinum. It will be spread very thinly on a large surface area of support material. As the platinum will not be used up in the process, it will be recovered when the unit stops working efficiently and recycled.

◀ Catalytic converters ▶

CATALYTIC CONVERTERS – AUTOCATALYSTS

As the name suggests, these are catalysts used on *auto*mobiles – cars and lorries. They are also used on stationary engines used in industry for power generation. (See Fig. C.7.)

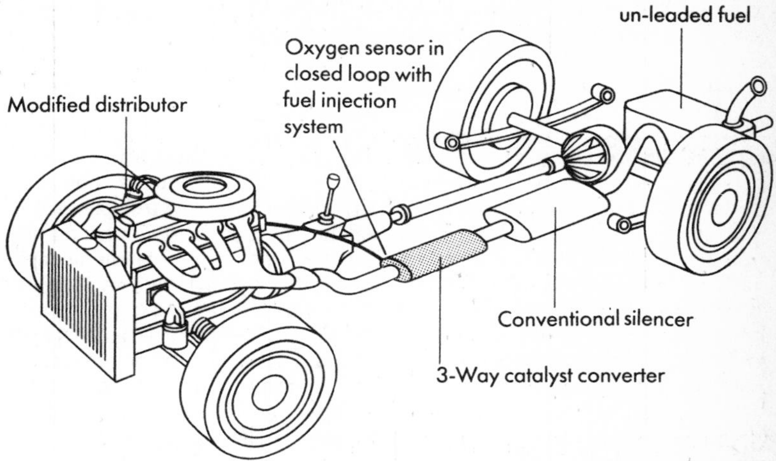

Fig. C.7 3-way catalyst fitted on a car (courtesy of Johnson Matthey Catalytic Systems Division)

Chemical principles

The chemical principles behind their working are not difficult to understand. The exhaust gases from motor cars contain toxic gases such as carbon monoxide, nitrogen oxides and hydrocarbons. The molecules of these compounds react together but very slowly. The catalyst's job is to ensure that they react together before they leave the exhaust system.

The reactions occurring are:

- In a platinum **oxidation** catalyst system for 'lean-burn' engines;

$$2CO(g) + O_2(g) \rightarrow 2CO_2(g)$$
$$HC(g) + O_2(g) \rightarrow CO_2(g) + H_2O(g)$$

NO_x (see acid rain) is not removed by this type of catalyst.

- In a platinum-rhodium **three-way** catalyst system for high performance engines with fuel injection; the pollutant gases, CO and HC are made to combine with NO to form harmless nitrogen, water vapour and carbon dioxide. See Table C.2.

Note: **Petrol** is a mixture of many hydrocarbons (HC); the equations using the abbreviation HC do not balance but give an idea of the reaction occurring.

Pollutant gases		Clean exhaust gases
	3-way	
$2CO(g) + 2NO(g)$	$\rightarrow$	$2CO_2(g) + N_2(g)$
	catalyst	
$HC(g) + NO(g)$	$\rightarrow$	$CO_2(g) + H_2O(g) + N_2(g)$
	converter	
$HC(g) + O_2(g)$	$\rightarrow$	$CO_2(g) + H_2O(g)$

Table C.2 The effect of a 3-way catalytic converter on exhaust gases

The structure of catalytic converters

Because the gases passing through car exhausts travel rapidly, their reaction on the catalyst surface must also be fast. For this reason, the platinum catalyst is thinly spread on a heat-resistant ceramic which contains thousands of very fine channels. The channels are large enough to allow free passage of exhaust gases. The total surface area of the channels is several thousand square metres which means a large surface area of platinum coating for rapid reaction. The platinum is coated so thinly on the ceramic support that the converter itself is not very expensive. However, as with most attempts to preserve and improve our environment, the total cost of fitting an autocatalyst will be large because of the engine modifications needed to provide the correct conditions for the catalyst to work without reducing the performance of the car. Catalysts are 'poisoned' by **lead** and **sulphur** compounds, so these must not be present in fuels used with autocatalysts. The increasing sales of unleaded petrol will allow British cars to be fitted with the catalysts that have been fitted to cars in America and Japan for more than ten years. Experience in these countries has shown that the concentration of carbon monoxide, nitrogen oxides and hydrocarbons has fallen considerably since the introduction of autocatalysts in the mid-seventies.

CATHODE

The cathode is the electrode connected to the negative pole of the d.c. electrical supply in an electrolysis cell. Electrons enter the electrolyte through the cathode which, because of its negative charge, attracts the positively charged ions in the electrolyte. Electrons are transferred from the cathode to the metal ions so forming metal atoms. For example, in the electrolysis of copper (II) sulphate solution:

copper ions	+	electrons from cathode	$\rightarrow$	copper deposit on cathode
$Cu^{2+}(aq)$	+	$2e^-$	$\rightarrow$	$Cu(s)$

CATIONS

Cations are the ions attracted to the **cathode** during **electrolysis.** They are positively charged ions. All cations are metal ions with the exception of hydrogen and ammonium ions, H^+ and NH_4^+.

CATION TESTS

When we test for the presence of cations in a mixture or compound we are usually trying to discover whether there are any metal ions present. Only two cations are not metal ions, they are the hydrogen ion, H^+ and the ammonium ion NH_4^+. Table C.3 shows a scheme of tests for cations.

Cation	*Test reagents*	*Results of positive test*
hydrogen ion	indicator solution	red/orange solution
ammonium ion	add sodium hydroxide solution	ammonia produced on warming turns damp indicator paper blue
zinc aluminium		white precipitate which dissolves in excess reagent
copper		pale blue precipitate
iron(II)		dirty green precipitate
iron(III)		rust-brown precipitate
calcium magnesium		white precipitate not soluble in excess reagent

Table C.3 A scheme of tests for cations

Cation tests using a flame – flame tests

Some cations are more easily detected by flame tests; they are, Na^+, K^+, Ca^{2+}.

◀ Flame tests ▶

CAUSTIC SODA

The term caustic means that the substance is corrosive to the skin and flesh. The common name for **sodium hydroxide**, NaOH, is caustic soda.

CAVENDISH, HENRY (1731–1810)

Cavendish was a great experimenter. On his father's death in 1783 he became a wealthy man and turned his home into a series of workrooms and laboratories. He greatly preferred his own company to that of others. He discovered hydrogen in 1766 (but mistakenly thought it came from the metal he used to make it) and synthesised water from hydrogen and oxygen. In 1785, he determined the main components of air – oxygen and nitrogen. In the process he discovered that air contained a small portion of a gas that could not be nitrogen, oxygen or carbon dioxide. More than one hundred years later this portion was found to contain the **noble gases**.

CELLS

The term cell is used to mean either an electrolysis cell or a 'battery'. In an electrolysis cell electricity is consumed and the electrolyte decomposes into its elements. In a 'battery', a chemical reaction occurs which produces electricity. The two can be distinguished if we call them **electrolysis cells** and **electrical cells** respectively.

ELECTRICAL CELLS

Electrical cells make electricity from chemical reactions. They depend on the tendency of reactive metals to lose electrons and the ions of unreactive metals to gain electrons. For example, in the cell below (see Fig. C.8), magnesium is the reactive metal. It gives up electrons as it reacts.

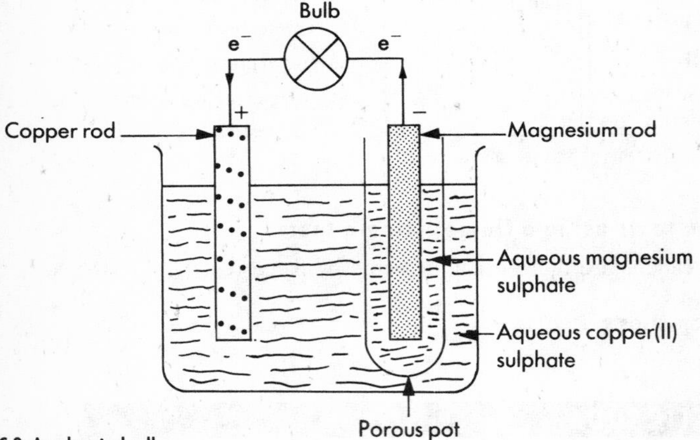

Fig. C.8 An electrical cell

magnesium	→	magnesium ions	+	electrons released
Mg(s)	→	Mg^{2+}	+	$2e^-$

The electrons released by the magnesium as it reacts travel to the copper where they combine with copper ions. Copper is the unreactive metal and therefore does not react.

copper ions	+	electrons from magnesium	→	copper deposit
Cu^{2+}(aq)	+	$2e^-$	→	Cu(s)

As they travel in the wire connecting the magnesium rod with the copper rod, the electrons are able to light the bulb. A flow of electrons is an electric current. Eventually all the magnesium will have reacted and all the copper ions will have formed copper metal. The electrical cell will then be 'dead'. The total reaction that has occurred here is:

magnesium	+	copper sulphate	→	copper	+	magnesium sulphate
Mg(s)	+	$CuSO_4$(aq)	→	Cu(s)	+	$MgSO_4$(aq)

If a cell is made in such a way as to allow the reacting chemicals to be fed in continuously, it never 'dies'. Such a cell is called a **fuel cell.** (See Fig. C.9.)

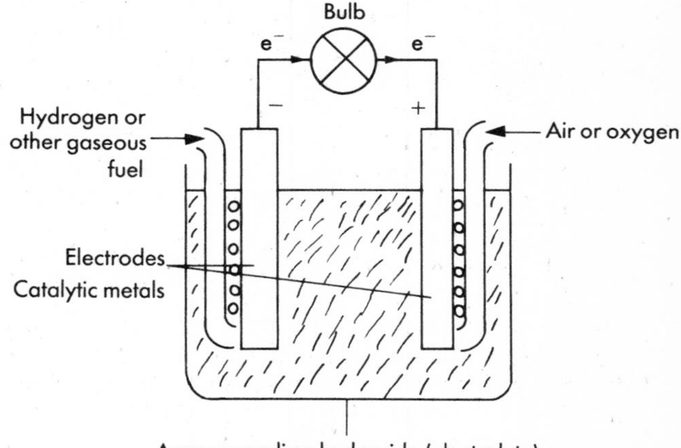

Fig. C.9 A fuel cell

Types of electrical cell

Table C.4 lists several common cells and illustrates the principle that a reactive and unreactive metal are used to produce electricity.

A normal electrical cell must be thrown away when the chemicals sealed inside it have completely reacted. The cell is then 'dead'. There are two alternatives to this wasteful process:

- to make the cell so that the reacting chemicals can be fed in continously; this solution creates a **fuel cell.**
- to choose a chemical reaction that can be reversed in the cell; this creates a **rechargeable cell.**

Rechargeable cells

The commonest rechargeable cell is the car **battery**. In this the chemical reaction that produces electricity eventually 'runs down' the battery. The

Electrical cell	*Reactive metal (−)*	*Unreactive metal (+)*	*Cell voltage*	*Advantage/disadvantage*
simple cell used as an example	magnesium	copper	1	rods easy to replace, spills too easily
common 'dry' cell	zinc	manganese (IV) oxide	1.5	cheap, reliable, voltage not constant, bulky
mercury cell	zinc	mercury oxide	1.5	small in size, constant voltage, pollution problem on disposal
silver cell	zinc	silver oxide	1.5	small size, constant voltage
air/sea survival cell	magnesium	silver metal	3	high voltage to light bright bulb, expensive

Table C.4 Types of electrical cell in common use

battery can be recharged by passing an electric current through the cell in the reverse direction. In motor vehicles this is done automatically by the alternator.

The fuel cell

The fuel cell (Fig. C.9) is a continuously fed electrical cell. The usual fuel consists of hydrogen or an organic gas or liquid fuel at the negative electrode (anode). The positive electrode (cathode) is fed with air (oxygen). The overall reaction which produces the electricity is the oxidation of the fuel.
For example,

at the anode	$2H_2(g)$			$\rightarrow$	$4H^+(aq) + 4e^-$
at the cathode	$O_2(g)$	$+$	$2H_2O(l) + 4e^-$	$\rightarrow$	$4OH^-(aq)$
added together	$2H_2(g)$	$+$	$O_2(g)$	$\rightarrow$	$2H_2O(l)$

In passing from anode to cathode through the external circuit, electrons can be made to do work, produce light or sound etc. Fuel cells have been used in spacecraft. They make use of the hydrogen and oxygen that are also used by the craft as rocket fuels. The principle of the fuel cell is very attractive to electricity producers because the fuel is converted into electricity almost three times more efficiently than at coal burning power stations.

The USA and Japan have several very large pilot plants testing the feasibility of this method of electricity production. It is likely to cause less pollution than fossil-fuel burning power stations.

ELECTROLYSIS CELLS

◀ Electrolysis ▶

CEMENT

Strongly heating chalk or limestone with clay or shale produces a grey powdery product, cement. Reaction between the two raw materials produces a mixture of calcium silicate and calcium aluminate. The grey colour of ordinary cement comes from the iron compounds in clay. For economic reasons, centres of cement manufacture tend to be on the edges of limestone or chalk areas where the rock-type changes to clay or shale. Here, both raw materials are readily available. Mixtures of cement, sand and water produce mortar. Adding water to cement produces an alkaline mixture which is corrosive to skin and flesh.

CHALK

Chalk is a form of calcium carbonate found naturally in the chalk hills of the South West of Britain – the Chilterns and the Downs. Blackboard 'chalk' is mainly calcium sulphate not calcium carbonate.

CHARCOAL

Charcoal is a reasonably pure form of carbon made by heating wood or animal bones in the absence of air. It is a porous solid.

Uses

Charcoal is used in many countries as a smokeless fuel for cooking. In industrialised countries, charcoal has many other uses.

- it is used in cooker hoods to absorb cooking smells
- it will remove the brown colour from raw sugar solutions enabling white, refined sugar to be made
- it is used in 'gas masks' to allow the wearer to breathe air containing toxic gases
- it is present in so-called 'water filters' where it removes chlorine and chlorine compounds which give water an unpleasant taste
- it is used increasingly by water companies to remove colour, odour and unpleasant tastes before the water reaches household consumers. Charcoal made from coconut husks is usually used for this process

CHARGES ON IONS

The charge on an ion is determined by two factors:

- the number of electrons in the outer shell of the atom from which the ion forms
- the excess of charge (negative or positive) on the ion formed

ANIONS

Elements which form anions have atoms with more than four electrons in their outer shell. They are in groups 5 – 7. Their atoms gain electrons to produce a full outer shell of eight electrons for the ion formed.

Group 7 atoms gain 1 electron and so produce ions with one negative charge in excess of the positive charge on the nucleus. Examples are F^-, Cl^-, Br^- and I^-.

Group 6 atoms gain 2 electrons producing ions with two negative charges in excess of the positive nuclear charge.
Examples are: O^{2-} and S^{2-}.

Element	*Charge on the atom's nucleus*	*Charge on the atom's electrons*	*Electron structure of the atom*	*Electron structure of the ion*	*Charge on the ion's nucleus*	*Charge on the ion's electrons*	*Excess of charge on the ion*
O	8+	8−	2 6	2 8	8+	10−	2−
F	9+	9−	2 7	2 8	9+	10−	1−
Na	11+	11−	2 8 1	2 8	11+	10−	1+
Mg	12+	12−	2 8 2	2 8	12+	10−	2+
Al	13+	13−	2 8 3	2 8	13+	10−	3+

Table C.5 The origin of charges on ions

CATIONS

Elements which form cations have less than four electrons in their outer shell. They are in groups 1–3. Their atoms lose one or more electrons to produce a complete outer shell of electrons for the ion produced. Group 1 elements lose the single outer electron to form singly positive ions, e.g. Li^+, Na^+ and K^+.

Group 2 elements lose two electrons to form ions, e.g. Mg^{2+}, Ca^{2+}.

Group 3 elements lose three electrons, e.g. Al^{3+}

CHEMICAL FEEDSTOCK

The chemical industry uses many materials to make its products. These materials are called raw materials or chemical feedstock. A complete list is beyond the scope of this guide, but it is useful to be aware of some of these materials. They include, air, coal, crude oil, limestone, metal ores, natural gas, river water, sea water, salt, sand and sulphur.

CHEMICAL INDUSTRY

The chemical industry is the U.K.'s fourth largest industry. It employs one-third of a million people and is the country's main export earner. The major sectors of the industry are shown in the pie-chart, Fig. C.10.

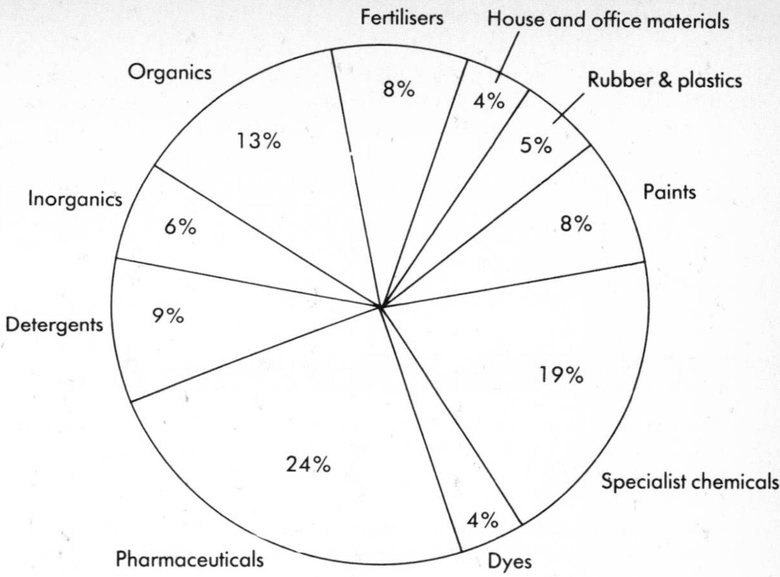

Fig. C.10 The main products of the UK chemical industry

CHLORIDES

Chlorides are compounds of chlorine. Metallic chlorides contain the chloride as an ion, Cl^-. Non-metallic chlorides contain chlorine covalently bonded to the non- metal. (See Figs. C.11 and C.12.)

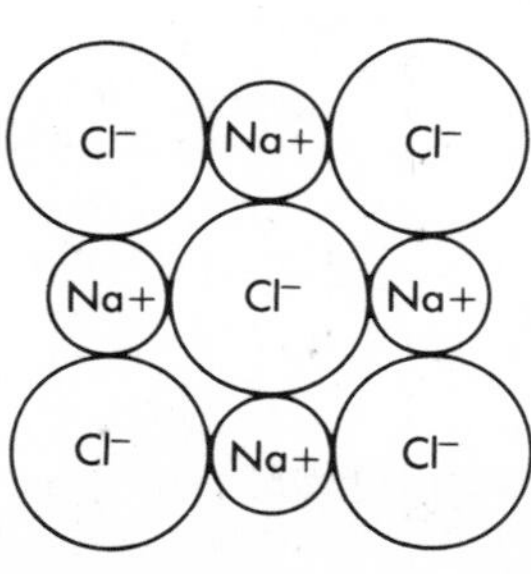

Fig. C.11 Sodium chloride – ionic crystal

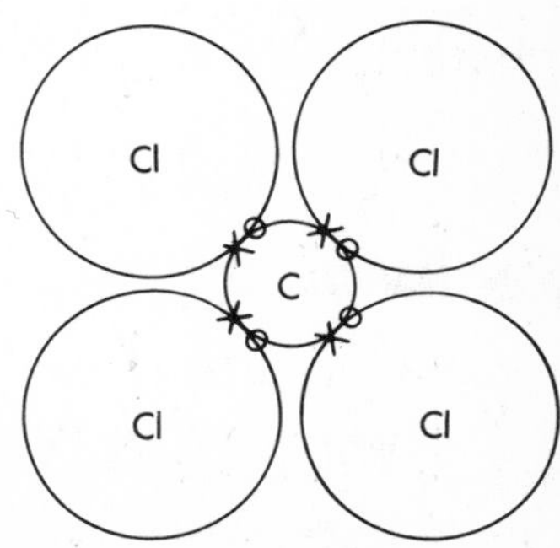

Fig. C.12 Tetrachloromethane molecule

TEST FOR A CHLORIDE

To test an unknown compound for ionic chloride, a solution of silver nitrate is added to a solution of the unknown. The appearance of a white precipitate shows that chloride ions are present in the unknown substance.

silver nitrate	+	chloride	→	silver chloride	+	nitrate
$AgNO_3(aq)$	+	$XCl(aq)$	→	$AgCl(s)$	+	XNO_3

◄ Anions ►

CHLORINE, Cl_2

Chlorine was discovered by **Scheele** in 1774. Scheele did not know that the gas he had prepared was an element. It was left to **Humphry Davy** to prove that in 1810. Ever since its discovery chlorine has found many uses that affect our daily lives.

Chlorine is a non-metallic element in group 7 of the periodic table. It is a green gas, much denser than air. It has a characteristic smell and is very toxic.

Structure

Chlorine is a molecular gas. Its molecules contain two atoms joined by a single covalent bond. (See Fig. C.13)

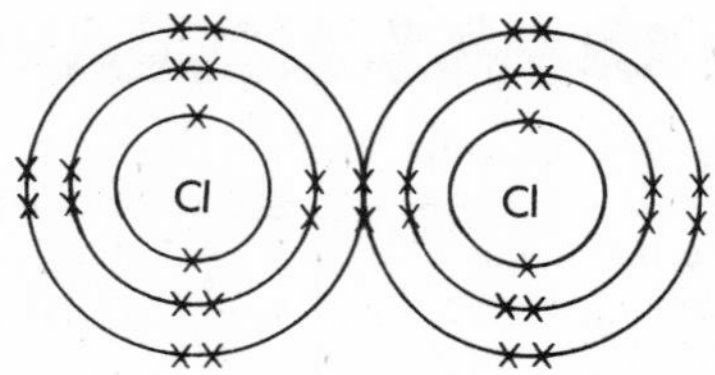

Fig. C.13 A chlorine molecule

The small molecules do not attract each other strongly and so the melting and boiling points of chlorine are very low.

MANUFACTURE

Preparation in the laboratory

This gas is most often made by adding concentrated hydrochloric acid to potassium permanganate crystals, through a tap funnel. Chlorine cannot be collected over water because of its solubility. It is usually collected by delivering it downwards into a gas jar fitted with a loose-fitting lid, but a small quantity can be collected in a gas syringe. (See Fig. C.14)

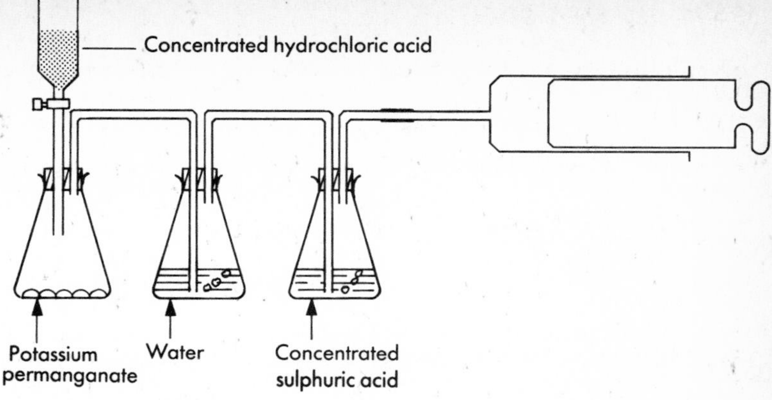

Fig. C.14 The preparation of chlorine

A simpler method of making chlorine uses **domestic bleach**. Bleach is a solution of chlorine combined with sodium hydroxide. Adding any dilute acid to bleach solution will produce chlorine gas.

bleach	+	acid	→	salt	+	water	+	chlorine
$NaOCl(aq)$	+	$2HCl(aq)$	→	$NaCl(aq)$	+	$H_2O(l)$	+	$Cl_2(g)$

If the chlorine is required pure and dry it must be washed first with water to remove hydrochloric acid gas and then with a drying agent to remove water vapour, as in Fig. C.14.

Manufacture in industry

Chlorine must be made as cheaply as possible in industry. It is industrially made by the electrolysis of **brine**. There are three different processes in use, the **diaphragm cell**, the **mercury cell** and the **membrane cell**. In each one the chlorine is formed at titanium anodes.

chloride ions	minus	electrons	→	chlorine gas
$2Cl^-(aq)$	$-$	$2e^-$	→	$Cl_2(g)$

The gas is dried by washing with concentrated sulphuric acid. It is compressed to liquefy it and then put into cylinders.

Properties

Chlorine is chemically a very reactive element. It will react with most other elements:

- it reacts with **metals** to form ionic metal chlorides e.g.

sodium	+	chlorine	→	sodium chloride
$2Na(s)$	+	$Cl_2(g)$	→	$2NaCl(s)$

- it reacts with **non-metals** to form covalently bonded molecular chlorides, e.g.

phosphorus	+	chlorine	→	phosphorus(V) chloride
$2P(s)$	+	$5Cl_2(g)$	→	$2PCl_5(s)$

- it reacts with **water** to form a solution which is both acidic and a bleach, e.g.

chlorine	+	water	→	hydrochloric acid	+	oxygen for bleaching
$Cl_2(g)$	+	$H_2O(l)$	→	$2HCl(aq)$	+	[O]

[O] is not oxygen gas; it shows that the solution has oxygen to use if there is a chemical like a dye present to oxidise. This reaction explains why we usually test for chlorine using damp indicator paper. The hydrochloric acid formed turns the indicator red and the oxygen [O] bleaches the indicator dye.

Reaction of chlorine with halides

Chlorine is more reactive than the elements below it in group 7 – bromine and iodine.

If chlorine is bubbled into a solution of a bromide or an iodide, the less reactive halogen is displaced.

chlorine	+	potassium bromide solution	→	bromine	+	potassium chloride solution
$Cl_2(g)$	+	$2KBr(aq)$	→	$Br_2(aq)$	+	$2KCl(aq)$
chlorine	+	potassium iodide solution	→	iodine	+	potassium chloride solution
$Cl_2(g)$	+	$2KI(aq)$	→	$I_2(aq)$	+	$2KCl(aq)$

These reactions indicate that chlorine displaces both bromine and iodine from their salts. Therefore chlorine is more reactive than both bromine and iodine.

Safe use of chlorine

Chlorine gas must be handled with care. It should be made or used only in a fume cupboard if more than test tube quantities are being made.

Uses

- Chlorine is toxic to most forms of life. One of its important uses is in sterilising domestic water supplies. When the water is free from bacteria, excess chlorine is removed by further chemical treatment with sulphur dioxide.
  (Note that water that has been chlorinated is biologically sterile (contains

no harmful bacteria) but is not chemically 'pure'. Tap water contains dissolved solids and chlorine does not purify it of these solids.

- Most of the chlorine manufactured is used to make PVC (**poly(vinyl chloride)**).
- Swimming pool water is usually chlorinated to disinfect it.
- Wood pulp for paper-making is bleached with chlorine.
- Chlorine forms useful compounds with hydrocarbons. For example, perchloroethene is used as a dry cleaning solvent; 1,1,1-trichloroethane is the solvent in correcting fluid. Some organic chlorine compounds, for example DDT, are powerful pesticides. Unfortunately, they are not quickly biodegraded and have become concentrated in the bodies of predatory animals and birds. Here they have toxic effects which have brought some birds of prey to the verge of extinction in Britain. These compounds are no longer used.

◀ Gas ▶

CHLOROFLUOROCARBONS (CFCs)

CFCs are molecular compounds composed of chlorine, fluorine, carbon and sometimes hydrogen. They are usually identified by numbers following the letters CFC. For example, CFC – 11 is the commonest. The public knows them mainly as aerosol propellants but they are also used as a foaming agent (they make polymers swell – like a rising cake) in the manufacture of expanded polymers – such as polystyrene for food packaging and polyurethane for insulation. They are also the working fluids (called refrigerants) in freezers and refrigerators.

CFCs were discovered in the 1920s by an American, **Thomas Midgley** and at the time were acclaimed for their useful properties and safety. They do not burn and are not toxic. They quickly replaced toxic ammonia in refrigerators. They were not suspected of doing any damage until 1985 when the British Antarctic Survey first detected a 'hole' in the **ozone** layer 30km above the South Pole.

The numbering system for CFCs

The numbers are a code for the formulae of CFCs. The code is as follows reading the numbers from left to right:

- First number is the number of carbon atoms minus one (C−1)
- Second number is the number of hydrogen atoms plus one (H+1)
- Third number is the number of fluorine atoms (F)
- All other atoms in the molecule are chlorine atoms

The formula of the CFC can then be worked out by constructing a molecule based on these atoms and giving each element its normal number of bonds. The first number is often zero, for C = 1, and so is omitted. This is recognised by a two digit number instead of a three digit number.

The commonest CFC is CFC−11. Its formula is based on the number 011. Using the above code this gives $CFCl_3$, which has the structure

$$\begin{array}{c} Cl \\ | \\ F-C-Cl \\ | \\ Cl \end{array}$$

See also a different numbering system in fire extinguishing Halons.

◀ Fire extinguishers ▶

CHLOROPHYLL

Chlorophyll is the green colouring matter in plants. It acts by catalysing the action of sunlight in photosynthesis.

		sunlight		
carbon dioxide	+ water	→	glucose	+ oxygen
		chlorophyll		
$6CO_2(g)$	+ $6H_2O(l)$	→	$C_6H_{12}O_6(aq)$ +	$6O_2(g)$

CHROMATOGRAPHY

Chromatography is a method of separating the ingredients (components) of a mixture.

- At its simplest, chromatography will tell us how many components there are in a mixture, for example, the mixture in Fig. C.15 contains three components.

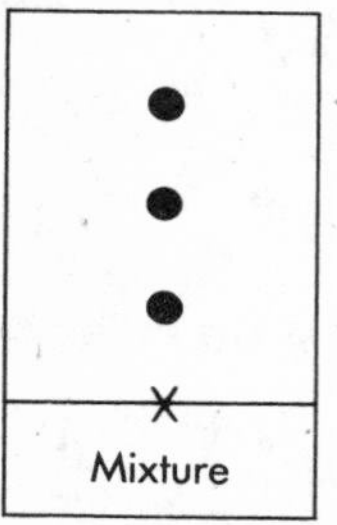

Fig. C.15 Chromatogram showing three different components in a mixture.

- If we add spots of known substances to the chromatogram we may be able to identify the components of the mixture, for example, the mixture in Fig. C.16 contains the substances A, B, C, and D.
- The mixture does not even need to be coloured for a chromatogram to be made. Fig. C.17 shows a chromatogram of the mixture which is left after hydrolysing **starch** with dilute acid. The hydrolysate, H, is seen to

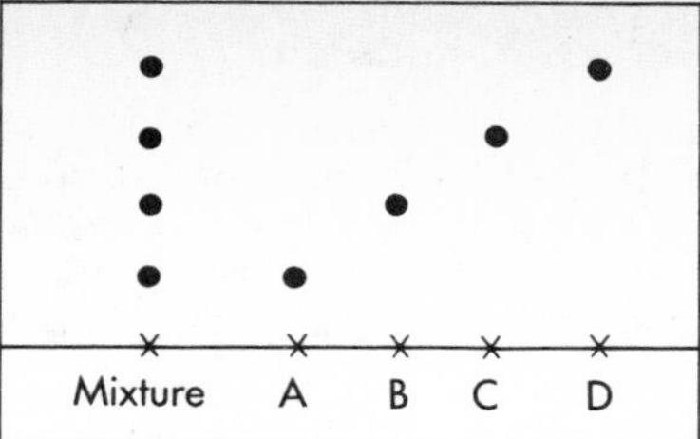

Fig. C.16 Chromatogram showing four different components in a mixture

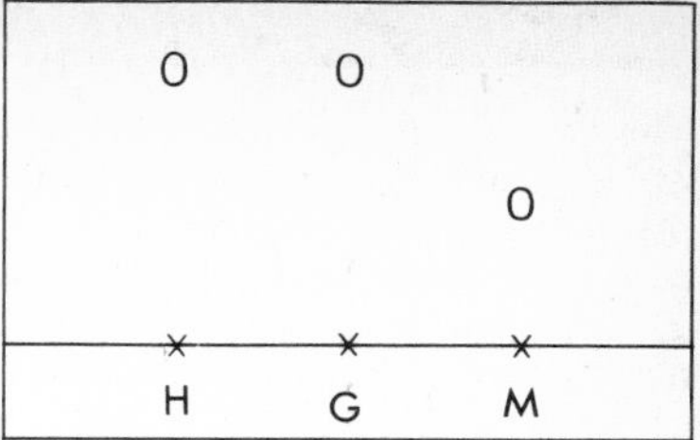

Fig. C.17 Identification of glucose by chromatography

contain the sugar, glucose, but not the sugar, maltose. The spot from the hydrolysed starch is at the same height above the bottom line as the spot from pure glucose, but not at the same height as the spot from maltose. Sugars are white and will not show on the white chromatography paper. However, they are 'located' by dipping the paper into a liquid 'locating agent' which makes them coloured and therefore visible. (See Fig. C.17.)

CITRIC ACID

Citric acid is the **weak acid** present in citrus fruits such as oranges and lemons. It is commonly used to add a 'tang' to fruit drinks and lemonade. Mixed with sodium hydrogencarbonate (commonly called bicarbonate of soda) and sugar it becomes 'sherbet'.

CLEAN AIR ACT

This Act of Parliament became law in 1956. It forbids the use of smoky fuels in many towns and cities of the UK. Since 1956, there is much less smoke and **sulphur dioxide** in the air we breathe.

COAL

Coal is a solid fossil fuel. It formed over a long period of time beginning 300 million years ago. Coal is the result of slow chemical and physical changes occurring in large masses of tree and plant material buried under great depths of rock. Over millions of years of decomposition, the plant material has lost most of the hydrogen and oxygen it contained when living (plants are largely cellulose which is a **carbohydrate**, $C_nH_{2m}O_m$). Most of the carbon in the plant material is not lost and remains as coal.

COKE

The process of coal formation has occurred under hot, airless conditions far underground. If poor quality coal (containing a low percentage of carbon) is placed in special heating chambers – called 'retorts' and heated without air, the process of 'coal making' can be continued, but more quickly than in nature. The end product is coke which is almost pure carbon. Coke is used in iron manufacture and is a smokeless-fuel.

COLLISIONS THEORY AND CHEMICAL REACTION

The collisions theory states that in order to react particles (molecules or ions) must:

- collide
- have enough energy to react

For the speed of a reaction to change:

- either the frequency of collision must change
- or the energy of the particles must change
- or both must occur

To increase the number of collisions per second and so make the reaction faster we can:

1) Heat the reactants; this will:
   - Make the particles move about faster; faster moving particles will collide more often and so the reaction will be faster (see Fig. C.18.)

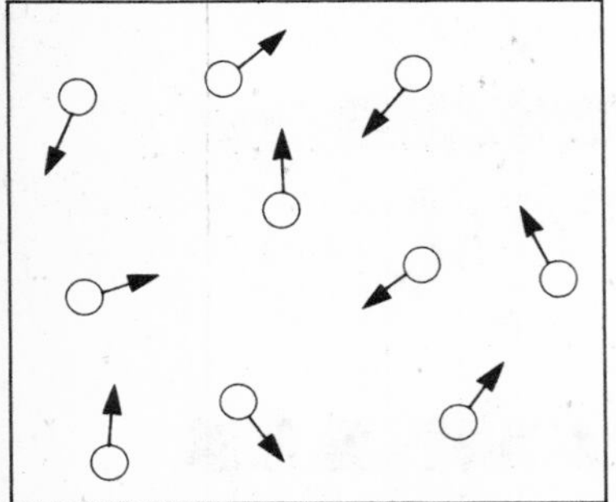

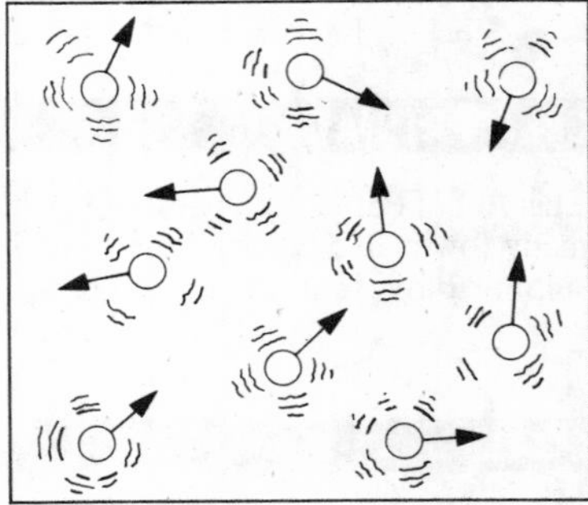

Fig. C.18 Molecules move about faster if they are 'hotter'

- give more of the particles the minimum amount of energy to react; this will ensure more 'reactive collisions' per second and so speed up the reaction

2) Increase the concentration of the reactants; this will:
   - increase the number of particles in the reacting 'space' more particles in the same space means more frequent collisions. (See Fig. C.19.)

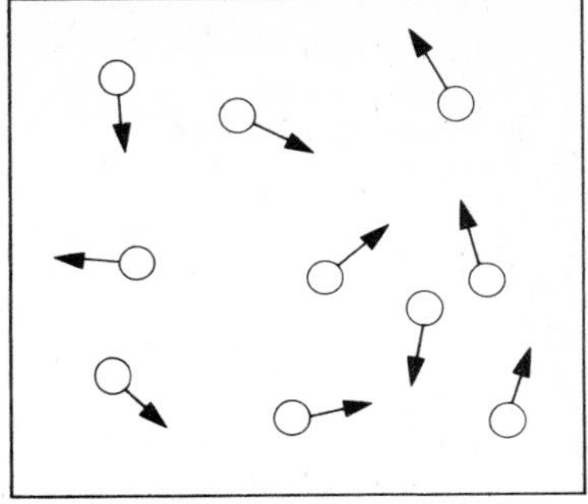
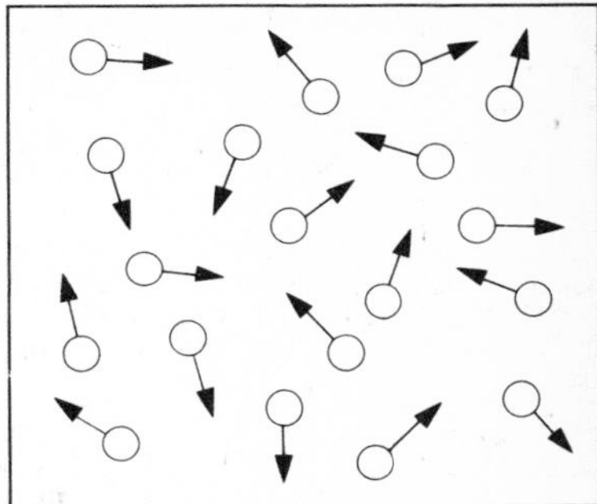

Fig. C.19 Molecules collide more often if there are more of them in a given space

- for **gases**, increasing the concentration is done by increasing the pressure. Doubling the pressure means packing twice the number of particles into the same volume.
- for **aqueous solutions**, increasing the concentration means dissolving more of the reactants in the same volume of water.

3) Increase the surface area of any solid reactant; this will:
   - expose more particles of solid to collision with particles of a reacting solution or gas (see Fig. C.20.)

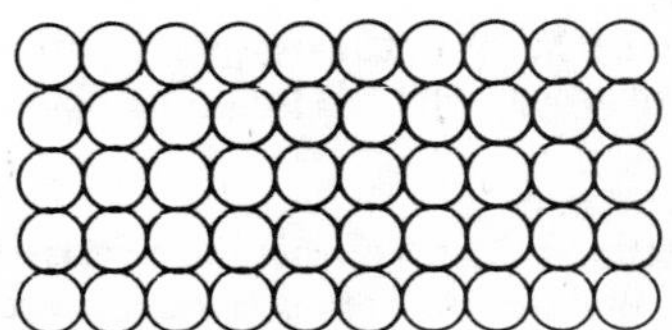

A single lump of reactant containing 50 particles. The number of particles exposed to reaction at the surface of the lump is 26

Fig. C.20 a) The effect that breaking up a lump of solid has on the exposure of surface particles

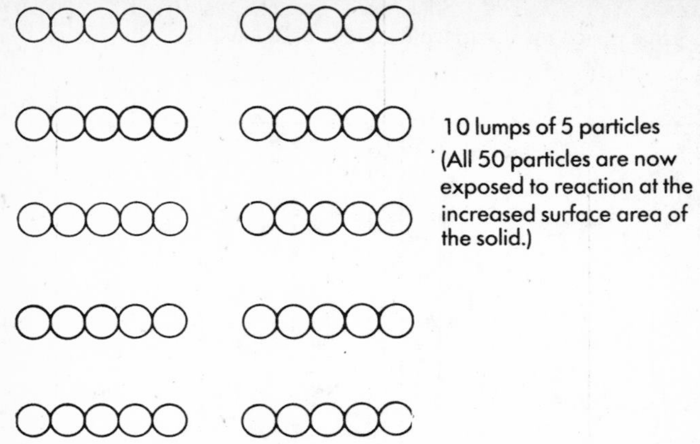

Fig. C.20 b)

In the example shown in Figs. C.20 a) and C.20 b) the speed of reaction would be twice as high for the ten lumps as for the single lump because twice as many particles are exposed to the reaction. Note, though, that to compare speeds 'fairly', the same number of particles (same mass) has been taken in each case.

COMBUSTION

Combustion usually refers to substances burning in air or oxygen. It is another term for burning. Chemists and engineers use the term in preference to burning in such phrases as;

- 'products of combustion' – compounds formed when a substance burns, for example, the products of combustion of petrol are carbon dioxide and water if combustion is complete
- 'internal combustion engine' – a motor car engine which runs on a burnable fuel such as petrol or ethanol. Combustion occurs inside the cylinders of the engine, that is internally
- 'incomplete combustion' occurs when a fuel has too little oxygen to burn completely. Incomplete combustion of hydrocarbon fuels produces toxic **carbon monoxide**

Combustion processes are **exothermic reactions.** Many of them are carried out specifically to obtain the heat from the combustion. Some, however, are used to obtain a specific product. For example, sulphur is burnt in air to produce the sulphur dioxide used to make sulphuric acid in the **contact process.**

HEAT OF COMBUSTION

The price of any fuel is set by the amount of energy it gives out per unit of mass. The 'energy value' of coal, for example, will be in kilojoules per tonne. These values must be measured so that a comparison can be made between different fuels. This is done using a 'calorimeter' in the following way.

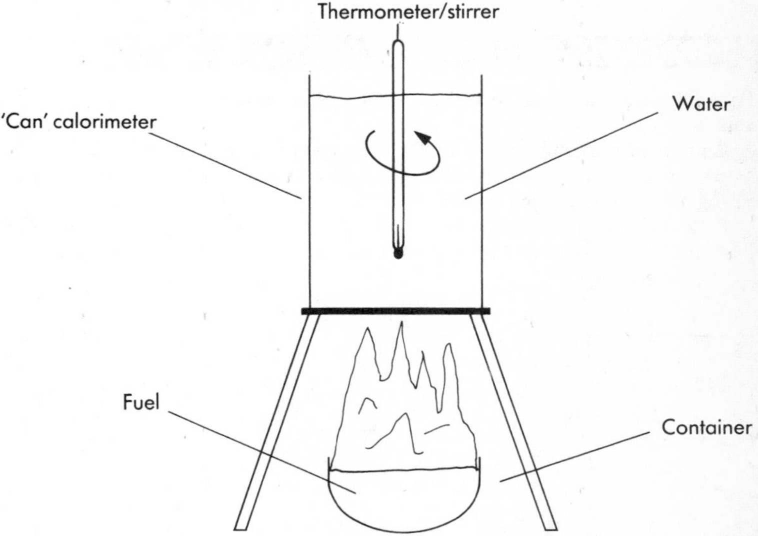

Fig. C.21 Finding the heat of combustion of a fuel

The apparatus is set up as in Fig. C.21 which shows a calorimeter used for determining the heat of combustion of a fuel.

- A known mass of water is placed in the 'tin' can (calorimeter)
- The temperature of the water is measured
- The weighed container of fuel is lit and immediately placed under the can
- The water is stirred steadily as it is being heated
- When a temperature rise of about 20 °C has occurred, the flame is put out
- The highest temperature reached with continued stirring is measured
- The burner + unburnt fuel is reweighed

The 'energy value' of the fuel burnt is calculated:

mass of water heated in kg.	×	4.2kJ per kg. per °C	×	temperature rise of the water in °C

This calculation gives the energy given out by the fuel in kilojoules. Let it be 4kJ.

- If this value is divided by the mass of fuel burnt in kilograms, say 0.01kg (10 grams), we get the energy value of the fuel in kJ per kg. In our example this is: $\frac{4\text{kJ}}{0.01\text{ kg}} = 400\text{kJ per kg}$
- To get the value in kJ per tonne this value would be multiplied by 1,000 (there are 1,000kg in a tonne).

COMPOUNDS

Any substance we care to name will be either an element, a compound or a mixture.

Compounds are substances (solids, liquids or gases) containing the atoms to two or more elements bonded together. The common feature of the diagrams in Fig. C.22 is that each shows

- at least two different atoms in the substance – so it cannot be an **element**
- each group of two or more atoms is exactly the same so it cannot be a **mixture**

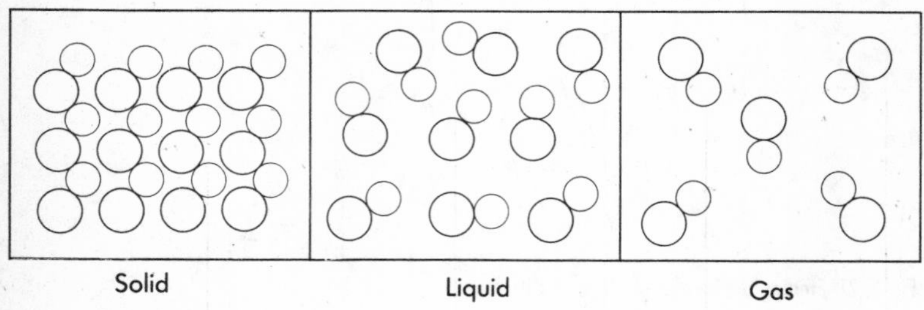

Fig. C.22 Molecules of a compound in the solid, liquid and gaseous states

A compound can be split up into its elements by a chemical reaction such as electrolysis and sometimes by heat alone. An element, of course, cannot be split up into anything simpler.

CONDENSATION POLYMERISATION

Some of the most familiar polymers are made by the process of condensation polymerisation. The nylons, polyesters, polyurethanes and epoxy resins are all families of condensation polymers. In another section we have seen that the other type of polymers – **addition polymers** – require only one reactive group to form; this group is the carbon-carbon double bond. Condensation polymers need two different reactive groups to form a long chain polymer. When these two groups react together water or some other small molecule is given off. For example, when nylon 6,6 forms, hydrogen chloride is given off:

hexane–1,6–diamine + hexanedioyl chloride →

$$nH{-}\underset{\displaystyle H}{\underset{|}{N}}{-}(CH_2)_6{-}\underset{\displaystyle H}{\underset{|}{N}}{-}H \quad + \quad nCl{-}\underset{\displaystyle O}{\underset{||}{C}}{-}(CH_2)_4{-}\underset{\displaystyle O}{\underset{||}{C}}{-}Cl \quad \rightarrow$$

nylon 6,6 + hydrogen chloride (small molecule)

$$H{-}\left[\underset{\displaystyle H}{\underset{|}{N}}{-}(CH_2)_6{-}\underset{\displaystyle H}{\underset{|}{N}}{-}\underset{\displaystyle O}{\underset{||}{C}}{-}(CH_2)_4{-}\underset{\displaystyle O}{\underset{||}{C}}\right]_n{-}Cl \quad + \quad nHCl$$

Because there are two different compounds reacting together in condensation polymerisation, changing these compounds results in a whole family of different polymers. Three nylons are in common use – nylon 6, nylon 6,6 and nylon 6,10.

CONDUCTORS

Conduction is a term used to describe either the passage of heat or the passage of electricity through a substance. **Metals** are good conductors of heat. Most other substances are not, with the exception of diamond which is an excellent heat conductor.

Processes of conduction

Metals and molten salts conduct electricity but by different processes:

- Metals conduct electricity because they consist of a collection of atoms in a 'sea of electrons'. When a metal conducts electricity, it is 'this sea of electrons' that conducts the electric current through the metal (see Fig. C.23.)

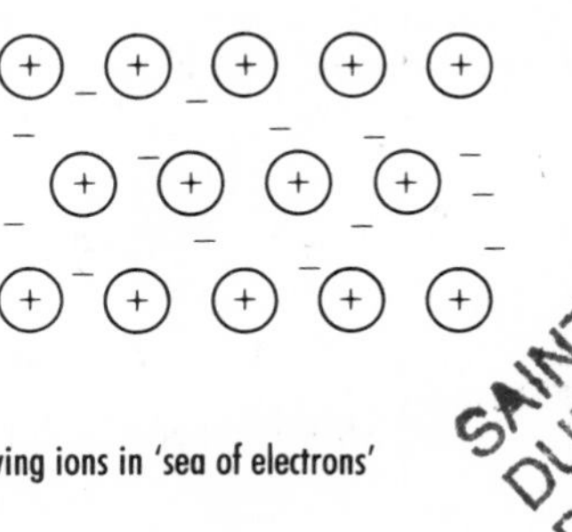

Fig. C.23 Metallic structure showing ions in 'sea of electrons'

- Molten salts do not conduct electricity in the same way. They consist of randomly moving ions. When positive and negative electrodes are placed in a molten salt, the ions are attracted to the electrode of opposite charge. When they reach the electrodes the ions discharge. It is this movement and discharge of ions that is the conduction process in molten salts. (See Fig. C.24.)

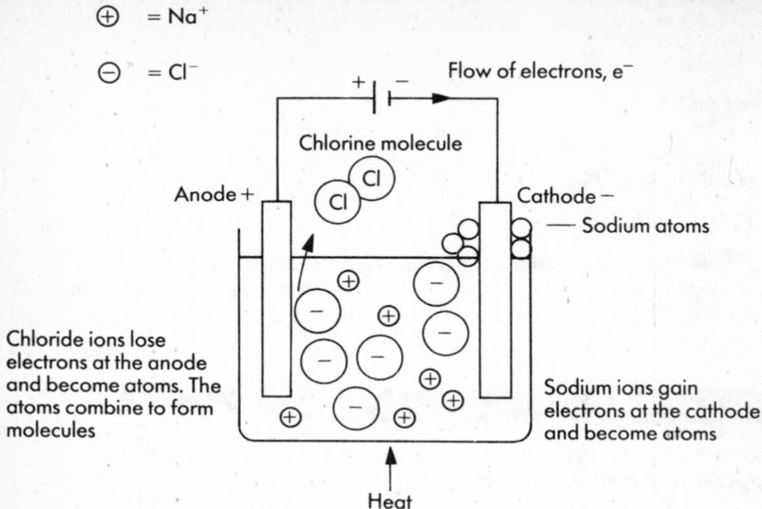

Fig. C.24

◀ Non-conductors ▶

CONTACT PROCESS

The contact process is the oxidation of sulphur dioxide by air using vanadium(V) oxide catalyst at 450°C and normal pressure.

The process occurs in 3 stages. (See Fig. C.25.)

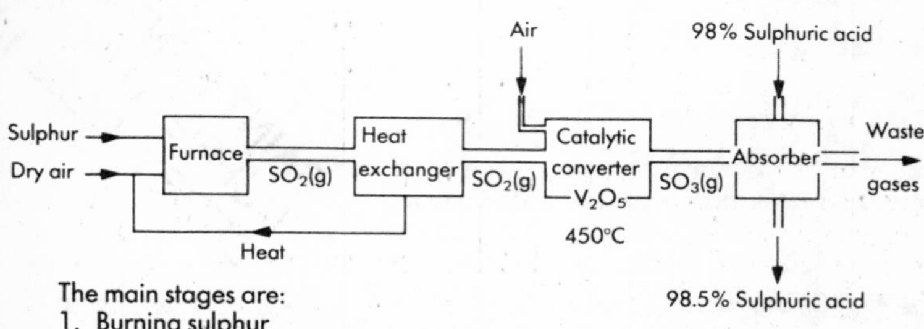

The main stages are:
1. Burning sulphur
2. Oxidising sulphur dioxide to sulphur trioxide
3. Converting the sulphur trioxide to sulphuric acid

Fig. C.25 The contact process – flow chart

- The first stage is the burning of sulphur to make sulphur dioxide.

molten sulphur	+	hot air	→	sulphur dioxide	+	heat
S(l)	+	$O_2(g)$	→	$SO_2(g)$		

- In the second stage, called the contact process, the sulphur dioxide mixed with air is oxidised to sulphur trioxide. This process occurs in a catalyst-contact chamber called a converter. The catalyst is vanadium (V) oxide and works at a temperature of between 400 and 450°C.

sulphur dioxide	+	oxygen	↔	sulphur trioxide	+	heat
$2SO_2(g)$	+	$O_2(g)$	↔	$2SO_3(g)$		

- In the last stage, the sulphur trioxide is hydrated to concentrated sulphuric acid. The overall reaction is:

sulphur trioxide	+	water	→	concentrated sulphuric acid	+	heat
$SO_3(g)$	+	$H_2O(l)$	→	$H_2SO_4(aq)$		

Attempts to react sulphur trioxide with water in one step results in dense mist which make the process impracticable and would result in loss of acid and atmospheric pollution. The third stage is therefore completed in two parts to avoid these process difficulties:

Sulphur trioxide is dissolved in 98% concentrated sulphuric acid, H_2SO_4, with no mist formation.

sulphur trioxide	+	98% acid	→	98.5% acid
$SO_3(g)$	+	$H_2SO_4(aq)$	→	$H_2SO_4(l)$

The acid is diluted back to 98% with water.

98.5% acid	+	water	→	98% acid
$H_2SO_4(aq)$	+	$H_2O(l)$	→	$H_2SO_4(aq)$

High efficiency process – lower pollution

In the most modern plant the oxidation of sulphur dioxide is carried out on 4 or 5 catalyst beds arranged in series. The reaction mixture goes through each of the beds in turn. In each catalyst bed, the reaction heats up the gases. They must be cooled before entering the next bed. The excess heat is extracted by '**heat exchangers**'. The yield of sulphur trioxide can be as high as 99.5%.

Economy of production

The heat of the reactions which has been removed by heat exchangers is used to:

- produce electricity in a steam turbine generator for use on the site

- produce steam for sale to nearby steam users
- to pre-heat the air entering the sulphur burner.

These economies offset the cost of the materials to make the acid. The process is therefore very economical, leading to a cheaper product. One chemical company in Britain operates a sulphuric acid manufacturing plant as a means of obtaining energy for their other chemical processes. That is, they use sulphur as a **fuel** and convert the products of combustion into a saleable **by-product** – sulphuric acid.

POLLUTION CONTROL

- The amount of sulphur dioxide passed out to the air from this process is now regulated by law. The modern process achieves 99.5% conversion. The amount of pollution is very low and is maintained at or below an allowed level.
- Sulphuric acid mist is avoided by carrying out the hydration of sulphur trioxide in two steps as discussed above. Sulphuric acid is the cheapest and most widely used mineral acid. For the uses of sulphuric acid, see **sulphuric acid**.

COPPER, Cu

The word copper is derived from the Latin; *cyprium aes* meaning 'metal from Cyprus'. It is an ancient metal – copper water pipes are known to have been used by the Egyptians 5,000 years ago!

Copper is one of only two metal elements that are not silver in colour – the other is gold. It is a dense pink solid melting at about 1080 °C. It is soft and can be shaped easily when cold. It is an excellent conductor of electricity and of heat.

Reactions

Copper is a very unreactive metal. However, in polluted air it slowly tarnishes and becomes covered with a green coating or 'patina'. This is often seen on old copper roofs and domes.

Properties

- it does not react with water
- it will not dissolve in dilute hydrochloric or dilute sulphuric acids because it is lower in the **reactivity series** than hydrogen
- it forms a black oxide, **copper (II) oxide**, CuO, if heated strongly in air.

COPPER REFINING

Copper is made from its ores by smelting. This process involves converting copper compounds such as copper sulphides into impure copper containing

98% copper. At this level of purity, copper is unsuitable for shaping, it must be refined – made purer. Copper can be refined in furnaces to a purity of 99.5%. This copper is then cast into anodes for the final electrolytic purification.

ELECTROLYTIC PURIFICATION

When electricity is passed through an aqueous solution of copper sulphate using copper electrodes, the copper anode dissolves and pure copper deposits on the the cathode.

In copper purification (see Fig. C.26) the anode is a thick sheet of impure copper and the cathode a thin sheet of pure copper. Both dip into a bath of copper (II) sulphate solution. Electrolysis then transfers pure copper from the anode to the cathode:
copper dissolves giving up electrons
forming copper ions
At the anode: $Cu(s) - 2e^- \rightarrow Cu^{2+}(aq)$
copper ions take up electrons forming copper
At the cathode: $Cu^{2+}(aq) + 2e^- \rightarrow Cu(s)$
'Electrolytic' copper is at least 99.95% pure.

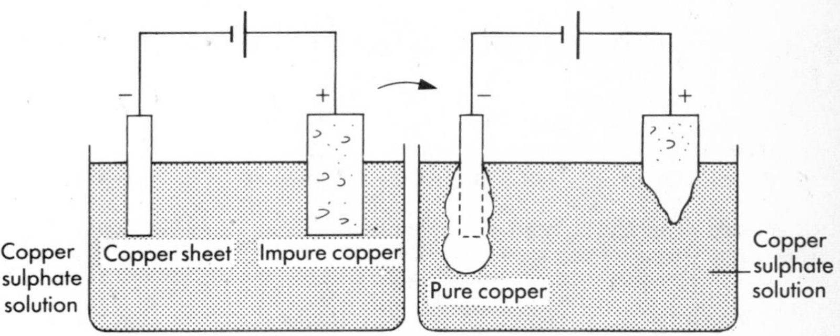

Fig. C.26 Purification of copper

Uses

Copper is used in manufacturing mainly because of four of its properties:

- it is very unreactive so does not corrode in water
- it is a good electrical conductor
- it is a good heat conductor
- it is soft and easily shaped

It is therefore used to make pans, water boilers, water pipes and taps. Electrical wire for indoor electricity supply is made only from copper. Good heat conduction is needed in pans and water boilers which are often made from copper. In spite of its useful properties, copper is an expensive metal. Alloying it with other metals widens its use, making it harder and often cheaper (e.g. brass).

Economies in copper use

Alloying copper with other metals uses less copper. Also, recycling copper scrap (about 40% is recycled) helps to extend the available supplies. It is estimated that the world's copper ore will not last more than 50 years!

◀ Alloys ▶

COPPER(II) OXIDE

This is the common, black, oxide of copper.

Preparation

It is difficult to make by reacting copper with oxygen, but it can be made by thermal decomposition of copper(II) carbonate or copper(II) nitrate. For example:

	heat			
copper(II) carbonate	→	copper(II) oxide	+	carbon dioxide
$CuCO_3(s)$	→	$CuO(s)$	+	$CO_2(g)$

Copper(II) oxide is a basic oxide. It neutralises acids to form copper(II) salts and water.

copper(II) oxide	+	sulphuric acid	→	copper(II) sulphate	+	water
$CuO(s)$	+	$H_2SO_4(aq)$	→	$CuSO_4(aq)$	+	$H_2O(l)$

The oxide is easily reduced to copper by natural gas or hydrogen. The reaction is strongly exothermic.

hydrogen	+	copper(II) oxide	→	copper	+	water
$H_2(g)$	+	$CuO(s)$	→	$Cu(s)$	+	$H_2O(l)$

This reaction can be used to determine the **formula** of copper (II) oxide.

Distinguishing copper(II) oxide from carbon

The black colour of copper (II) oxide may cause it to be mistaken for carbon. A simple test will distinguish them. If a black powder is warmed with dilute sulphuric acid a blue solution will form if the original black powder is copper (II) oxide. There will be no reaction with carbon.

COPPER(II) SULPHATE, $CuSO_4.5H_2O$

Copper(II) sulphate-5-water is the systematic name of this deep-blue solid. It contains 36% of its weight as **water of crystallisation**.

REACTIONS

It is soluble in water to give a solution containing copper ions, $Cu^{2+}(aq)$, which are blue. If blue copper(II) sulphate is heated, it **dehydrates** to a white powder known as **anhydrous copper(II) sulphate.**

copper(II) sulphate	$\rightarrow$	copper(II) sulphate	+	water
$CuSO_4.5H_2O(s)$	heat $\rightarrow$	$CuSO_4$	+	$5H_2O(l)$

The reaction is reversible and so white, anhydrous copper(II) sulphate can be used to test for the presence of water in a liquid by noting if the white powder turns blue on contact with the liquid.

'white' copper sulphate	+	water in the test liquid	$\rightarrow$	blue copper(II) sulphate	+	heat
$CuSO_4(s)$	+	$5H_2O(l)$	$\rightarrow$	$CuSO_4.5H_2O(s)$		

CORROSIVE

The term corrosive can be used to describe almost any substance. It means 'reactive'. For example, water is corrosive to metals such as sodium and iron; oxygen is corrosive to alkali metals. Also, substances we usually know to be corrosive are not always so, for instance, dilute sulphuric acid is not corrosive when in contact with gold metal. The term corrosive, therefore, is used as a warning that a substance is corrosive when in contact with living organisms or common materials.

The hazard symbol for corrosive illustrates these possible effects.

Fig. C.27 Hazard symbol – corrosive

COVALENT BOND

Covalent bonds are the bonds formed by the sharing of one or more *pairs of electrons* between two atoms. At the end of the process, each atom has its outer electron shell full, i.e. having eight electrons.

In covalently bonded elements, the atoms are identical, e.g. O_2, N_2.

Covalent bonds in compounds form between two different atoms, see Fig. C.32.

COVALENT BONDING

In elements

- A **single** bond is formed when two atoms share a pair of electrons. Usually, one electron comes from each atom. For example, the molecule of hydrogen. (See Fig. C.28.)
- A **double** bond is formed by the sharing of two pairs of electrons between two atoms; usually one pair from each atom. For example, the molecule of oxygen. (See Fig. C.29.)

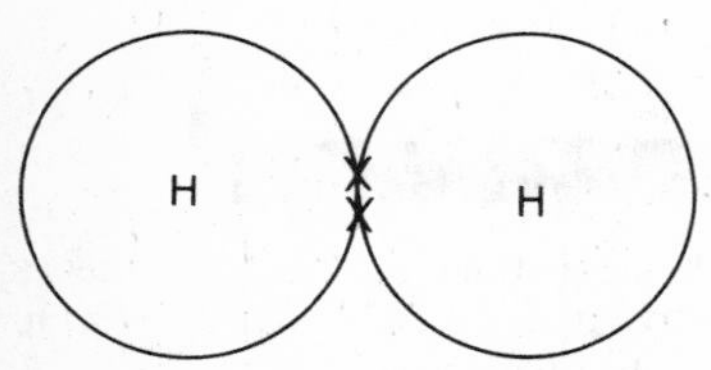

Fig. C.28 A hydrogen molecule

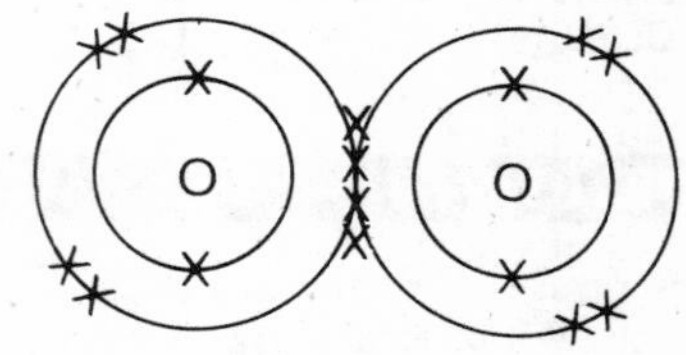

Fig. C.29 An oxygen molecule

- A **triple** bond forms when three pairs of electrons are shared between two atoms. For example, the nitrogen molecule. (See Fig. C.30.)

In compounds

The covalent bond formed between hydrogen and chlorine in hydrogen chloride is shown in Fig. C.31.

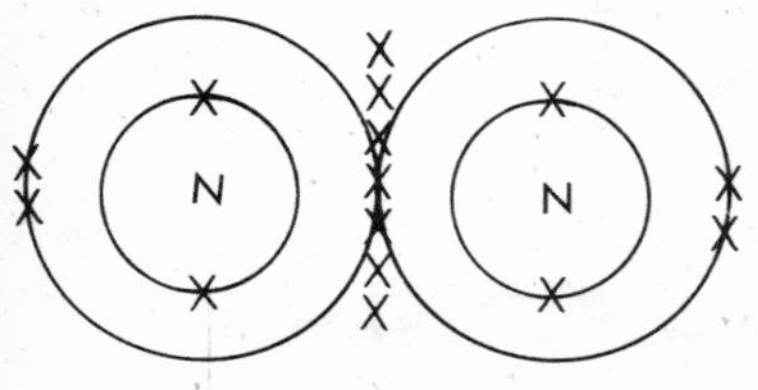

Fig. C.30 A nitrogen molecule

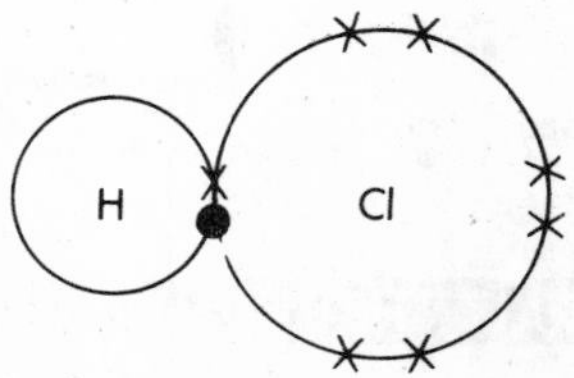

Fig. C.31 A hydrogen chloride molecule

The covalent bonds between hydrogen and oxygen in water are shown in Fig. C.32.

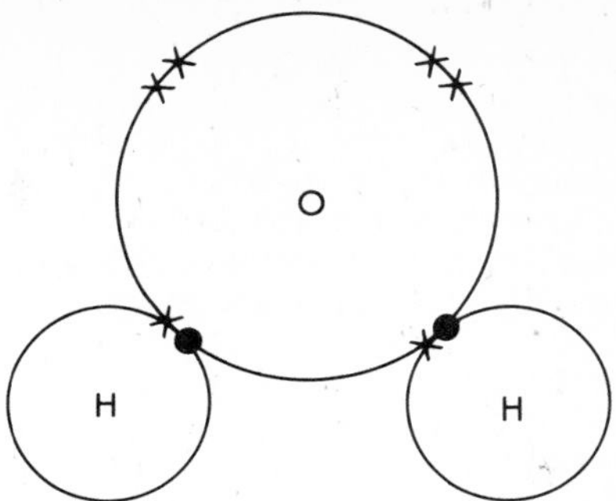

Fig. C.32 A water molecule

A double covalent bond is present in the molecule of ethene, C_2H_4. (See Fig. C.33.)

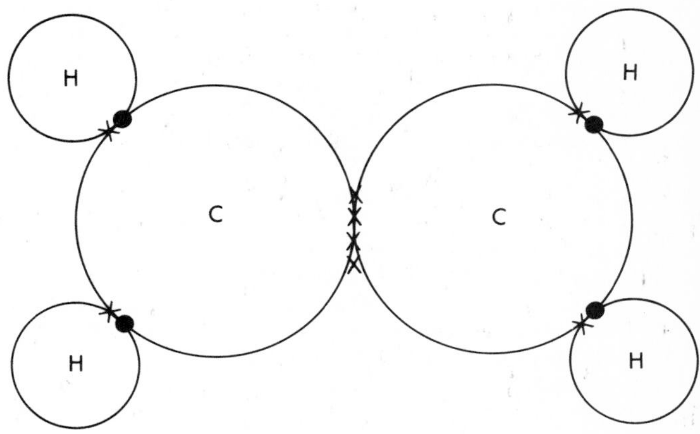

Fig. C.33 An ethene molecule

Properties of covalent compounds

Substances which contain covalent bonds have quite different properties from substances which have ionic bonds. Covalently bonded compounds have the following properties:

- low melting and boiling points
- do not conduct electricity in any state
- are usually soluble in organic solvents
- are not usually soluble in water

CRACKING

Cracking is a very appropriate term used to describe the breaking of a hydrocarbon molecule into smaller hydrocarbon molecules.

The process can be carried out:

- by heat (thermal cracking)
- by heat and a catalyst (catalytic cracking)

Crude oil fractions containing large molecules are not very useful. Cracking these fractions will convert them into mixtures of smaller molecules. These 'cracked' mixtures are used as fuels or for making addition polymers, for example:

decane → octane + ethene

$C_{10}H_{22}(l) \rightarrow C_8H_{18}(l) + C_2H_4(g)$

Octane and ethene are more valuable products than decane. Octane is a constituent of petrol, ethene can be made into poly(ethene).

CROSS-LINKING

Cross linking occurs when linear polymer molecules become linked together side-to-side by chemical bonds. This has the effect of making a large number of large molecules into fewer giant-molecules. The physical properties of the polymer are changed by cross-linking. Compared with a linear polymer, the cross-linked polymer:

- is harder and less flexible
- is more resistant to heat – it melts at a higher temperature or may not melt at all
- does not dissolve or swell in solvents.

Some examples of cross-linked polymers are:

- Bakelite, urea-formaldehyde; hard and heat-resistant.
- Car-tyre rubber, called 'vulcanised' rubber – partially cross-linked rubber. It is flexible and keeps it shape better than pure rubber.
- Ion exchange resins of cross-linked polystyrene.
- Epoxy resin adhesives such as Araldite.
- Ebonite – fully cross-linked rubber; a polymer substitute for the very hard wood ebony.

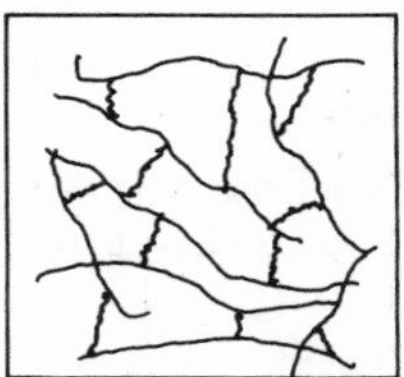

Fig. C.34 Cross-linking in a polymer

CRUDE OIL

It is generally believed that crude oil has formed from the remains of enormous numbers of sea creatures buried by ocean sediments. Over many millions of years, heat and pressure have converted these remains into the complex mixture of hydrocarbons we call crude oil. An alternative theory is that the formation has occurred deep in the Earth and that the crude oil has travelled up nearer to the Earth's surface through cracks in the crust.

Crude oil is our main source of petrol and other liquid hydrocarbon fuels. It is also the main source of chemicals for making polymers and useful organic chemicals like medicines, solvents, paints, and dyes. See **Fractional distillation** for products from crude oil. The combustion of any substance made from crude oil produces the 'greenhouse gas', carbon dioxide, as one of its combustion products. For this reason and also because crude oil is a diminishing natural resource, it would be much more sensible to use it as a **chemical feedstock** than as a fuel.

CRYOLITE, Na_3AlF_6

Cryolite is sodium aluminium fluoride. It is found naturally as Greenland Spar but is now made synthetically for use in aluminium production. The discovery that molten cryolite would dissolve alumina made the cheap production of aluminium possible from 1886.

◀ Alumina ▶

CRYSTALLISATION

This is the process that we see when crystals form from a molten substance or from saturated solutions. The process is slightly different in each case.

Crystals from a saturated solution

Consider the crystallisation of salt solution. The ions in the solution are moving about at random. They collide frequently but do not stick together. As the water in the solution evaporates there is less space for the ions to move in. Eventually, at the point we call 'saturation', the ions become so close together that they stick together in a lattice which we call a crystal. The more water that evaporates the bigger the crystal becomes.

Crystals from a molten substance

Consider the crystallisation of molten sulphur. Sulphur molecules in the liquid state are moving about at random. They collide with such energy that they cannot stick to each other but bounce apart. On cooling, the sulphur molecules lose energy. With less energy they no longer bounce off each other. They collect in an orderly arrangement – a crystal forms. Further cooling causes the crystal to become larger until the whole liquid 'crystallises' into one solid mass.

The solidification of metals is also a crystallisation process. It is possible for molten metals to form a single crystal on controlled cooling. Single-crystal metals are extremely strong. The titanium alloy turbine blades of many jet engines are now cast as single crystals.

DALTON, JOHN (1766–1844)

John Dalton could be regarded as the founder of modern chemistry. Every time we write an equation or calculate a reacting mass we are using an up-to-date version of Dalton's ideas on atoms and how they combine. In his Atomic Theory of 1808, Dalton suggested that:

- atoms are indivisible and cannot be created or destroyed
- atoms are the tiniest particles of matter imaginable
- atoms of different elements have different sizes and masses
- when atoms combine together they form compound atoms

Dalton gave us our first symbols for atoms. Some of Dalton's symbols are shown in Fig. D.1.

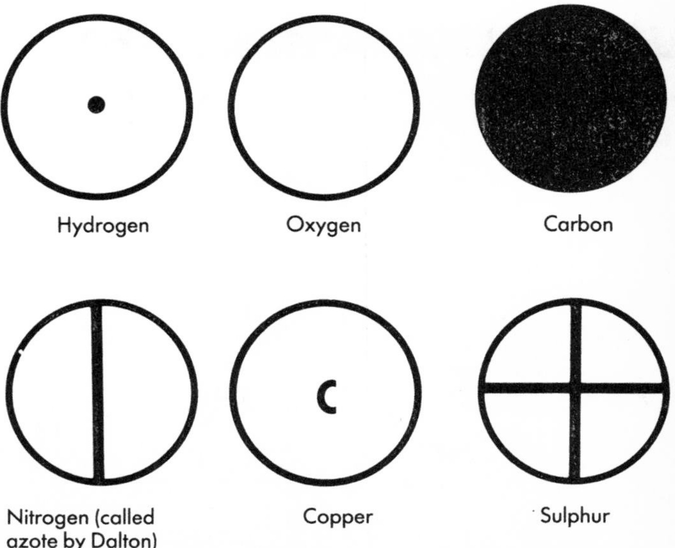

Fig. D.1 Dalton's atomic symbols

Today, his ideas seem very obvious but modern chemists realise what a great step forward Dalton's ideas about atoms have been and how helpful they were in advancing the study of chemistry. The relative atomic masses he gave atoms are known more accurately today and modern symbols use letters rather than designs on circles. In most other ways, Dalton's ideas are still in use.

DAVY, SIR HUMPHRY (1778–1829)

Humphry Davy was one of Britain's greatest chemists. His discoveries and inventions have benefitted people all over the world. He found a way of making pure samples of a newly discovered gas we now call nitrous oxide. Davy tried the gas out on himself. He discovered it to have strange properties. It produced a feeling of drunkenness and it stopped one of his wisdom teeth aching. It was later used as an anaesthetic – and is still in use to dull the pain of childbirth. Davy was one of the first chemists to use electricity to decompose molten compounds – the process of **electrolysis**. He was the first to prepare sodium, potassium, magnesium, calcium, strontium and barium metals. Further work in electrochemistry led him to discover the action of zinc in protecting metal ships from corrosion – called **sacrificial protection**. Towards the end of his life he invented the miners' safety lamp after investigating the combustion of methane found in coal mines. He found that a flame would not travel through a metal gauze so he made a lamp that had the flame surrounded by a metal gauze; air could get in but the flame could not explode the gases outside.

DECANTATION

This is a technique for separating a solid from a liquid. (See Fig. D.2.) It has the same purpose as **filtration**. It relies on the solid part of the mixture being

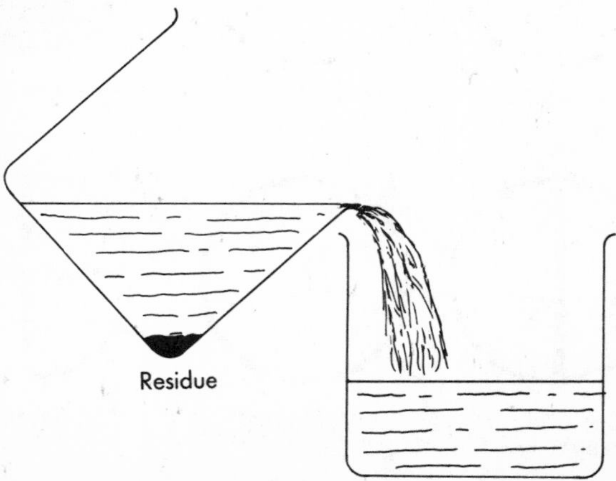

Fig. D.2 Decantation

much denser than the liquid. When the solid has sunk to the bottom of the vessel the liquid above it is carefully poured out. Decanting works best with heavy solids, like metals or heavy metal compounds. The process of panning for gold uses the technique of decanting.

DEHYDRATION

One type of dehydration is the removal of chemically combined water. An example is the removal of water of crystallisation from a compound. It is carried out by heating the compound and allowing the steam produced to escape. We are then left with the **anhydrous** substance. For example copper(II) sulphate crystals, $CuSO_4.5H_2O$ or magnesium sulphate crystals, $MgSO_4.7H_2O$ are hydrated crystals. On heating:

crystals of magnesium sulphate hydrate	→	dehydrated crystals of anhydrous magnesium sulphate	+	steam given off
$MgSO_4.7H_2O(s)$	→	$MgSO_4(s)$	+	$7H_2O(g)$

This type of dehydration is not the same as drying. For example, if we have made some crystals of copper (II) sulphate, $CuSO_4.5H_2O$ or magnesium sulphate, $MgSO_4.7H_2O$ and they are wet, we would wish to *dry* them but not *dehydrate* them. The difference is that in a warm place the wet crystals would dry, for example:

wet crystals of hydrated copper(II) sulphate	gentle heat →	dry crystals of hydrated copper(II) sulphate
$CuSO_4.5H_2O(s)$	gentle heat →	$CuSO_4.5H_2O(s)$

The dry crystals still contain **water of crystallisation.**

- Dehydration can also mean removing the elements of water, hydrogen and oxygen in the ratio 2:1, from a compound.

For example, ethanol, C_2H_6O, can be dehydrated by passing it over a heated catalyst. The produce is ethene, C_2H_4.

ethanol	→	ethene	+	water
$C_2H_6O(g)$	→	$C_2H_4(g)$	+	$H_2O(g)$

This dehydration can also be carried out using concentrated sulphuric acid as the dehydrating agent.

DELIQUESCENCE

Substances which are deliquescent absorb water from the air and dissolve in it. Deliquescent substances usually form damp, caked masses and eventually solutions in their containers if these are frequently left open. Examples include sodium hydroxide and calcium chloride.

Calcium chloride is the chemical in de-humidifiers currently sold in DIY shops. It begins as a dry powder and after absorbing several pints of water from the air in the room, is thrown away.

DENSITY

One substance is denser than another if its mass is greater for the same volume. Density is not heaviness or lightness. To calculate the density of any substance we divide its mass in grams by its volume in cubic centimetres (for solids or liquids) or in litres for gases

$$\text{density of a solid} = \frac{\text{mass in grams}}{\text{volume in cm}^3} \qquad \text{density of a gas or liquid} = \frac{\text{mass in grams}}{\text{volume in litres}}$$

Densities of solids and liquids fall in the range 0.5 g/cm^3 to 22 g/cm^3 (lithium to osmium). The densities of gases are in the range 0.08 g/l to 8.9 g/l (hydrogen to radon).

DETERGENT

Detergents are substances which wet and suspend (emulsify) grease and oil. The word comes from the Latin, *tergere*, which means 'to wipe clean'. Soap the oldest detergent was in use at least four thousand years ago.

Structure

The structure of the detergent molecule is the key to its action. Synthetic detergents (syndets) and soap are similar in having a hydrocarbon 'tail' and a charged 'head'. The detergent molecule-ion can be drawn as a 'tadpole-like' structure with a charged, water-loving head and an uncharged, oil-loving tail. The 'tail' consists of a long chain, hydrocarbon section. The 'head' is a COO$^-$ group. It is often drawn as a 'tadpole-like' figure.

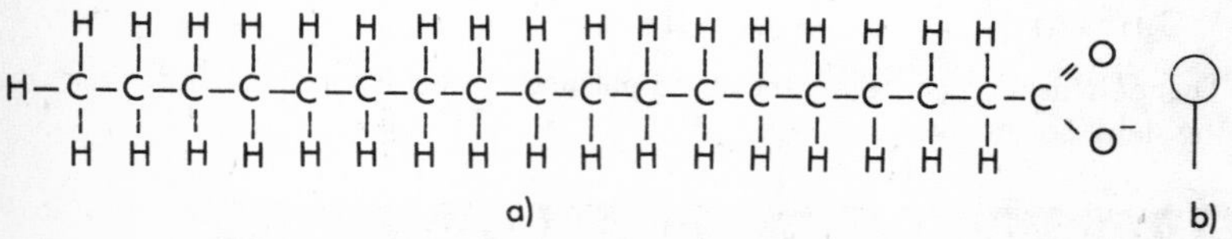

```
   H H H H H H H H H H H H H H H H H
   | | | | | | | | | | | | | | | | |    //O
 H-C-C-C-C-C-C-C-C-C-C-C-C-C-C-C-C-C-C
   | | | | | | | | | | | | | | | | |    \O⁻
   H H H H H H H H H H H H H H H H H
                  a)                          b)
```

Fig. D.3 A soap molecule: a) structure; b) simple representation

Action

The action of a detergent is shown in the series of diagrams in Fig. D.4. Because of its attraction to oil and grease, the tail of the detergent molecule embeds itself in the oil or grease on the surface of a fibre or greasy dish. Agitation of the fabric or dish then disperses the oil as drops. Each drop is 'coated' with negative charges which cause the drops to repel each other and so stay suspended in the water. The result is an emulsion of oil/grease in water. This is easily washed away without the oil and water separating. The detergent has emulsified the oil/grease.

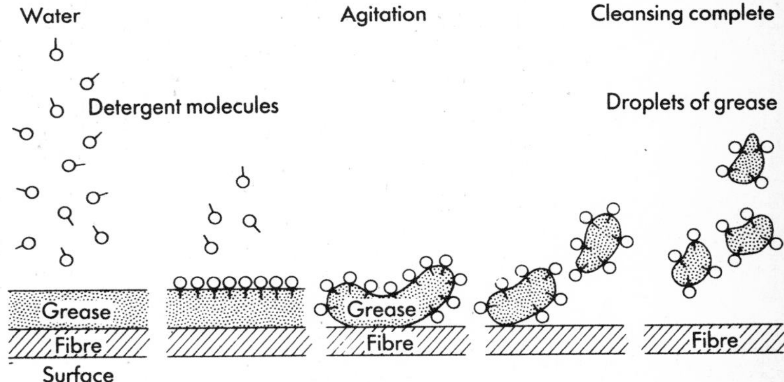

Fig. D.4 Action of a detergent

Syndets and soap

Man made detergents (syndets) are now used more than soap because they do not react with calcium salts in water forming a scum as soaps do. A comparision of the properties of syndets and soap is given in Table D.1.

Comparison	*Soaps*	*Synthetic detergent*
raw materials for manufacture	fats or oils + caustic soda	hydrocarbons from crude oil + sulphuric acid
biodegradable?	yes	yes
suitable for hard water?	no	yes
type of particle	hydrophobic tail hydrophilic head	hydrophobic tail hydrophilic head
main advantage	made from renewable resources	works in hard water, cheap
main disadvantage	forms scum in hard water	usually contains phosphates which cause river pollution, uses non-renewable resources

Table D.1 Properties of syndets and soaps

DEUTERIUM, $^{2}_{1}H_2$

The isotope of hydrogen of mass number 2 is called deuterium. The nucleus of a deuterium atom contains one proton and one neutron. When burned in oxygen it forms heavy water, D_2O.

DIAMOND

Diamond is one of the allotropes of carbon. It is the hardest known substance. Diamonds are believed to have been formed in the earth from carbon containing material subjected to great pressures and high temperatures. They are found in 'pipes' which are huge cylinders of rock and earth which must be mined to extract the diamonds.

Diamond is a colourless crystalline solid. It does not conduct electricity but is an excellent heat conductor. It is because of this property that a diamond feels cold to the touch and from this originated its slang name – 'ice'. The great hardness of diamond results from the very strong covalent bonds linking carbon atoms to each other in a giant structure called a **macromolecule.** (See Fig. D.5.)

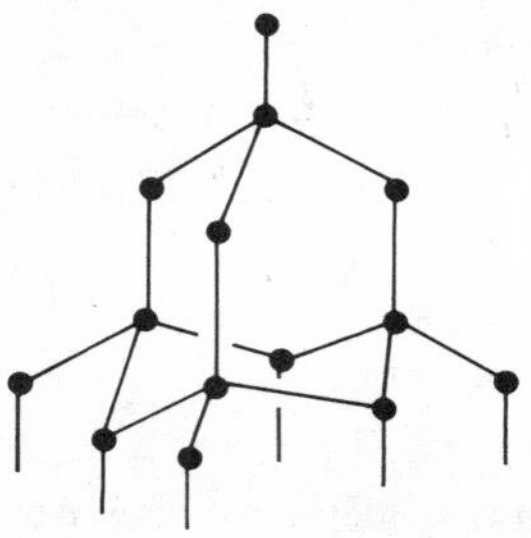

Fig. D.5 Diamond – a macromolecule

Diamond is pure carbon. This is easily proven but at considerable cost! A small diamond will burn completely in air and form carbon dioxide as the only product.

DIAPHRAGM CELL

One method of electrolysing brine (concentrated salt solution) is in a diaphragm cell. In this cell the anode and cathode are separated by a porous asbestos partition called a diaphragm The diaphragm prevents the chlorine formed at the anode from reacting with the hydrogen and **sodium hydroxide** formed at the cathode. At the same time, the electrolyte (brine) is made to flow from the anode to the cathode to carry sodium hydroxide solution out of the cell for purification. (See Fig. D.6.)

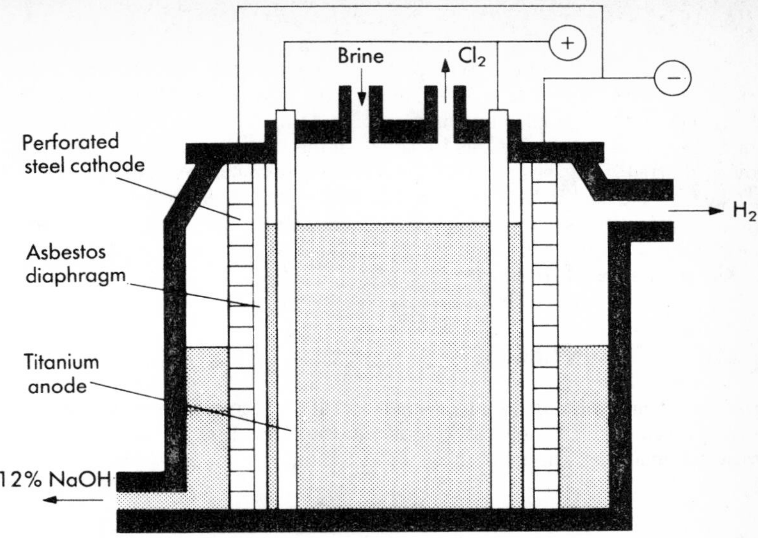

Fig. D.6 Diaphragm cell

At the anode: $2Cl^-(aq) - 2e^- \rightarrow Cl_2(g)$
At the cathode: $2H^+(aq) + 2e^- \rightarrow H_2(g)$

These equations do not tell the whole story. There are ions present which are not discharged and these are important in this process. At the cathode, one hydroxide ion, $OH^-(aq)$, accumulates for every hydrogen ion, $H^+(aq)$, that discharges. Since sodium ions are also attracted to the cathode, sodium hydroxide solution will be formed there. Note that the sodium hydroxide is not one of the substances *discharged.*

Purification of the sodium hydroxide solution

The mixture that comes out of the diaphragm cell contains 12% sodium hydroxide and 15% sodium chloride. When it is evaporated to about one-fifth volume, sodium chloride crystallises out leaving a solution which contains only 1% of salt and 50% sodium hydroxide. This level of impurity is acceptable in many applications of sodium hydroxide.

DIFFUSION

Diffusion is a mixing process caused only by the natural motion of the particles making up the diffusing substances. Diffusion usually involves two substances. They diffuse into each other.

Why does diffusion occur?

Diffusion is evidence that the particles which make up all matter are in continuous, random motion. When two substances are brought into close contact, particles from these substances spread into each other in the way that two crowds of people coming into contact might mingle freely with each other. We would not expect this to happen if the particles or people were not moving. Particles in gases move faster and have more space around them than particles in liquids. This is why gases diffuse into each other faster than liquids. Particles in solids do not move about freely, they only vibrate from side to side. Hence, solids diffuse extremely slowly into each other.

◀ Kinetic theory of gases ▶

DIFFUSION IN GASES

Bromine vapour will diffuse into the air and at the same time air will diffuse into the bromine in the apparatus shown in Fig. D.7. In a few minutes, both jars will contain the same pale-brown gas mixture.

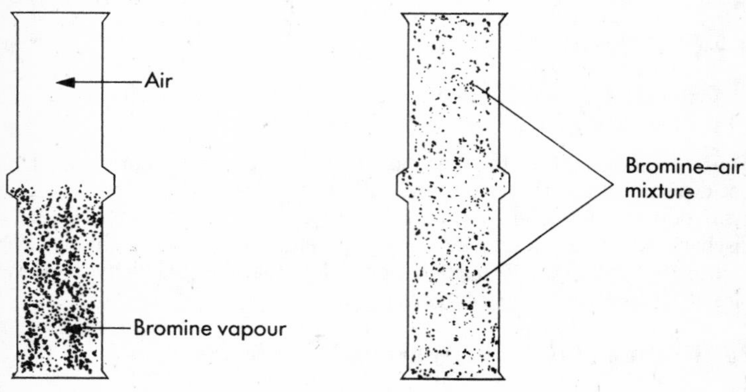

Fig. D.7 Bromine diffusion

The molecules in gases are widely spaced and move about with great speed. This allows molecules of gases to mix with each other very quickly. The speed of mixing depends on the speed of the molecules involved. Molecules move faster if they are light or have high energies. Hydrogen will diffuse faster than chlorine at room temperature because its molecules are lighter.

DIFFUSION IN LIQUIDS

If a concentrated solution of copper (II) sulphate is carefully placed underneath water in a beaker, diffusion of each liquid into the other will occur. This will usually take a few days to complete when a uniform, pale-blue coloured solution will result. (See Fig. D.8.)

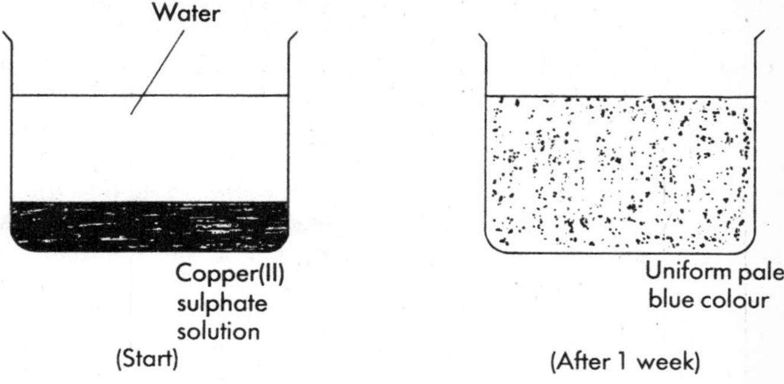

Fig. D.8 Diffusion in liquids

DIFFUSION IN SOLIDS

Diffusion of one solid into another is a very slow process. It can only be made to occur in a short time if two solids are pressed closely together at high temperatures. Particles in solids vibrate faster at high temperatures.

DIRECT CURRENT, d.c.

Direct current is a current of electricity which flows in one direction only. A direct current is a flow of electrons through a wire from the negative terminal of the source to the positive terminal. It is the type of electric current obtained from an electrical source such as a battery or a lab-pack – which has a positive and a negative terminal.

DISCHARGE OF IONS IN ELECTROLYSIS

Ions are either positively charged particles (cations) or negatively charged particles (anions). In electrolysis, ions are attracted to the electrode of opposite charge. At the electrodes ions lose their charge and become atoms or molecules. This process of losing charges is called discharge. Examples of discharge in electrolysis are:

	charged ions	→	electron transfer	→	uncharged atoms or molecules
at cathode	$Cu^{2+}(aq)$	+	$2e^-$	→	$Cu(s)$
at anode	$2Cl^-(aq)$	−	$2e^-$	→	$Cl_2(g)$

DISINFECTANTS

Any substance used to destroy disease bacteria outside the human body is called a disinfectant. Disinfectants are one section of a group of chemicals called **germicides**. Common household disinfectants are bleach solution, and 'Dettol'.

Disinfection of household water supplies to make them safe for drinking is carried out at the water works mainly by using **chlorine** gas. An excess of chlorine is then removed by reaction with sulphur dioxide. In some other countries, **ozone** is used in place of chlorine because it leaves no taste or odour in the treated water. Ozone is used in Britain where lowland water is coloured by dissolved organic compounds. The ozone removes the colour from the water. Ozone treatment is just starting in Britain and there are plans to extend its use in the future.

DISPLACEMENT

Displacement is a type of chemical reaction in which an element displaces a less reactive element from one of its compounds.

For example, chlorine will displace bromine from potassium bromide solution:

chlorine	+	potassium bromide	→	bromine	+	potassium chloride
$Cl_2(g)$	+	$2KBr(aq)$	→	$Br_2(aq)$	+	$2KCl(aq)$

Displacement among metallic elements occurs when zinc displaces copper from copper(II) sulphate solution.

zinc	+	copper sulphate	→	copper	+	zinc sulphate
$Zn(s)$	+	$CuSO_4(aq)$	→	$Cu(s)$	+	$ZnSO_4(aq)$

Displacement reactions can be explained by the idea of a **reactivity series** of metals or non-metals.

◀ Replacement ▶

DISTILLATION

The process we know as distillation originated in ancient times. Distillation is a technique for separating a liquid from a mixture by boiling the mixture and condensing the vapour given off. There are two types of distillation:

Simple distillation

This will separate a liquid from a solution of a solid. An example of this is:

- the production of distilled water from a salt solution. (See Fig. D.9.)

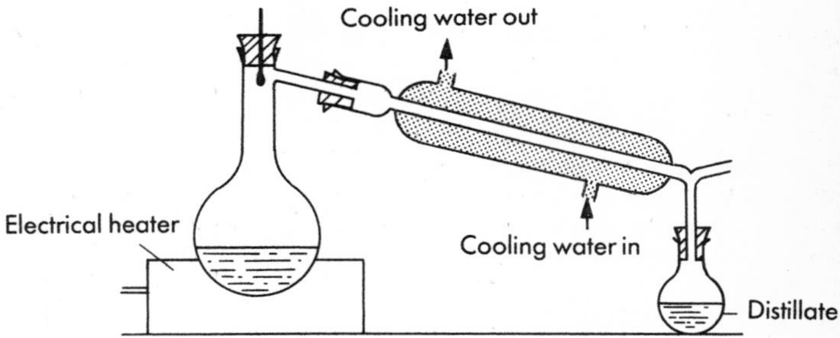

Fig. D.9 Simple distillation

Fractional Distillation

This will separate one liquid from a mixture of two or more liquids. (See Fig. D.10). Common examples are:

- the fractional distillation of wine to produce ethanol
- the‘ fractionation’ of crude oil to obtain petrol and other ‘fractions’

◀ Fractional distillation ▶

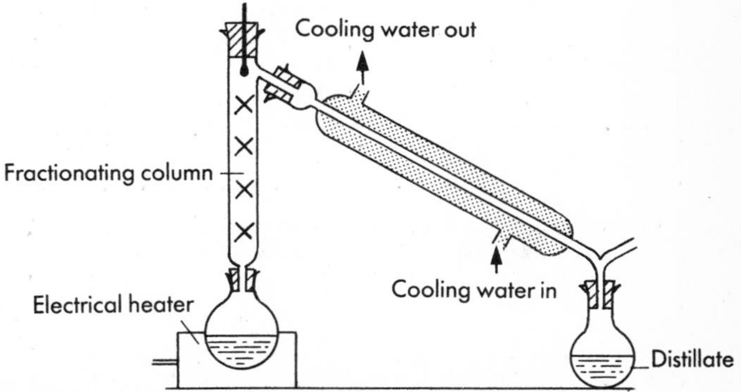

Fig. D.10 Fractional distillation

DOMESTIC BLEACH

All brands of domestic bleach (Domestos, Vortex etc.) are dilute solutions of sodium hypochlorite (sodium chlorate(I)), NaOCl(aq). They vary in concentration up to about 12%. Domestic bleach is made by reacting chlorine gas with sodium hydroxide solution. Its chief domestic use is as a disinfectant rather than as a **bleach**. Containers display a hazard warning symbol to state that bleach is both harmful and an irritant. It also warns against mixing it with acidic cleaners. The basis of this warning can be understood from the equation for the reaction:

bleach	+	acid from cleaner	→	chlorine gas				
2NaOCl(aq)	+	2HCl(aq)	→	$Cl_2(g)$	+	2NaCl(aq)	+	$H_2O(l)$

It can be seen that the poisonous gas – chlorine – is formed on mixing bleach with an acid cleaner. The above reaction – carried out in a fume cupboard in a chemistry laboratory – is a convenient way of making a small amount of chlorine gas.

DOUBLE BOND

◄ Covalent bonds ►

DRY CLEANING

As the name suggests, this is cleaning without water. The chemicals used are grease **solvents**. The commonest dry-cleaning solvent is the chlorinated hydrocarbon perchloroethene (the 'P' on cleaning instructions). Any solvent used must dissolve grease or oil; must be non-toxic; and is safer if it is non-flammable. Dry-cleaning solvents are expensive and must be reused for the process to be economical. They are therefore chosen to have low boiling points so that the solvent can be **distilled** from the grease and oil and recycled.

DRYING AGENT

Drying agents are chemicals that remove liquid water by absorbing it or reacting with it.

- Silica gel will dry gases by absorbing water from them. It is used commonly in chemical laboratories.
- Concentrated **sulphuric acid** and anhydrous salts such as anhydrous copper(II) sulphate will dry gases by reacting with water in them.

EARTH'S CRUST

The Earth's crust consists of the top ten miles of the whole Earth including the sea. The estimated approximate percentage of the common elements is shown in Fig. E.1. The Earth's crust provides our major source of chemicals.

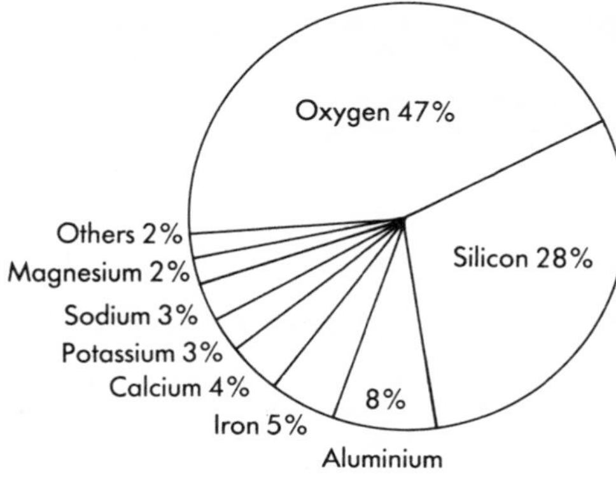

Fig. E.1

ELECTROCHEMISTRY

The science of electrochemistry began in 1800 when the first means of producing an electric current was invented by **Alessandro Volta**. In that same year, water was decomposed by electricity into hydrogen and oxygen. This led **Humphry Davy** to carry out his impressive series of electrolysis experiments by which he produced six elements that had not been isolated previously.

ELECTRODES

In electrolysis

An electrode is an inert solid rod or plate used to carry electrons into (cathode) or out of (anode) an electrolyte in electrolysis. The materials usually used are carbon, nickel, stainless steel or titanium. Small platinum electrodes are sometimes used in laboratories.

- In electroplating, the anode is not inert, it dissolves to maintain the electrolyte concentration.

In electrical cells

Electrodes are used also in electrical cells. Here they may not be inert, they may react to produce the electrical energy. The electrodes are also differently named in an electrical cell. The anode is the negative electrode and the cathode the positive electrode.

As a general rule the chemical reaction at the anode is always oxidation and at the cathode it is reduction in both processes.

ELECTROLYSIS

The decomposition of a compound into its elements by an electric current is called electrolysis. Although electrolysis involves conduction of electricity, it is a different process from metallic conduction. Metals conduct without decomposition.

Apparatus

The apparatus needed to carry out electrolysis is shown in Fig. E.2. The features worth noting are:

- the electrodes A and C must be electrical conductors and must not, usually, react with the products or the electrolyte – in other words they must be inert
- the source of electricity must be d.c.
- the electrolyte must be an ionic compound in liquid form – it must contain mobile ions – not electrons!

If gases are produced in the electrolysis, then the cell must be modified so that gas collection is made easier. This can be effected as shown in Fig. E.3.

Products of electrolysis

Electrolysis produces **elements**. If the compound is a pure binary salt – one that contains only a single metal and a single non-metal – the metal will be formed (discharged) at the cathode and the non-metal at the anode. If the electrolyte is a solution of a compound in water, it is a mixture. In this case the elements discharged may come from the salt or the water in the mixture. If

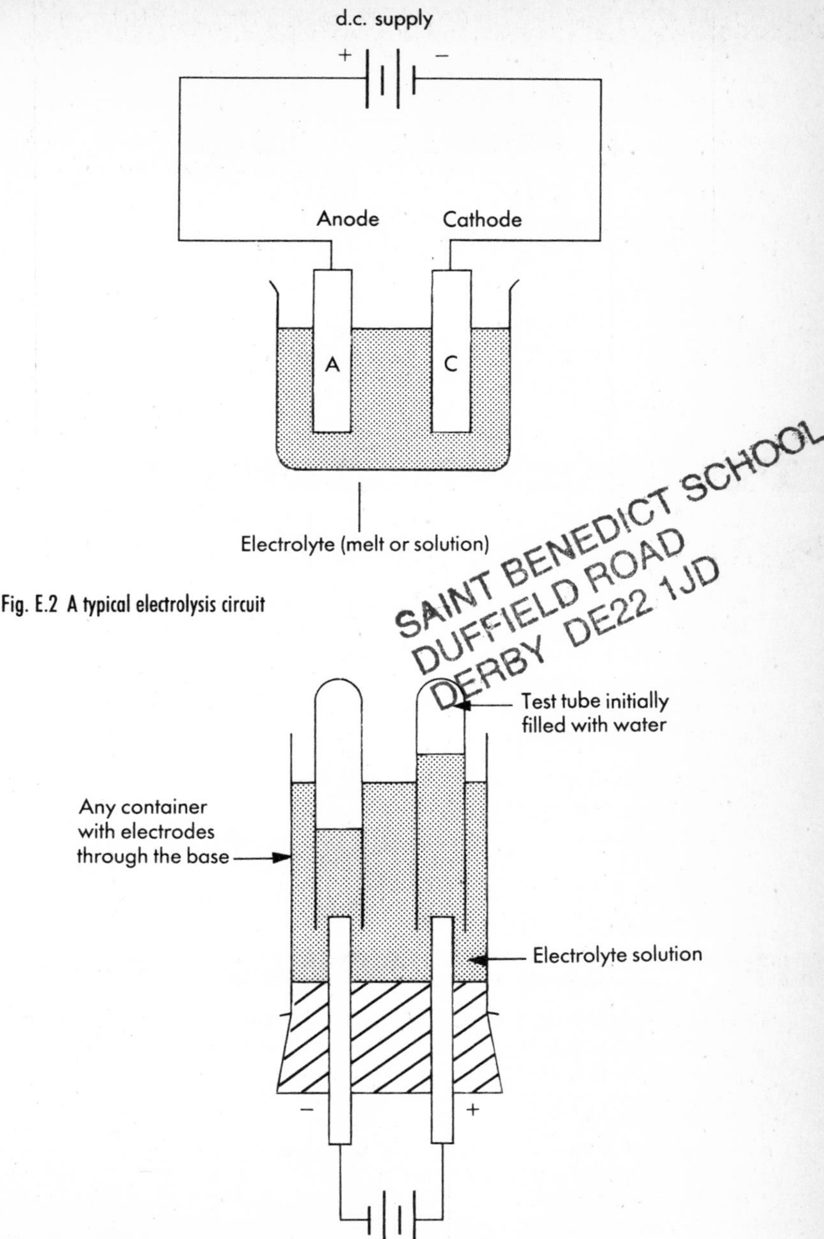

Fig. E.2 A typical electrolysis circuit

Fig. E.3 Gas collection

we consider the electrolysis of sodium chloride both as a pure molten salt and as a solution in water, different products are obtained as detailed in Table E.1.

Electrolyte	*Anode (+) product*	*Cathode (−) product*
pure molten sodium chloride	chlorine	molten sodium
aqueous sodium chloride	chlorine if concentrated, oxygen if dilute	hydrogen at any concentration

Table E.1 Products of the electrolysis of sodium chloride

◀ Lead (II) bromide ▶

ELECTROPLATING

This process deposits a thin layer of metal onto an object.

- The object must be made the cathode in the electrolysis of a solution of the plating metal.
- The anode must be made of the plating metal.
- The electrolyte must be a solution containing ions of the plating metal.

For example, electroplated nickel-silver cutlery is made by placing the nickel-silver items in a basket which is the cathode. The cathode basket and a silver anode are immersed in a silver salt solution. Electroplating is stopped when the required thickness of silver has been deposited. Electroplating may make objects:

- more resistant to corrosion
- visually more attractive
- harder wearing

ELECTROSTATIC PRECIPITATOR

Electrostatic precipitators are used in industry to remove dust from waste gases before they are discharged into the air. Dust usually has a negative charge and is attracted to any positively charged surface. By passing the dusty gases through a container which has a surface charged positively to over 10,000 volts, the dust is deposited and removed from the waste gases. Fig. E.4 shows a diagram of an electrostatic precipitator.

Electrostatic precipitators are used in:

- power stations
- lime kilns
- metal smelters

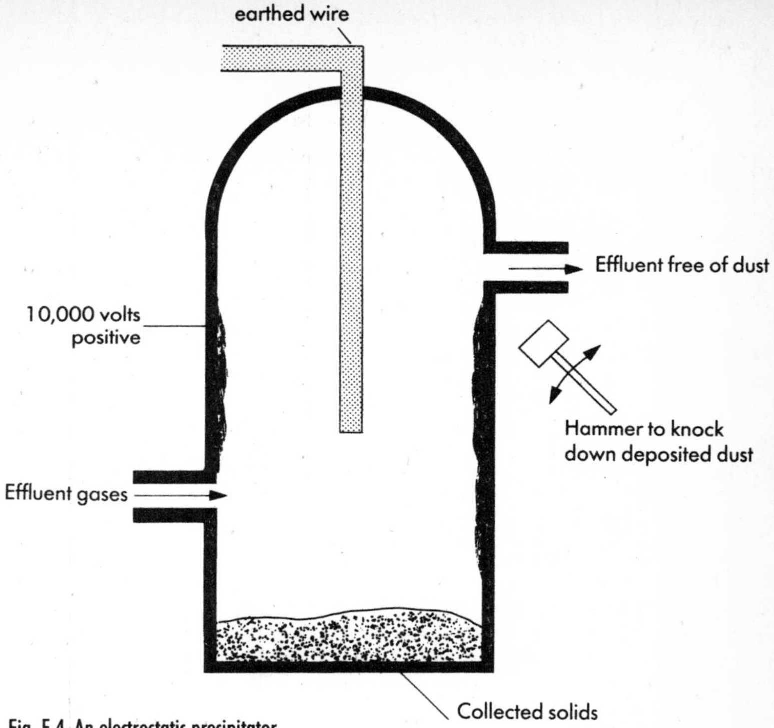

Fig. E.4 An electrostatic precipitator

ELEMENTS

An element is a substance that cannot be broken down into anything simpler. In the last century, when only about half the elements had been discovered, any new substance which was thought to be an element was tested to see if it could be broken down into simpler substances. For example, at one time, **Humphry Davy** believed that nitrogen, carbon, sulphur and phosphorus were not elements. However, he tried – and failed – to break them down into simpler substances and had to admit their elemental nature.

The 89 naturally-occurring elements, when combined in different ways have produced more than five million known **compounds** and probably there are many more yet to be discovered. Of the naturally-occurring elements, 68 are metals and 21 non-metals.

NATIVE ELEMENTS

Only a few elements are found *uncombined* in rocks or oceans. Metallic elements that are sometimes found uncombined are called 'native' metals. These are the elements known since ancient times. Examples of native metals are the less-reactive metals gold, silver, copper and lead. Non-metallic elements found uncombined in nature are sulphur and carbon.

SYMBOLS OF ELEMENTS

Element	*Symbol*	*Origin of name*	*Date of discovery and discoverer*
hydrogen	H	Gr. *hydro*, water *genes*, forming	1766 – Cavendish
helium	He	Gr. *helios*, the sun	1868 – Janssen
lithium	Li	Gr. *lithos*, stone	1817 – Arfvedson
beryllium	Be	Gr. *beryllos*, beryl (a precious stone)	1828 – Wohler
boron	B	Ar. *buraq*	1808 – Davy
carbon	C	L. *carbo*, charcoal	ancient
nitrogen	N	L. *nitrum*, soda *genes*, forming	1772 – Rutherford
oxygen	O	Gr. *oxys*, acid *genes*, forming	1774 – Priestley
fluorine	F	L. *fluere*, flow	1886 – Moissan
neon	Ne	Gr. *neos*, new	1898 – Ramsay & Travers
sodium	Na	Eng. *soda*; L. *natrium*	1807 – Davy
magnesium	Mg	*Magnesia*, in Greece	1808 – Davy
aluminium	Al	L. *alumen*, alum	1827 – Wohler
silicon	Si	L. *silex*, flint	1824 – Berzelius
phosphorus	P	Gr. *phosphoros*, light-bearing	1669 – Brand
sulphur	S	Sanskrit, *sulvere*	ancient
chlorine	Cl	Gr. *chloros*, green	1774 – Scheele
argon	Ar	Gr. *argon*, inactive	1894 – Rayleigh & Ramsay
potassium	K	Eng. *potash*, pot ashes	1807 – Davy
calcium	Ca	L. *calx*, lime	1808 – Davy

Table E.2 The discovery and naming of the first 20 elements

(Key to language abbreviations: Ar. Arabic; Eng. English; Gr. Greek; L. Latin)

THE DISCOVERY AND NAMING OF ELEMENTS

The discovery of the 107 known elements (some of them man-made) shows the international nature of chemistry. It has taken chemists from many countries several centuries to discover, prepare and name all the known elements. The names of the 107 known elements have many different origins. Some are named after their discoverers, some after countries. Yet others are named after one of their important properties or after one of their common compounds. (See Table E.2.)

MAN-MADE ELEMENTS

Elements beyond uranium in the periodic table are man-made. They have been formed by 'shooting' small atoms at heavier atoms in order to form an atom of increased size by sticking these colliding particles together. Many are named after famous scientists, e.g. einsteinium (element 99) and mendelevium (element 101).

Elements beyond 103 are now named on a number-based system. (See Table E.3.)

Element	*Symbol*	*Name*	*Interpretation*
104	Unq	unnilquadium	un, one; nil, zero; quad, four
105	Unp	unnilpentium	un, nil, pent (five)
106	Unh	unnilhexium	un, nil, hex (six)
107	Uns	unnilseptium	un, nil, sept (seven)

Table E.3 Names of newly discovered elements

◀ Symbols ▶

EMULSIONS AND EMULSIFICATION

The process we call emulsification causes oil to mix with water. This can be done by making the oil into very tiny drops which mix into the bulk of the water. The mixture formed is called an emulsion. In time, an emulsion made in this way will separate into oil and water layers. To prevent this an emulsifying agent is added which stops the tiny oil droplets from rejoining. Examples are:

- Milk is an emulsion of oil in water in which a protein coats each oil droplet
- Salad cream is an emulsion of oil in vinegar in which each oil droplet is coated with egg yolk
- Used dishwashing water is an emulsion of oil and grease in water; washing-up liquid molecules coat the oil droplets.

In each case the 'coating' on the oil droplets prevents them from joining together and forming an oil layer on top of the mixture. The material of these coatings is the emulsifying agent or emulsifier. Emulsifiers are much-used in the preparation of cosmetics, food and medicines. They allow the oils or fats which are the essential ingredients of these items to be blended with water to make a smooth, uniform cream.

◀ Detergents ▶

ENDOTHERMIC

Endothermic means 'takes in heat' (Gr. *endo*, inside; *therme*, heat). Chemical reactions in which the products have taken in heat from the surroundings will cool the surroundings. If the reaction is carried out in an aqueous solution, heat will be taken *from* the water (surroundings) and the solution will be cooled. For example, the reaction of citric acid and sodium hydrogencarbonate mixture when water is added lowers the temperature of the aqueous mixture.

sodium hydrogencarbonate + citric acid → sodium citrate + water + carbon dioxide

'Health Salts' give cool drinks because of this reaction.

◀ Energy ▶

ENERGY

Energy is the capacity for doing work. It is measured in joules. There are various forms of energy which can be interconverted.

Heat energy

Exothermic reactions give out heat energy; endothermic reactions take in heat energy.

Chemical energy

This is the energy contained in chemical bonds. It is a 'stored energy'. In an exothermic reaction the stored energy can be released. For example, fuels contain chemical energy that is released as heat energy when they are burned. In an endothermic reaction the absorbed energy is stored in the bonds of the products.

Electrical energy

This is the energy of the moving electron stream that is an electrical current. Chemical energy is converted into electrical energy in an electric cell. Electrical energy is converted into chemical energy in an electrolysis cell.

Nuclear energy

This is the energy given out during a nuclear reaction. It is also called atomic energy. It results from the conversion of mass into energy. It is made use of in nuclear reactors where nuclear energy is converted into heat energy which is then converted into electrical energy by a turbine.

EXCHANGE OF ENERGY

There is usually an exchange of energy when a chemical reaction occurs. The reactants either give out or take in energy as they form products. This exchange occurs between the reactants and the surroundings. It is called the enthalpy change or just the energy change for the reaction. It is given the symbol ΔH, pronounced delta aitch. The energy exchange is caused by changes in the energy of the bonds before and after reaction.

Total energy of all bonds in products minus total energy of all bonds in reactants = ΔH.

Energies are usually quoted in kilojoules per mole of reaction, kJ mol^{-1}

Reactions in which energy is given out to the surroundings are called **exothermic reactions.** If energy is taken in from the surroundings the reaction is **endothermic.** Anything which is in contact with the reacting substances is considered to be part of the surroundings. If the reaction involves solutions in water, then the water is the most obvious part of the surroundings. For reactions in aqueous solution therefore, a thermometer placed in the solution will show a rise or fall in temperature because the temperature of the water in the solution will be measured. In the end, heat energy will pass through the sides of the reaction vessel and the outside surroundings will also gain or lose energy. Given time the products which are left will reach the same temperature as the reactants at the start. It will then be obvious that the products have more (if energy has been taken in) or less (if energy has been given out) energy than the reactants had before reaction. The commonest type of energy change is the exothermic change. Endothermic changes are less common. There are a few reactions in which the energy change is zero.

ENERGY LEVEL DIAGRAMS

An energy level diagram shows the energy change for a chemical reaction on a scale. It is not a graph. The scale may have energy values on the vertical axis, but it is more usual to show only the energy value for the difference between the levels. The energy level diagram for the endothermic reaction discussed in the previous section is shown in Fig. E.5.

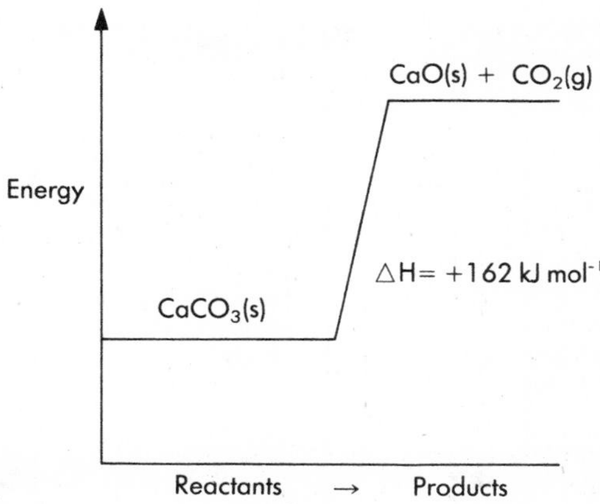

Fig. E.5 Energy diagram of an endothermic reaction

The energy level diagram for an **exothermic reaction** is shown for the neutralisation of an acid by an alkali. (See Fig. E.6.)

sodium hydroxide	+	hydrochloric acid	→	sodium chloride	+	water	
NaOH(aq)	+	HCl(aq)	→	NaCl(aq)	+	H_2O(l)	$\Delta H = -58 kJmol^{-1}$

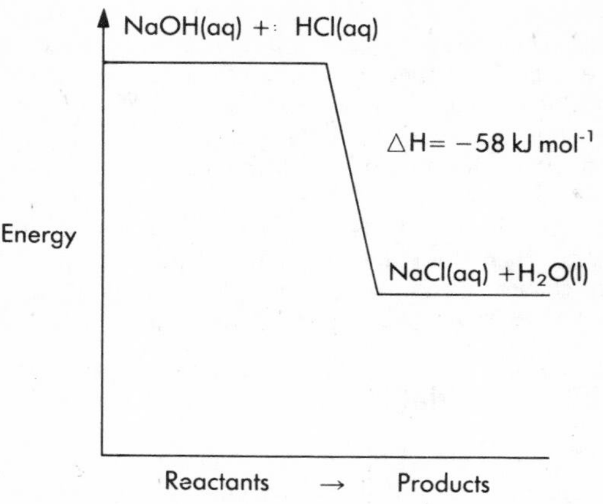

Fig. E.6 Energy level diagram for an exothermic reaction

◀ Bonds ▶

ENERGY SAVING

The chemical industry uses enormous quantities of energy. Energy costs money. Research chemists and chemical engineers are constantly looking for ways to reduce the energy needs of the industry. Most chemical reactions are exothermic. It makes sense, therefore, to try to make use of the energy given out in industrial chemical reactions. This energy can be used by collecting it in **heat exchangers**. In addition more efficient **catalysts**, alternative chemical processes, and **recycling** all help to reduce energy use and conserve fuel supplies. By such methods great increases in the energy efficiencies of iron-making, aluminium smelting and ammonia production have been achieved over the past 50 years.

ENZYMES

Enzymes are biological catalysts produced within living organisms (Gr. *En*, in; *zyme*, yeast).

Enzymes from yeast convert sugars into ethanol;

sugars	enzyme	ethanol	+	carbon dioxide
$C_6H_{12}O_6(aq)$	$\rightarrow$	$C_2H_5OH(aq)$	+	$2CO_2(g)$

Enzymes in the human body are responsible for the rapid conversion of the food eaten into muscle, skin, bone, energy and a few waste products.

We hear a lot about enzymes in washing powders. These were introduced in the early 1960s. To begin with, they were extracted from bacteria such as *bacillus subtilis*. Now they are man-made. Their purpose in the bacterium is to speed up the digestion of proteins. In the washing powder they do the same to stains such as egg, blood, grass, and sweat. Enzymes are used in the food-processing trade to make poorer quality meat steaks more tender. The enzyme, amylase, hydrolyses starch to maltose, $C_{12}H_{22}O_{11}$.

			enzyme	
starch	+	water	$\rightarrow$	maltose
$2(C_6H_{10}O_5)_n(aq)$	+	$nH_2O(l)$	$\rightarrow$	$nC_{12}H_{22}O_{11}(aq)$

EQUATIONS

An equation is a summary of what has happened in a chemical reaction. It represents, in symbols and formulae, the atoms, molecules or ions taking part in the reaction.

WORD EQUATIONS

An equation may be a very brief summary as when we write a word equation, say, for the burning of carbon in oxygen.

burning
carbon + oxygen → carbon dioxide

This word equation tells us only that carbon burns in oxygen to form carbon dioxide.

We can add more information by describing the states of the reactants and products.

solid carbon + oxygen gas burning → carbon dioxide gas

We now see that the burning carbon is a solid and that it reacts with oxygen gas to form the product, carbon dioxide, which is also a gas.

We can take the equation a step further by putting in the energy change for the reaction.

solid carbon+ oxygen gas burning → carbon dioxide gas + heat

Our equation now gives the additional information that the reaction is exothermic – heat is produced as carbon burns in oxygen. However, the word equation is already looking like a full, written description of the reaction. If we add any more information we will no longer have a summary but a short essay!

SYMBOLIC EQUATIONS

Symbolic equations, formulae, allow us to both add more information and reduce the space taken up by the equation.

$$C(s) + O_2(g) \xrightarrow{\text{burning}} CO_2(g) \quad \Delta H = -394 kJmol^{-1}$$

We have substituted formulae for names. We have balanced the equation. We have used **state symbols** so that we can visualise what is happening accurately. Finally we have indicated exactly how much energy the reaction gives out.

Using relative atomic masses of carbon and oxygen, C = 12; O = 16, and knowing that one mole of any gas has a volume of 24 000cm^3 at normal temperature and pressure (**Avogadro's law**) this equation is a summary of the following statement.

'When 12g of carbon is burnt in oxygen gas, it reacts with 32g (24 000cm^3) of oxygen gas and forms 44g (24 000cm^3) of carbon dioxide gas. In the process 394 kilojoules of heat energy is given out'.

A balanced chemical equation as described is therefore a very compact method of giving information about a reaction.

BALANCED CHEMICAL EQUATIONS

Word equations are simple descriptions of reactions, they do not need to be balanced because they do not indicate the numbers of atoms involved in the reaction. When symbolic equations are written, the final equation must obey the laws of nature.

One natural law of interest to chemists can be stated as 'matter cannot be created or destroyed'.

When a reaction occurs there will always be exactly the same number of atoms of each element among the products as there was among the reactants. So in a symbolic chemical equation there must be the same number of atoms of reactants and products. If they are not equal then we are either creating atoms or destroying atoms; this can never happen in a chemical reaction!

Writing balanced equations

- Sometimes, simply writing the correct formulae of the reactants and products results in a balanced equation. This can be seen in the example used above.
- Usually, putting in the correct formulae does not give a balanced equation and a process of 'balancing' must be carried out. For example: sodium metal reacts with water forming sodium hydroxide and hydrogen gas.

The word equation is

sodium + water → sodium hydroxide + hydrogen

substituting formulae gives an unbalanced equation:

$Na + H_2O \rightarrow NaOH + H_2$

Although each formula is correct, there are only two hydrogen atoms among the reactants but three among the products. It looks as if a hydrogen atom has been created out of nothing!

It is quite possible to find by measurement how much sodium and water react together and also how much sodium hydroxide and hydrogen are produced. The results of these measurements are:

23g of sodium	reacts with	18g of water	to form	40g of sodium hydroxide	plus	1g of hydrogen

As expected the mass of reactants is exactly the same as the mass of products, 41g of each. Matter has not been created or destroyed!

Converting these measurements to moles using the following data:
1 mole of sodium atoms is 23g
1 mole of water molecules is 18g
1 mole of sodium hydroxide is 40g
1 mole of hydrogen molecules is 2g
indicates to us that 1 mole of sodium atoms reacts with 1 mole of water molecules to form 1 mole of sodium hydroxide and ***half a mole of hydrogen molecules***.

The balanced equation is therefore:

$$Na(s) + H_2O(l) \rightarrow NaOH(aq) + \tfrac{1}{2}H_2(g)$$

or

$$2Na(s) + 2H_2O(l) \rightarrow 2NaOH(aq) + H_2(g)$$

ELECTRODE EQUATIONS

In electrolysis, atoms of elements are discharged at the electrodes. Atoms of non-metallic elements deposit at the anode. Atoms of metallic elements deposit at the cathode. Each of these reactions involves ions of the element and electrons. For example, in the electrolysis of molten sodium chloride, the following equations summarise what happens at the electrodes.

At the anode (+)
$Cl^-(l) \rightarrow Cl(g) + e^-$
followed by $2Cl(g) \rightarrow Cl_2(g)$
(Chlorine atoms cannot exist singly; they instantly pair to form diatomic molecules.)

At the cathode (−)
$Na^+(l) + e^- \rightarrow Na(l)$

- The number of electrons involved in the electrode equation equals the number of charges on the ion being discharged.
- Electrons are added to the cation at the cathode and removed from the anion at the anode.
- Non-metal atoms discharged in electrolysis always combine in pairs to form diatomic molecules, e.g. Cl_2 and O_2.

IONIC EQUATIONS

Many chemical reactions involve ionic compounds. In these we usually find that some of the ions present in the reactants do not take part in the reaction.

They are called 'spectator ions'. Any substance not taking part in a reaction need not be shown in the equation. If we leave out the spectator ions we get an equation with reacting ions in it, called an ionic equation. For example, when magnesium reacts with any acid, only the hydrogen ions of the acid react with the magnesium.

The equation is best written:

magnesium	+	any acid	→	magnesium ions	+ hydrogen
$Mg(s)$	+	$2H^+(aq)$	→	$Mg^{2+}(aq)$	+ $H_2(g)$

This is an ionic equation.

NUCLEAR EQUATIONS

The principles of writing nuclear equations are exactly the same as for chemical equations. Nuclear reactions, however, involve only the nuclei of atoms of elements.

Two examples of radioactive decay are considered below.

1) Uranium–238 decays by losing an alpha particle.
- Uranium is element 92. Uranium atoms have an **atomic number** of 92.
- The symbol for a uranium atom of **mass number** 238 is $^{238}_{92}U$.
- The decay product of U–238 is an **isotope** of thorium (Th), atomic number 90.
- The total mass of products must equal the total mass of the reactants.
- From this data we can produce the equation:

$$^{238}_{92}U \rightarrow \ ^{234}_{90}Th + \ ^{4}_{2}He$$

← both sides total 238

← both sides total 92

2) Carbon–14 decays by losing a beta-particle.

$$^{14}_{6}C \rightarrow \ ^{14}_{7}N + \ ^{0}_{-1}e$$

Once again:
- The sum of the mass numbers of the products equals those of the reactant.
- The sum of the atomic numbers of the products equals that of the reactant.
- The nuclear equation balances.

EQUILIBRIUM

Many chemical reactions are reversible. **Reversible reactions** can go in the forward or the reverse direction depending on the conditions – temperature, pressure or concentration. It is also possible for any reversible reaction to come to an equilibrium position somewhere in between complete reaction in either direction. Examples of equilibrium reactions are:
- The water equilibrium:

$H_2O(l) \rightleftharpoons H^+(aq) + OH^-(aq)$

In pure water at room temperature hydrogen ions, hydroxyl ions and water molecules all exist at constant concentrations. Although these concentrations do not change there are still chemical changes occurring. Hydrogen ions and hydroxyl ions are continually recombining to form water molecules. Water molecules are continually decomposing into hydrogen and hydroxyl ions. Equilibrium or balance is reached by the opposing changes taking place at the same speed – ions recombine to form water molecules as fast as water molecules split up into ions. This is called dynamic equilibrium.

- The weak acid equilibrium:

$$CH_3CO_2H(l) + H_2O(l) \rightleftharpoons H_3O^+(aq) + CH_3CO_2^-(aq)$$

When ethanoic (acetic) acid is added to water a reaction occurs. However, only about 1% of the acid molecules react with water molecules before equilibrium is reached. After that, water molecules and acid molecules continue to react but the ions formed recombine equally quickly. The result is a balance or equilibrium in which the concentrations of all the particles involved do not change. It is this *incomplete reaction* which makes aqueous solutions of compounds like ethanoic acid **weak acids.**

- The ammonia synthesis equilibrium:

nitrogen + hydrogen $\rightleftharpoons$ ammonia

$$N_2(g) + 3H_2(g) \rightleftharpoons 2NH_3(g)$$

Nitrogen and hydrogen react together to form a mixture with ammonia which has reached equilibrium. No matter how long the mixture is left the proportions of ammonia, hydrogen and nitrogen do not change. This reaction is the basis of the Haber process. The equilibrium can be *manipulated* by change of pressure or temperature to increase the proportion of ammonia at equilibrium. Increasing the pressure produces a greater percentage yield of ammonia. Decreasing the temperature has a similar effect.

In the industrial process the unreacted gases are not wasted; ammonia is removed and the unreacted elements are recycled into the process.

◀ Haber process ▶

ESTERS

When organic acids react with alcohols, compounds called esters are formed. Many esters are found naturally in animal and vegetable products.

The esters with small molecules generally have sweet, fruity smells. Small molecular esters are simple to synthesise and are well known as flavourings for sweets, jellies and synthetic perfumes. (See Table E.4.)

Ester	*Alcohol and acid reactants*	*Flavour*
amyl ethanoate	amyl alcohol + ethanoic acid	banana
propyl ethanoate	propanol + ethanoic acid	pear drops
ethyl methanoate	ethanol + methanoic acid	rum
ethyl butanoate	ethanol + butanoic acid	pineapple

Table E.4 Esters in common use

MAKING ESTERS

Acids and alcohols react together slowly. A catalyst, a few drops of a strong acid, is usually added to speed-up the reaction.

$CH_3CO_2H(l)$	+	$C_2H_5OH(l)$	↔	$CH_3COOC_2H_5(l)$	+	$H_2O(l)$
ethanoic acid	+	ethanol	↔	ethyl ethanoate		water

The reverse process – conversion of ester to acid and alcohol is called **hydrolysis**.

Long-chain esters

Giant-molecule esters are found in fats and oils. Soap, detergents and margarine are manufactured from them. Fats are esters of the alcohol, glycerol and long-chain fatty acids such as stearic acid or oleic acid.

The common ester in animal fat is tristearin (see Fig. E.7).

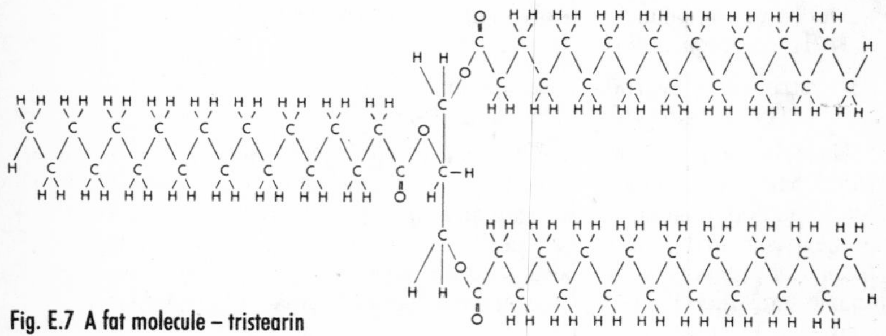

Fig. E.7 A fat molecule – tristearin

Hydrolysis of tristearin produces glycerol and stearic acid.

tristearin + water ⇌ stearic acid + glycerol

If sodium hydroxide is used instead of water for the hydrolysis, the reaction produces glycerol and sodium stearate (a soap).

tristearin	+	sodium hydroxide	→	glycerol	+	sodium stearate

This hydrolysis is given the specific name – **saponification**.

ETHANE, C_2H_6

Ethane is the second member of the hydrocarbon series called **alkanes**. It is a colourless, flammable gas. It must not be confused with ethene. Its formula can be displayed as

```
   H  H
   |  |
H—C—C—H
   |  |
   H  H
```

The molecule contains six C–H bonds and one C–C bond. All bonds are single bonds.

OCCURRENCE AND USES

It is present in **natural gas** in varying amounts. Its main use is in the manufacture of **ethene** by **cracking**.

ethane	→	ethene	+	hydrogen
$C_2H_6(g)$	→	$C_2H_4(g)$	+	$H_2(g)$

Chemical properties

Ethane burns, like all hydrocarbons, to form carbon dioxide and water if sufficient oxygen is present.

ethane	+	sufficient oxygen	→	carbon dioxide	+	water
C_2H_6	+	$3\frac{1}{2}O_2(g)$	→	$2CO_2(g)$	+	$3H_2O(l)$

If combustion is incomplete, carbon monoxide will be produced.

ethane	+	insufficient oxygen		carbon monoxide		water
$C_2H_6(g)$	+	$2\frac{1}{2}O_2(g)$	→	$2CO(g)$	+	$3H_2O(l)$

Unlike ethene, ethane does not decolourise bromine solution.

ETHANOIC ACID, CH_3CO_2H

Ethanoic acid is the **systematic name** for acetic acid. It is the second member of the homologous series of **carboxylic acids**. The prefix ethan – shows that its molecule contains two carbon atoms. It is a colourless liquid with a sharp smell. **Vinegar** is a 5% solution of ethanoic acid in water.

Reactions

Ethanoic acid forms by accidental or deliberate bacterial oxidation of ethanol. This reaction is responsible for the souring of wine – the commercial production of vinegar from low quality wine.

ethanol	+	air	→ bacteria	ethanoic acid	+	water
$C_2H_5OH(aq)$	+	$2[O]$	→	$CH_3CO_2H(aq)$	+	$H_2O(l)$

Synthetic ethanoic acid is made by the oxidation of butane, ethene or methanol.

An aqueous solution of ethanoic acid is a **weak acid**. Its reactions are typical of acids but being a weak acid it reacts more slowly. It reacts with the more reactive metals to give hydrogen, e.g.

magnesium + ethanoic acid → magnesium ethanoate + hydrogen

$$Mg(s) + 2CH_3CO_2H(aq) \rightarrow Mg(CH_3CO_2)_2(aq) + H_2(g)$$

It neutralises alkalis, e.g. sodium hydroxide and metal oxides, e.g. copper (II) oxide.

Note: although it is a *weak* acid, ethanoic acid reacts with exactly the same amounts of alkalis and bases as *strong* acids do.

It will react slowly with carbonates giving carbon dioxide.

ethanoic acid + calcium carbonate → calcium ethanoate + carbon dioxide + water

$$2CH_3CO_2H(aq) + CaCO_3(s) \rightarrow Ca(CH_3CO_2)_2(aq) + CO_2(aq) + H_2O(l)$$

It reacts with alcohols to form **esters**.

ETHANOL, C_2H_5OH

Ethanol, is the best known alcohol. It is a colourless liquid with a faintly sweet smell. Pure ethanol is called 'absolute' ethanol. It is rarely used because it carries a large excise duty which makes it very expensive. Ethanol is present to smaller or larger extents in beers, wines, and spirits.

MANUFACTURE

By fermentation

Yeast will convert sugars to ethanol and carbon dioxide if the process is carried out in an air-free container. This anaerobic process is called **fermentation**. The resulting solution contains up to 12% ethanol, the rest is mainly water. Nearly pure ethanol can be made by **fractional distillation** of this alcoholic solution. The product is a colourless solution containing 96% ethanol.

By synthesis

Ethanol is synthesised from **ethene**. Ethene is hydrated using a catalyst at about 300°C. About 5% conversion is obtained but, by recycling the unreacted gases, 95% of the ethene is eventually converted to ethanol.

ethene + water ⇌ ethanol

$$C_2H_4(g) + H_2O(g) \rightleftharpoons C_2H_5OH(l)$$

Uses

- It is the main ingredient of methylated spirit – 'meths'.
- Meths is used as a fuel in stoves specially designed to burn it.
- Ethanol is a solvent for varnishes, polishes and printing inks.
- It can be used as a motor fuel either pure or blended with petrol – 'Gasohol'. It is used for this purpose in Brazil.

Note: 'Blue' methylated spirit contains a dye to distinguish it from water and a smelly substace – pyridine – to make it easily recognised by blind people. The term 'methylated' means that it has methanol as an additive. This makes 'meths' toxic to drink in large amounts. It is added to try to prevent its use in alcoholic drinks. Colourless, distilled ethanol is used as a solvent for the fragrances in perfumes.

Ethanol as a fuel is not likely to be less polluting than unleaded petrol. Some of the products of combustion have unpleasant effects. When completely burnt both petrol and ethanol should produce only carbon dioxide and water.

ETHENE, C_2H_4

Ethene is the first member of the unsaturated hydrocarbon series called **alkenes.**

The structure of ethene is

```
H   H
 \ /
  C
  ||
  C
 / \
H   H
```

The molecule contains four C–H single covalent bonds and one C=C double covalent bond.

The presence of the C=C double bond makes ethene a very reactive compound. Many substances can react with ethene producing useful chemicals such as ethanol, antifreeze and poly(ethene).

Properties

Ethene is a colourless, sweet smelling gas. It does not dissolve in water and is neutral to indicators. It is highly flammable, burning to carbon dioxide and water in an adequate supply of air. Because of its unsaturated nature, ethene reacts by addition across the carbon-carbon double bond. It also polymerises by **addition polymerisation** forming **poly(ethene).**

A laboratory test for ethene

The reactivity of the carbon-carbon double bond enables the detection of ethene by its reaction with orange/brown bromine solution. *Ethene decolourises bromine solution.*

Uses

- The main use for ethene is in the manufacture of poly(ethene).
  $nC_2H_4(g)$ catalyst → catalyst $(C_2H_4)_n(s)$
- Another major use is to make vinyl chloride and styrene for conversion to **poly(vinyl chloride)**, PVC, and **poly(styrene).**

ethene	+	water	catalyst	ethanol
$C_2H_4(g)$	+	$H_2O(g)$	$\rightarrow$	$C_2H_5OH(l)$

- Ethene is also converted into **antifreeze**, terylene, **detergents** and **solvents.**
  Ethene–1,2–diol (ethylene glycol)

```
   HO  OH
    |   |
H — C — C — H
    |   |
    H   H
```

This compound is the familiar antifreeze.

◀ Addition reactions ▶

ETHYNE, C_2H_2

The common name for ethyne is acetylene. Ethyne is an unsaturated hydrocarbon having a carbon–carbon triple bond. (See Fig. E.8.) It is a fuel gas and is used mixed with oxygen to produce a flame hot enough to cut many metals by melting – the oxy-acetylene flame.

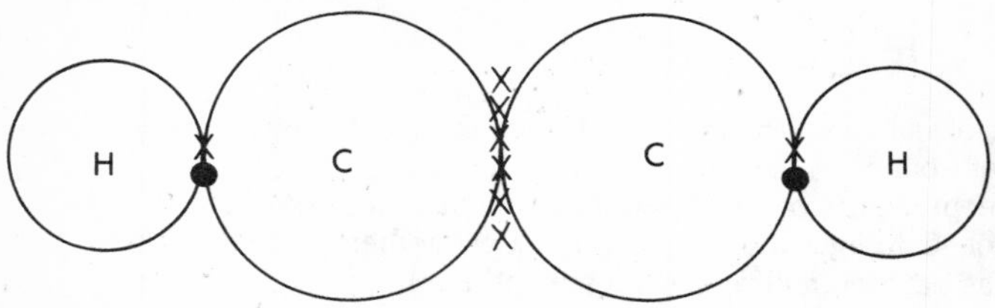

Fig. E.8 Ethyne molecule

EUTROPHICATION

Any chemical that is a plant food can cause eutrophication if it finds its way into rivers or lakes. Eutrophication is a biological process. It occurs as excessive plant growth in rivers or lakes leading to a reduction in dissolved oxygen in the water and death of animal and plant life. Nitrates from fertilisers and animal manures can enter rivers from farm land drainage. Phosphates from washing powders can enter rivers through sewage works. Both can cause a rapid growth in plant life which has several effects:

- the river or lake becomes choked with plants
- sunlight cannot penetrate to lower level plants and these die
- dead plants decay by bacterial action; bacteria remove oxygen from the water as they consume the dead plants; when the oxygen is gone other bacteria take over and produce 'rotten' smells – hydrogen sulphide – as they finish the decay process
- without oxygen, animal life is threatened and plants cease to grow
- the river or lake becomes eutrophied – dead

EVAPORATION

This is the familiar process in which a liquid gradually 'disappears into the air'. In fact molecules from the liquid have gained enough energy to escape into the air. Once in the air they diffuse away. Evaporation of many liquids occurs slowly at room temperature but heating speeds up the process by giving the molecules in the liquid more energy to escape. Liquids evaporate fastest at their **boiling points**. The escaping molecules are the **vapour**. Evaporation, sometimes called *vaporisation*, is the first step in **distillation**.

In the laboratory

Evaporation is often carried out to reduce the volume of an aqueous solution – to concentrate it. It is done in an evaporating basin – a vessel designed to expose a large surface area of liquid for more rapid escape of vapour molecules. Most commonly, this produces crystals when the hot, concentrated solution cools. (See Fig. E.9.)

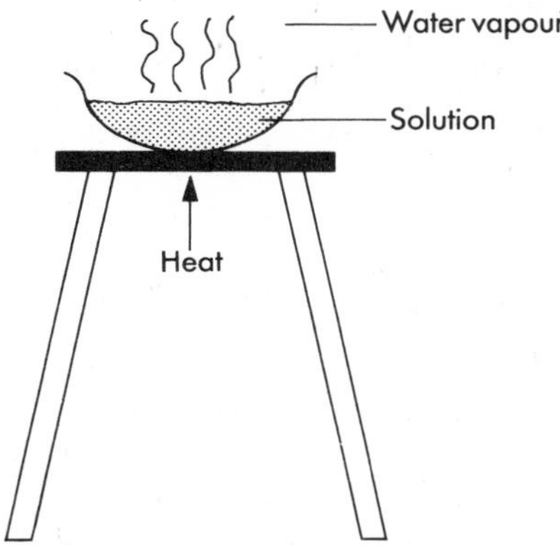

Fig. E.9 Evaporation in the laboratory

In industry

Evaporation on a large scale is carried out in the production of crystalline chemicals, e.g. common salt. It is usually done by boiling the solution in a vacuum. In a vacuum, a solution boils at much lower temperatures than normal and the steam produced is used to heat the next batch of solution. This makes the process more energy efficient.

◀ Crystallisation ▶

EXOTHERMIC REACTIONS

Exothermic means 'gives out heat' (Gr. *exo*, outside; *therme*, heat). Chemical reactions in which heat is given out will become hot and warm up the surroundings. An example of an exothermic reaction is:

copper oxide	+	hydrogen	→	copper	+	water
$CuO(s)$	+	$H_2(g)$	→	$Cu(s)$	+	$H_2O(l)$

We use exothermic reactions in different ways:

- as major heat sources, e.g. fuel burning
- as minor heat sources, e.g. the use of packs of rusting iron, speeded up by a catalyst, to warm the hands of climbers and hikers
- the use of the reaction of quicklime with water in the self-heating stew cans used by the military

◀ Energy ▶

FARADAY CONSTANT

The Faraday constant is a quantity of electrical charge equal to 96,500 coulombs. It is often called a mole of electrical charge because it is the total charge on one mole of electrons.

To calculate the moles of electrical charge passed in electrolysis, the equation below is used:

$$\text{Moles of electrical charge} = \frac{\text{current passing in amps} \times \text{time in seconds}}{96{,}500}$$

IONIC CHARGE AND ELECTROLYTIC DISCHARGE

The charge on an ion is a measure of the moles of electrons required to deposit one mole of atoms at an electrode.

For example, one mole of aluminium ions, Al^{3+}, is converted to one mole of aluminium atoms by passage of 3 moles of electrons.

Similarly, 1 mole of electrons is required to deposit one mole of sodium atoms from sodium ions, Na^{1+}.

The rule followed by discharging atoms is simple:

- For **metals**: the number of moles of electrons **added** to each mole of ions equals the group number
- For **non-metals**: the number of moles of electrons **removed** from each mole of ions equals 8 minus the group number

These quantities are seen from the **electrode equations**:

$Al^{3+}(l) + 3e^- \rightarrow Al(l)$

Adding 3 moles of electrons deposits 1 mole of aluminium atoms or 1 mole of any other group 3 metal

$Na^+(l) + e^- \rightarrow Na(l)$

Adding 1 mole of electrons deposits 1 mole of sodium atoms or 1 mole of any other group 1 metal

$Cl^-(aq) - e^- \rightarrow Cl(g)$

Removing 1 mole of electrons deposits
1 mole of chlorine atoms or 1 mole of atoms of any other group 7 element.

$O^{2-}(aq) - 2e^- \rightarrow O(g)$

Removing 2 moles of electrons deposits 1 mole of oxygen atoms or 1 mole of atoms of any other group 6 element

FARADAY, MICHAEL, (1791-1867)

Faraday started his scientific career as assistant to **Humphry Davy**. He did much work on the relation between electricity and magnetism and discovered the principle of the dynamo in 1831. His note-books show that he made over sixteen thousand experimental observations in his career. The modern electrochemical industry is founded on his discovery of the laws of electrolysis.

FATTY ACIDS

Fatty acids are organic acids found in animal or vegetable oils and fats. They are usually present in the form of **esters** from which they are extracted by **hydrolysis.** They are also called carboxylic acids. They can be divided into two groups, saturated and unsaturated fatty acids.

Examples of **saturated fatty acids** are, ethanoic acid (in vinegar), butyric acid (in rancid butter) and stearic acid (in animal fat as a glyceride ester); see Fig. F.1. The general formula of saturated fatty acids is $C_nH_{2n+1}CO_2H$.

Unsaturated fatty acids may have one carbon-carbon double bond or more than one. They are called mono-unsaturated acids and polyunsaturated acids respectively.

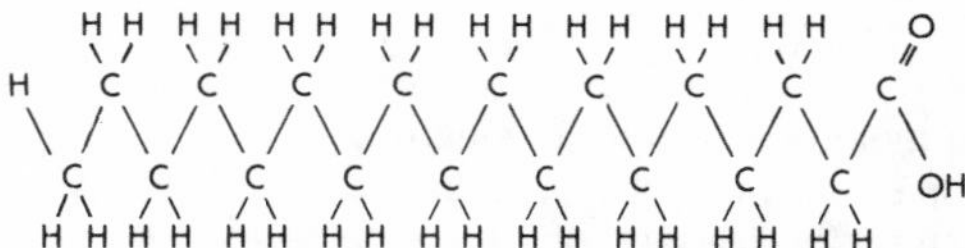

Fig F.1 A stearic acid molecule

Fig. F.2 An oleic acid molecule

An example of a mono-saturated fatty acid is oleic acid, see Fig. F.2, the most common of all fatty acids. It is found in olive oil as a glyceride ester. The general formula of mono-saturated fatty acids is $C_nH_2nCO_2H$.

Examples of poly-unsaturated acids include linoleic acid which is essential to human growth and is found in soya bean and sunflower oils. Polyunsaturated fatty acids reduce the cholesterol levels in the human body and help to prevent heart disease. Many soft margarines now contain polyunsaturated fatty acids for health reasons.

FEHLING'S SOLUTION

The common test for **reducing sugars** is to boil the unknown substance with Fehling's solution. A brown, yellow or green precipitate forms if a reducing sugar is present. **Benedict's solution** is similar in its reaction. It has the advantage that it does not need to be mixed immediately before use.

FERMENTATION

Fermentation is the anaerobic (air-free) process by which yeast converts sugars to **ethanol** and **carbon dioxide**. Fermentation has probably been known since prehistoric times. If air is allowed into the process, the products are less desirable – carbon dioxide and water.

- Under **anaerobic** conditions – fermentation occurs:

			yeast			
glucose solution	+	no air	→	ethanol	+	carbon dioxide
$C_6H_{12}O_6(aq)$	+	no air	→	$2C_2H_5OH(aq)$	+	$2CO_2(g)$

- Under **aerobic** conditions the yeast just grows:

glucose solution	+	air	→	carbon dioxide	+	water
$C_6H_{12}O_6(aq)$	+	$6O_2(g)$	→	$6CO_2(g)$	+	$6H_2O(l)$

The product of all fermentation reactions on sugars is a dilute solution of ethanol in water with important but small quantities of other flavourful substances. It is the combination of the ethanol and the flavours which make beer, wine and spirits differ in taste. Fermentation requires a temperature of 12°C to 40°C. It is faster at the higher temperature. Above 40°C reaction stops because the yeast organism dies.

◀ Brewing ▶

FERTILISERS

A complete chemical analysis of animal and plant bodies would be a very difficult task. However, a rather crude chemical analysis of plants was made over a hundred years ago by Baron Liebig (the inventor of the water-cooled condenser!). He analysed the ash from burnt plants. The elements he found in the ash are among those shown in Table F.1; he did not find them all. This was the first time anyone knew for certain which chemical elements were present in plants. It was obvious to Liebig that these elements had come from the air, soil and rain. His discovery led to the beginning of the modern agricultural fertiliser industry.

Chemistry plays a large part in agriculture and animal rearing because animal and plant bodies rely on chemicals and chemical reactions for their growth. Animal and plant bodies are composed of a large number of chemical compounds which they arrange and use differently.

Plant and animal bodies are made up **fats, proteins** and **carbohydrates.** These three types of compound each contain carbon, hydrogen and oxygen atoms. In addition, protein molecules contain nitrogen atoms and sulphur atoms. If an organism is to grow, its food or nutrient supply must contain these elements in large amounts. Smaller amounts of other elements are also necessary. The molecules that control and regulate growth also contain phosphorus and potassium.

If we consider the elements mentioned above we see that there are two which *hardly ever* need to be supplied and one which *never* needs to be applied by farmers. Plants get all the hydrogen and oxygen they need from rainwater and all the carbon they need from the carbon dioxide in the air. The other elements are also found naturally in the soil but can be used up by heavy cropping and so may need continual replacement.

Elements needed in large amounts	*Elements needed in small amounts – trace elements*
carbon	sulphur
hydrogen	magnesium
oxygen	zinc
nitrogen	iron
phosphorus	chlorine
potassium	copper
	boron
	manganese
	molybdenum

Table F.1 Elements essential for plant growth

Higher plants cannot use molecules of nitrogen as nutrients. The nitrogen must always be in a combined (we say 'fixed') form as nitrates or ammonium compounds. It is for this reason that nitrogen compounds are synthesised on such a large scale in the chemical industry. Certain plants, called legumes, have bacterial colonies living in their roots. The bacteria are able to 'fix' nitrogen from the air. Legumes do not need added nitrogenous fertilisers to grow.

A fertiliser will usually have an analysis of the contents stated on the bag. For example, 'Growmore' contains 9% of each of the three main nutrients, N,P, and K.

◀ Haber process, percentage composition ▶

FILTRATION

This common laboratory and industrial process separates liquids from undissolved solids.

In the laboratory

Filter papers are used supported on a filter funnel. (See Fig. F.3.)

In industry

Synthetic fibre cloths may be used covering a revolving drum the inside of which is usually a vacuum. The mixture to be filtered is fed onto the outside of the drum and the liquid is 'sucked' into the drum through the cloth. A scraper removes the residue before the drum has completed one revolution leaving the filter cloth clear of residue for a repeat of the process. (See Fig. F.4.)

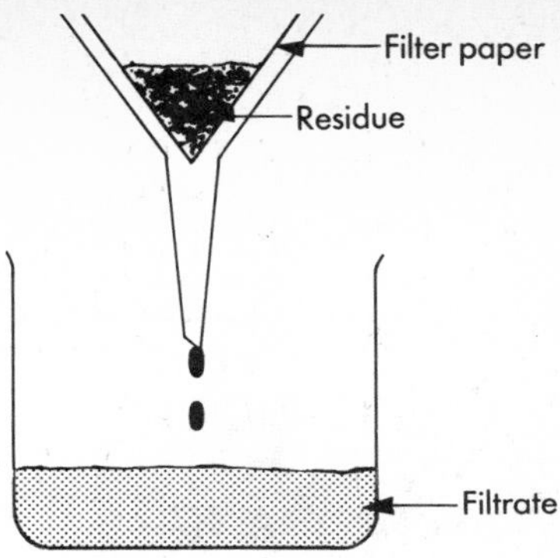

Fig. F.3 Filtration in the laboratory

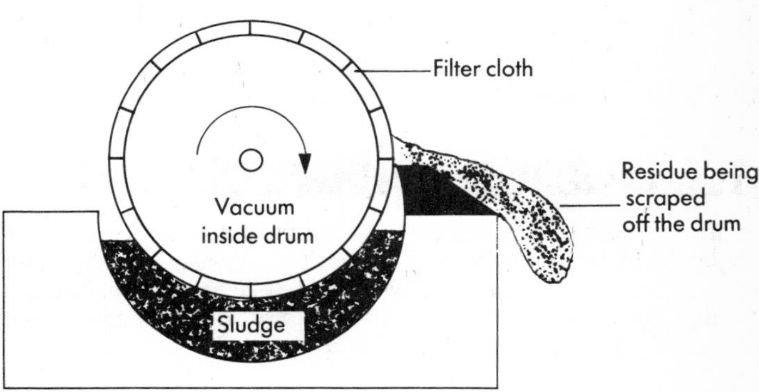

Fig. F.4 Vacuum drum filtration in industry

In the water industry

Filtration is done through filter beds. These are composed of gravel with finer sand on top. Water which filters through these beds leaves any particles behind on the top layer of sand. The advantage of such beds is that they are easily cleaned for re-use. The water flow is stopped and clean water is passed upwards from the bottom of the bed. The particles of impurity which have collected on the surface are 'floated off' and are discarded after removal of the flushing water. When cleaned, the sand and gravel mixture is allowed to settle and reforms the filter-bed. (See Fig. F.5.)

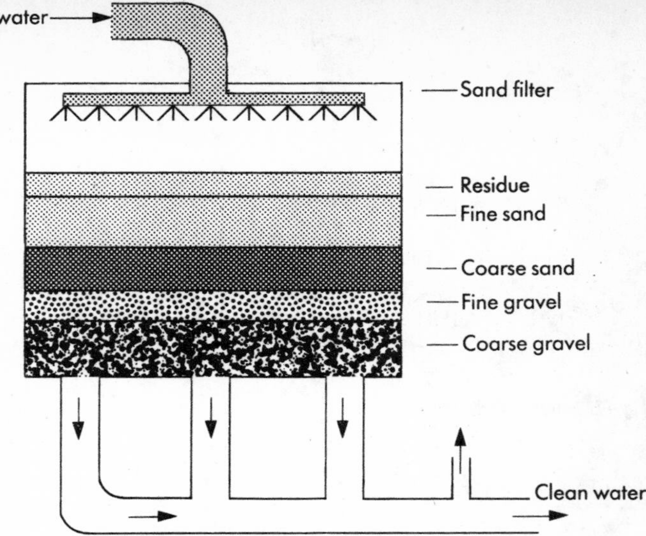

Fig. F.5 Filtration in the water industry – sand/gravel filter bed

FIRE EXTINGUISHER

The principle of fire extinguishing is easily understood in terms of the '**fire triangle**'. If any one of the three conditions for combustion can be removed a fire will go out. There are several types of fire extinguishers in common use. (See Figs. F.6a) and F.6b).) All will spray a fire with a chemical that either removes heat from the fire or excludes air.

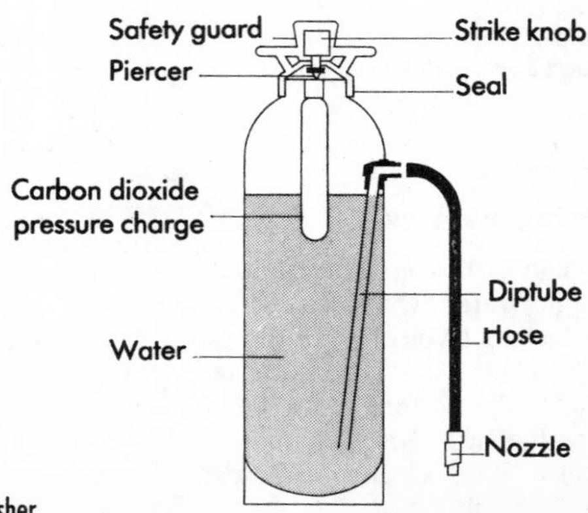

Fig. F.6 a) Water fire extingusher

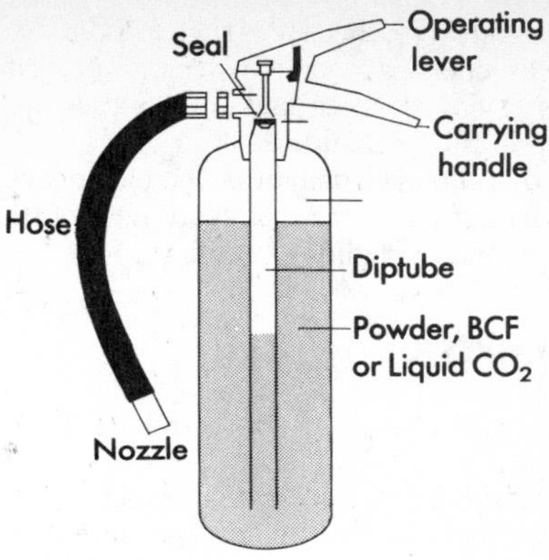

b) Fire extinguisher – oxygen excluder

The heat-removers

The simplest of these contains water which is expelled by carbon dioxide under pressure. Even as it vaporises, water cools the fire by taking heat of vaporisation from the burning fuel. Water extinguishers should not be used on electrical fires because of the danger of electrocution, or on fat or oil fires because of the danger of spreading the fire. For example, water poured into a chip-fat fire in a pan will sink below the fat, superheat and form steam. The superheated steam will 'blow' the burning oil out of the pan! The safest method of extinguishing such a fire is to place the lid on the pan or to cover it with a damp cloth to *exclude* air.

The oxygen-excluders

These can contain carbon dioxide or sodium hydrogencarbonate. They rely upon the formation of a dense, non-flammable, carbon dioxide 'blanket' to *smother* the fire. Few materials will burn in carbon dioxide. Sodium hydrogencarbonate is the constituent of dry-powder extinguishers. As the powder is sprayed onto the fire it decomposes with the heat, releasing carbon dioxide and steam.

The carbon dioxide and steam *smother* the fire. The process is messy since fine powder is spread over a large area. Less messy are extinguishers filled with liquid carbon dioxide under pressure. These eject carbon dioxide gas which smothers the fire but leaves no residue to damage salvaged equipment.

Specialised extinguisher

Bromochlorodifluoromethane, Halon 1211, was especially designed for flammable liquid fires such as aircraft-fuel or motor-fuel fires. It has very heavy vapour which *smothers* the fire. Halon 1211 also *slows down* the combustion reaction by chemical reaction. It is a very efficient extinguisher but it is an ozone-destroying chemical and is likely to be replaced with a more acceptable alternative in the near future.

Note: It is ironical that the main danger to the ozone layer of the earth from Halon 1211 arises from the more common use of the extinguisher in *fire-fighting drill* rather than in fighting real fires!

CLASSES OF FIRES

Fires are divided into four classes, A,B,C, and D. There are extinguisher chemicals for each type.

Class A fires are in wood, paper, straw, textiles and other carbon-containing materials. They can be extinguished by any type of extinguisher.

Class B fires are in petrol, oil, fats and other flammable liquids. All extinguishers except water are suitable for these fires.

Class C fires are in flammable gases such as methane or acetylene(ethyne). The best way to tackle these is to turn off the gas supply, but any extinguisher except water can be used.

Class D fires are in combustible metals. Special powders must be used on these. Carbon dioxide, for example, reacts strongly with burning magnesium.

All extinguishers except water are suitable for electrical fires. However, fires involving computers are usually extinguished by the Halon 1211 vapourising liquid. This does less damage than the powder extinguishers.

Note: Halon 1211 is an ICI product. The numbers indicate that there is 1 carbon, 2 fluorine, 1 chlorine and 1 bromine atom(s) in the molecule of the compound. The halogens are in order of increasing size. See also the different CFC numbering system.

FIRE TRIANGLE

The fire triangle (see Fig. F.7) is a simple display of the conditions necessary for a fire to exist.

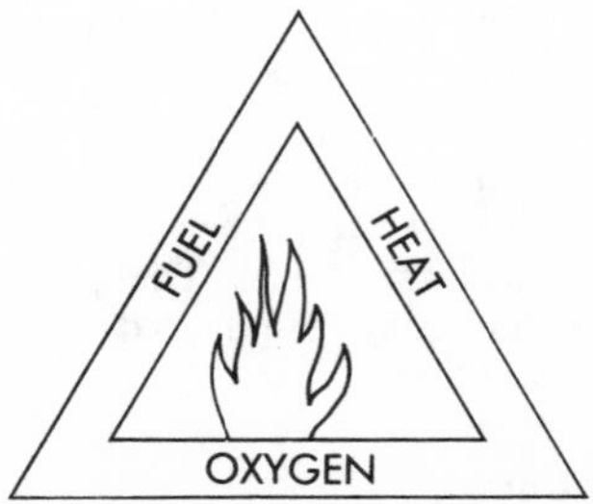

Fig. F.7 Fire triangle

It shows that a fire needs air (oxygen), something to burn (a fuel) and heat energy to maintain the combustion. If any one of these is missing or removed, the fire cannot begin or continue.

◄ Fire extinguishers ►

FIXATION OF NITROGEN

◄ Nitrogen cycle ►

FLAME TESTS

The perfection of the simple gas-burner we now call the bunsen burner in 1854 led **Robert Bunsen** to discover a method of chemical analysis called the flame test.

In his attempts to shape glass using the almost colourless hot flame of his burner, Bunsen noticed that when molten, glass made the flame yellow. He experimented with different substances in the flame using a platinum wire to insert them. He discovered that different elements in the substances gave different colours.

Process

To investigate the flame colour of a substance placed in a flame, it must first be converted into a chloride. Metal chlorides are more easily vaporised in a gas flame than sulphates, carbonates and nitrates. For example, if a lump of calcium carbonate is held in a flame, no flame colour is seen. If the lump is first dipped in hydrochloric acid, a red flame characteristic of calcium is seen. The hydrochloric acid has reacted with the calcium carbonate to form calcium chloride. Only very small amounts of metal chlorides are needed to produce quite strong flame colours.

Method

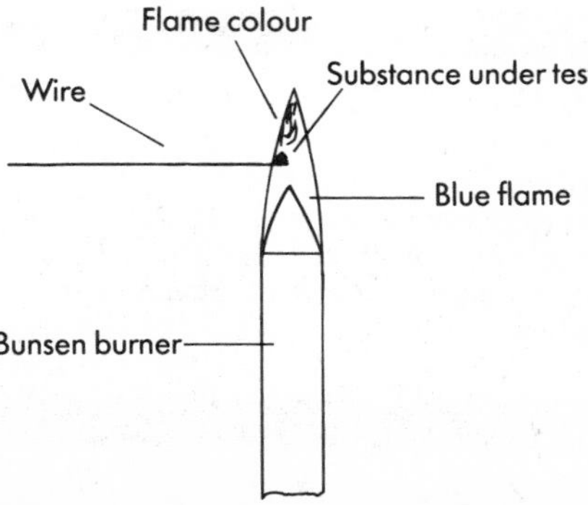

Fig. F.8 The flame test

A flame test is carried out in two steps:

i) the tip of a clean inert metal wire (platinum or nichrome) is dipped into a mixture of concentrated hydrochloric acid and the solid compound being analysed

ii) the loaded tip of the wire is then inserted into a faintly blue flame. The flame colour is observed. (See Fig. F.8 and Table F.2.)

Element	*Flame colour*
sodium	yellow
potassium	lilac
calcium	red flash
copper	green

Table F.2 Flame colours of common elements

FLAMMABLE

Substances which catch fire easily are said to be flammable. The term inflammable means the same but is now no longer used. To be classed as flammable, a substance must ignite after only a brief contact with a flame. Fig. F.9. shows the hazard symbol for flammable.

◀ Hazard warning symbols ▶

Fig. F.9 Hazard symbol – flammable

FLUORIDES

Many fluorides find uses in everyday life or industrial processes. Calcium fluoride, CaF_2 (fluorspar), is the most important source of fluorine compounds. Cryolite, Na_3AlF_6 is used in aluminium manufacture. Various fluorides are present in toothpaste to help prevent tooth decay. Some water authorities put soluble fluoride into drinking water for the same reason. Fluorides of carbon, such as poly(tetrafluoroethane), PTFE are used in non-stick pan coatings.

FLUORINE, $F_2(g)$

Fluorine, named from the Latin *fluere*; flow, was first recognised as an element by Humphry Davy in 1813 and first isolated by Henri Moissan in

1886. Fluorine is the most reactive halogen. It can only be produced from its compounds by electrolysis. This is one of the reasons it was not isolated until more than one hundred years after the discovery of chlorine.

Fluorine is a faintly yellow gas, paler than chlorine. It is the most powerful oxidising agent known. The chemical reactions of fluorine are not studied at school or college level because of its high reactivity. It is the most reactive of the **halogens** and is highly toxic.

FOOD ANALYSIS

Food analysis in school and college laboratories is usually practised to determine the elements present in the food. It is **qualitative analysis.** The main elements in food are carbon, hydrogen, oxygen and nitrogen. The presence of oxygen cannot be detected with certainty. The others are detected as described in Table F.3.

Element	*Test*	*Positive result*
carbon	heat food with dry copper(II) oxide	gas given off which turns lime-water milky – *carbon dioxide*
hydrogen		liquid formed on cool part of tube; turns cobalt chloride paper pink – *water*
nitrogen	heat food with soda-lime	gas formed which turns damp indicator paper blue – *ammonia*

Table F.3 Food analysis tests

FORMULAE

A formula is a convenient way of showing which **atoms** or **ions** are present in an **element** or **compound** and also their number or numerical ratio.

For example, the formula of the element **oxygen** is O_2 (See Fig. F.10). Oxygen consists of molecules each made up of two atoms. The formula of **sodium chloride** (common salt) is NaCl. (See Fig. F.11.) Sodium chloride contains equal numbers of sodium ions and chloride ions.

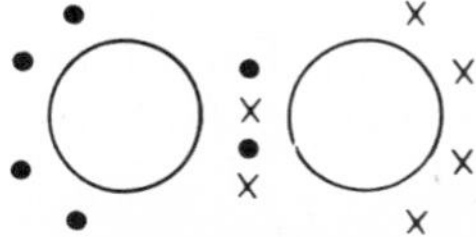

Fig. F.10 Oxygen molecule containing two oxygen atoms

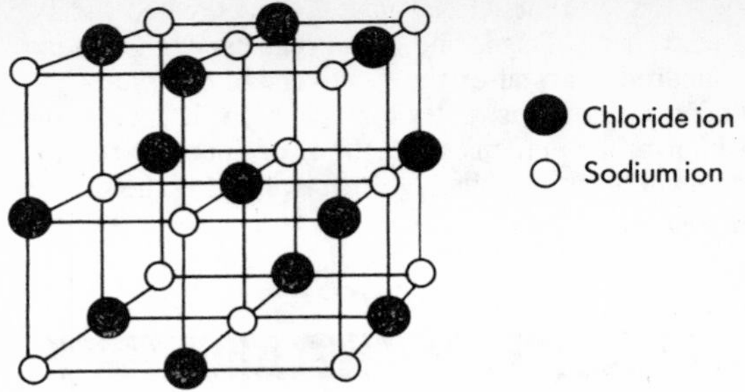

Fig. F.11 Sodium chloride crystal containing equal numbers of sodium ions and chloride ions

CALCULATING FORMULAE

The formula of a compound can be calculated from an **analysis** of the compound. The analysis must give the mass of each element in a given mass of the compound.

Method

i) find the mass of each element in a given mass of compound
ii) divide the mass of each element by its relative atomic mass, to get the moles of atoms of each element
iii) now divide each answer to ii) by the *smallest* answer to ii)
iv) this gives the relative moles of atoms of each element as whole numbers

Example

The following example shows these steps in practice.
8g of black copper oxide was reduced to copper by heating in a stream of hydrogen. 6.4g of copper was formed. The relative atomic masses are Cu=64; O=16.

i) the mass of copper is 6.4g; the mass of oxygen is 1.6g by subtraction.
ii) 6.4/64 = 0.1 moles of copper atoms
 1.6/16 = 0.1 moles of oxygen atoms
iii) dividing each by 0.1 gives
 0.1/0.1 = 1 mole of copper atoms
 0.1/0.1 = 1 mole of oxygen atoms

The simplest formula of black copper oxide is Cu_1O_1. The formula is usually written CuO since the symbol itself represents 1 mole of atoms. (Fig. F.12)

Simplest formula and molecular formula

There are two different types of formula for compounds, used in chemical studies. One is the empirical formula which is also called the simplest formula, the other is the molecular formula.

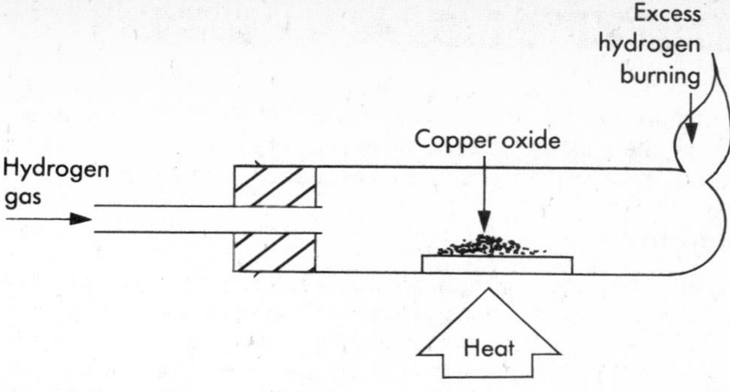

Fig. F.12 Reduction of copper oxide

- The simplest formula tells us the simplest ratio of the numbers of atoms present in the compound.
- The molecular formula gives the actual numbers of atoms in the molecule. The relative molecular mass must be known for this to be found.

The simplest formula is sometimes identical with the molecular formula, but not always. (See Table F.4.)

Compound	*Simplest formula*	*Molecular or chemical formula*
copper(II) oxide	CuO	CuO
ethene	CH_2	C_2H_4
ethanol	C_2H_6O	C_2H_6O
glucose	CH_2O	$C_6H_{12}O_6$
sodium chloride	$NaCl$	$NaCl$

Table F.4 Formulae of some common compounds

FOSSIL FUELS

Fuels which are extracted from the earth and which have taken millions of years to form are called fossil fuels. Coal, crude oil and natural gas are examples. Fossil fuels are also called non-renewable fuels because their rate of use is greater than their rate of formation. Fossil fuels are our most important source of organic compounds for the manufacture of drugs and medicines, plastics, paints, dyes, synthetic fibres etc. This is one of the reasons that makes it a priority for our society to reduce the use of fossil fuels as energy sources.

◀ Greenhouse effect ▶

FRACTIONAL DISTILLATION

This is the process of separating two or more **liquids** from each other by boiling the mixture and separately condensing the component vapours. The components of the mixture should mix completely with each other, like ethanol and water or the hydrocarbon components of crude oil.

In the laboratory

Fractional distillation of aqueous ethanol would be carried out in apparatus like that shown in Fig. D.10. Aqueous ethanol is heated in the distillation flask. When the mixture boils, ethanol vapour and water vapour travel up the fractionating column. Condensation and revaporisation take place on the packing material in the column. The vapour with the lowest boiling point (ethanol, b.p. 78°C) reaches the top first and enters the condenser. After condensing it flows into the receiver. When there is no more ethanol present, water (b.p. 100°C) will distill over.

Commercial distillation processes

Fractional distillation is an ancient process.

- Copper fractionating columns called 'stills' are used in many countries for producing traditional distilled spirits such as whisky, brandy and rum from fermented grapes or grains. The process is the same as described above but the vessels used are quite different in shape.
- **Crude oil** fractionation is carried out in industry on a large scale in tall columns as shown in Fig. F.13.

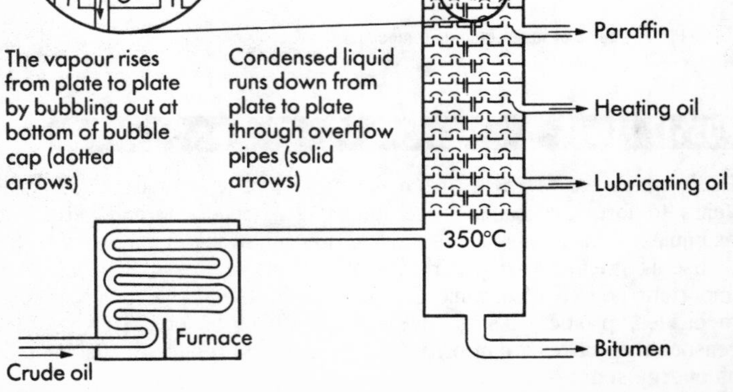

Fig. F.13 Crude oil distillation in industry

FRANCIUM, Fr

Francium is a synthetic **alkali metal** element, discovered in 1939. It has not been produced in amounts large enough to be seen. It would be expected to be the most reactive metal known.

FRASCH PROCESS

The *extraction of sulphur* from deep beneath the surface of the earth by the Frasch process was a triumph of imaginative thinking and technology in the late nineteenth century. The process was invented by Herman Frasch, a petroleum chemist. The problem to be overcome at the time was the extraction of sulphur from deposits below clay, gravel, quicksand and underground water containing toxic hydrogen sulphide gas. Mining was impossible through quicksand, water and toxic gas! Frasch noted that sulphur melts at a fairly low temperature. He suggested that injecting steam into the deposits would melt the sulphur which could then be pumped to the surface

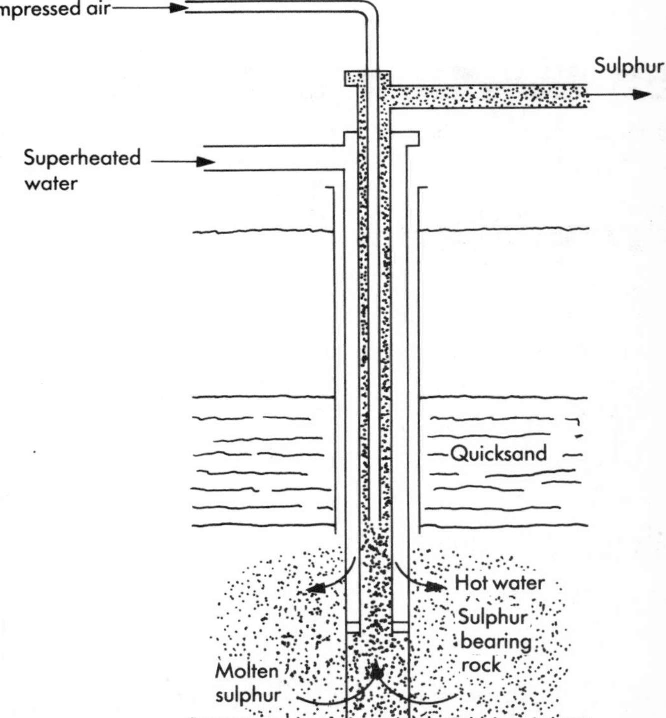

Fig. F.14 A Frasch well

like oil. This method is now used worldwide since it requires little labour and machinery. In addition, rocky impurities are left below ground which reduces both the cost of purification and the problem of waste disposal. The process is environmentally acceptable. It was first successfully tried in 1894. The details of the well are shown in Fig. F.14.

Method

Three concentric pipes are sunk into the sulphur deposits. The diameter of the largest pipe is only 20cm.

- Superheated water at 180°C passes down the outer pipe and enters the sulphur deposits; liquid sulphur forms below the water
- The liquid sulphur enters the inner pipe through holes in its lower part and rises only a short way up the pipe
- Compressed air is pumped down the centre pipe and mixes with the molten sulphur in the inner pipe, making it light and frothy; the froth rises to the surface
- Sulphur and water froth collect in huge vats, where the water separates and runs away, leaving commercially pure molten sulphur
- Most sulphur is converted into sulphuric acid.

FUELS

Any substances that can be used to release energy can be a fuel. In practice, only materials which are either cheap or give out a large amount of energy are regarded as fuels, e.g **fossil fuels**, wood and waste paper and **plastics** and **nuclear fuels**. Common fuels burn to give energy. Nuclear fuels undergo **nuclear fission** to give out energy.

GALVANI, LUIGI (1727–1798)

An eighteenth-century Italian professor of surgery, who is best known for an unusual discovery made whilst experimenting with muscle in a frog's leg. When the muscle was hung on a copper hook placed on an iron support, it was seen to twitch. Galvani considered this to be due to 'animal electricity'. Later his fellow countryman, **Alessandro Volta**, found that the electricity arose at the point of contact of the metals iron and copper. Volta found that an electrical current is produced whenever any two different metals are placed in a conducting solution. This effect led Volta to invent the voltaic 'pile', the prototype of the modern battery.

GALVANISING

Galvanising is the process of coating steel with zinc. It is done to prevent rusting. Steel waste bins, corrugated steel building panels and steel window frames are usually galvanised. Galvanising would prevent the rusting of car chassis' but few car models employ the process. Galvanised steel is easily recognised by its surface covering of grey irregularly-shaped flat crystals.

Protective action of zinc

The word, galvanising, arises from the electrical basis of the protective action of zinc. It is named after **Luigi Galvani**. The zinc coating protects the underlaying steel in two ways:

- it forms a complete covering preventing physical contact with water and oxygen
- exposed steel does not corrode from a scratch as zinc corrodes in preference to the iron because it is the more reactive of the two metals; the electrical origin of this effect can be seen in more detail in Fig. G.1 and the explanation below.

At the scratch, zinc and iron are in contact with water. In theory, both could react:

zinc coat	⇌	dissolved zinc	+	electrons	(1)
$Zn(s)$	⇌	$Zn^{2+}(aq)$	+	$2e^-$	

and

iron sheet	⇌	dissolved iron	+	electrons	(2)
$Fe(s)$	⇌	$Fe^{2+}(aq)$	+	$2e^-$	

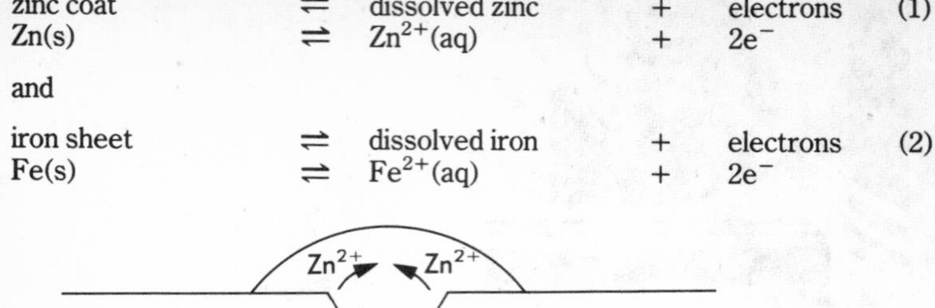

Fig. G.1 Sacrificial protection of steel by zinc

In practice, the zinc is the more reactive metal, being higher in the **reactivity series**; it produces electrons by reaction (1) faster than the iron. The excess electrons produced by the dissolving zinc enter the iron and reverse reaction (2) preventing the iron from corroding. The zinc is acting by a process called **sacrificial protection.**

GASES

The gaseous state is one of the three **states of matter.** The **state symbol** for the gas state is (g). Gases consist of molecules which move about freely and at random. There is very little attraction between gas molecules, so they can completely fill any container. Substances which are gases at room temperature have small molecules. They include the non-metallic elements and their compounds which have low **relative molecular masses.** Molecules of gases move at high speeds. At room temperature the average speed of an oxygen molecule is 1 700 km per hour – about 900 miles per hour! Lighter molecules will move faster, heavier ones slower, e.g. hydrogen molecules 4 000mph and bromine 450mph. They collide with each other over a million times a second. The speed of molecules and their distance apart control the speed of mixing of gases – **diffusion.**

GAS PRESSURE

The rate of collision of gas molecules with the sides of the container is the cause of gas pressure. Squashing the molecules of gas into a smaller volume or increasing the temperature both increase the rate of collision of molecules with the sides of the vessel. Gas pressure rises with an increase in temperature or a decrease in volume. The volume of 1 mole of any gas at room temperature and normal pressure is 24 000cm^3.

The properties of the more common gases are given in Table G.1.

Name	*Formula*	*Colour*	*Solubility in water*	*Relative density*	*Chemical test*	*Test result*
ammonia	NH_3	colourless	very soluble	0.6	damp indicator	high pH blue colour
carbon dioxide	CO_2	colourless	fairly soluble	1.5	add to lime water	milkiness
chlorine	Cl_2	pale green	fairly soluble	2.5	damp indicator	bleached
hydrogen	H_2	colourless	insoluble	0.07	lighted splint	explosion
hydrogen chloride	HCl	colourless	very soluble	1.3	mix with ammonia gas	white smoke
methane	CH_4	colourless	insoluble	0.6	lighted splint	blue flame or explosion
nitrogen	N_2	colourless	insoluble	0.96	(i) lighted splint, (ii) lime water	puts out flame/no effect on lime water
oxygen	O_2	colourless	insoluble	1.1	glowing splint	rekindles splint
sulphur dioxide	SO_2	colourless	soluble	2.2	acidic dichromate	turns from orange to green

Table G.1 Properties of common gases

Notes:

- Solubility: in this table, a 'very soluble' gas is roughly at least 5 × more soluble than a 'soluble' gas. A 'soluble gas' is at least 1000 times more soluble than an 'insoluble gas'. No gas is totally insoluble e.g. oxygen dissolves enough in water to support aquatic life.
- Relative density: this is the number of times the gas is denser than air.

GAS COLLECTION METHODS

The method of collecting a gas depends on its properties:

- Gases which are less dense than air can be collected in gas jars by upward delivery (see Fig. G.2) e.g. H_2 and NH_3
- Gases which are denser than air can be collected by downward delivery (see Fig. G.3) e.g. Cl_2, CO_2, SO_2, HCl
- Any gas can be collected in a gas syringe but the air in the reaction vessel will be mixed with it unless it is displaced first by the gas being produced (see Fig. G.4)
- Gases which do not dissolve in water can be collected 'over water' (see Fig. G.5) Soluble gases such as Cl_2, HCl, SO_2, CO_2, NH_3 cannot be collected over water.

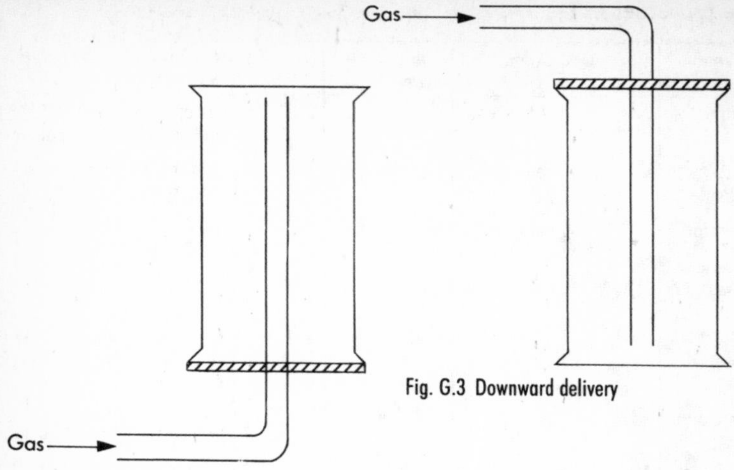

Fig. G.2 Upward delivery

Fig. G.3 Downward delivery

Fig. G.4 Gas syringe

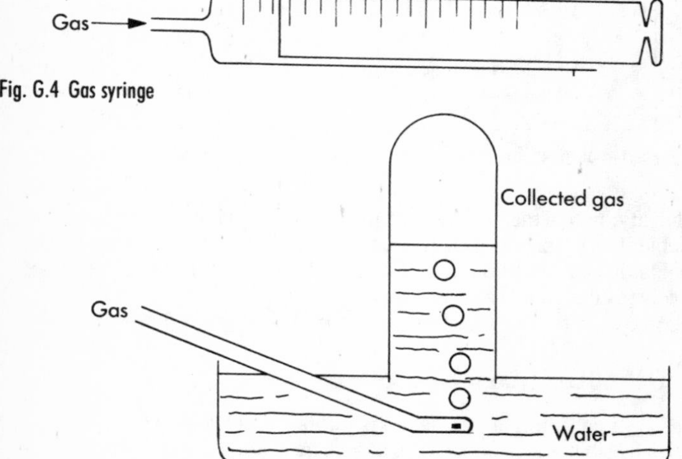

Fig. G.5 Collection over water

GERMICIDE

Any chemical that kills bacteria, moulds or yeasts is called a germicide. **Disinfectants** and **antiseptics** are both types of germicide.

GIANT STRUCTURES

Giant structures contain particles (atoms or ions) that are bonded together by a network of bonds which extend to the edges of the crystal. An alternative name is **macromolecules**. There are three types of structure.

Giant molecules

Any diamond is a single molecule, a giant structure of atoms called a giant molecule.

Giant ionic structures

A salt crystal, e.g. a sodium chloride crystal, is also a giant structure (see Fig. G.6). It is a giant ionic structure consisting of ions held together by a network of ionic bonds extending throughout the crystal.

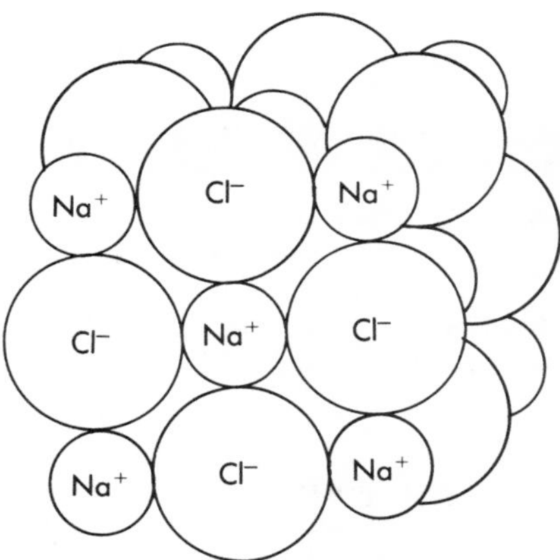

Fig. G.6 Sodium chloride crystal

Giant metallic structures

All solid metals are giant structures of atoms. Fig. G.7 shows a diagram of a copper crystal.

PROPERTIES

A characteristic property of giant structures is their high melting and boiling points. The **alkali metals** are an exception.

Fig. G.7 Copper crystal

GLASS

Glass is one of the oldest and commonest materials. It has been made since at least 4,000 BC when sand and wood ashes were melted together forming beads of glass.

Glass is a **supercooled liquid** – a liquid that has been cooled too quickly to form crystals and so solidifies in a non-crystalline form.

Types

There are many different types of glass:

- The common type, used to make window panes and bottles, is called soda-glass.
- More specialised glasses are the heat-resistant borosilicate glass (Pyrex) and the ornamental glass (lead crystal).
- Glass can be made from a single substance, **silica**, SiO_2. Silica glass is very resistant to the effects of heating and cooling that would destroy other glasses. A red-hot silica-glass tube can be plunged into ice-cold water and will not crack. Ordinary soda-glass cracks easily if heated or cooled quickly.

MANUFACTURE

Common soda-glass results from mixing sodium carbonate and limestone with sand. When heated in a furnace, these additional ingredients react with the silica to form the mixture of sodium silicate and calcium silicate which is known as soda-glass.

limestone	+	silica	→	calcium silicate	+	carbon dioxide
$CaCO_3(s)$	+	SiO_2	→	$CaSiO_3$	+	$CO_2(g)$

sodium carbonate	+	silica	→	sodium silicate	+	carbon dioxide
Na_2CO_3	+	SiO_2	→	Na_2SiO_3	+	CO_2

The addition of potassium carbonate and boron compounds produces borosilicate (Pyrex) glass. Addition of lead oxide makes lead crystal glass.

Float glass

Before 1958 the surfaces of plate glass had to be ground and polished after manufacture to obtain a finish suitable for shop windows, mirrors and vehicles.

Float glass is made by pouring a layer of molten glass onto a bath of molten tin. The principle of the method is simple. The smoothest flat surfaces known are those of liquids. By floating liquid glass on liquid tin both surfaces of the glass are as smooth as possible. The glass is cooled enough to retain its shape and smoothness before it leaves the tin bath to be annealed and cut.

A slight modification of the process will produce tinted glass. Using electrodes touching the top and bottom of the molten glass metallic ions can be dissolved in the glass from the anode. If a copper anode is used, copper ions enter the glass. The ions are reduced to copper metal later in the process and tint the glass.

Properties

Glass is a very strong material, twenty times stronger than the strongest metal alloy. However, manufacturing conditions reduce its strength and so it cracks easily. Methods of strengthening glass have been devised and we now have toughened glass in car windscreens, bullet-proof glass, glass fibre for increasing the strength of plastics ('fibre-glass') and optical fibres that can be bent into almost any shape. Glass may be the material of the future as well as one of the first materials used in the past.

Recycling glass

Glass is one of the most easily recyclable materials. New glass is made using up to 20% of broken, recycled glass. A scheme to encourage the public to recycle glass – the 'bottle bank' scheme – started in 1977. Since then the number of bottle banks has increased from about 20 in the first year to nearly 3000. About 15% of all bottles produced in Britain are recycled through bottle banks. Recycling saves energy and chemical resources.

GLUCOSE, $C_6H_{12}O_6$

Glucose is a carbohydrate and a reducing sugar. It is a common ingredient in processed foods. It is manufactured on a large scale by hydrolysing starch with dilute hydrochloric or sulphuric acid. After reaction, the acid, which is a catalyst and so is not used up, is neutralised with sodium carbonate. Glucose reduces Fehling's solution to a red/brown precipitate.

GLYCERINE (GLYCEROL)

Glycerine is a by-product of the **saponification** of fats and oils in the soap industry.

```
    OH OH OH
    |  |  |
 H—C—C—C—H
    |  |  |
    H  H  H
```

GOLD, Au

Gold is a rare, unreactive metal. Because of its extreme unreactivity it is found uncombined in nature (native gold). It is however rare to find it in visibly large lumps. It is also found as a natural alloy with silver – called electrum. The symbol for gold is derived from the Latin name *aurum*.

Gold is a very soft metal. For ornamental use it is hardened by alloying with copper or silver. The purity of gold is measured in carats – pure gold is 24 carat. 9 carat gold has nine parts of gold and fifteen parts of an alloying element.

Glass takes on a pink or red colour when small amounts of gold are included in the melt.

GRAPHITE

Graphite is one of the two **allotropes** of carbon, the other being diamond. Graphite (Gr. *graphos*; 'I write') is a soft grey solid.

STRUCTURE

Its characteristic properties arise from its crystalline structure (see Fig. G.8). Graphite has a layer structure. Each layer is composed of carbon atoms covalently bonded in hexagonal 'rings'. The bonding in these layers is very strong. The layers are packed together like playing cards. The bonding between layers is weak.

Uses

When put under pressure, the layers slide over each other giving the graphite a slippery nature. This is why graphite is used as a dry lubricant – it will not evaporate and so can be used in space.

Applying a piece of graphite to paper with hand-pressure causes some layers to be smeared onto the paper surface, making a grey mark. This

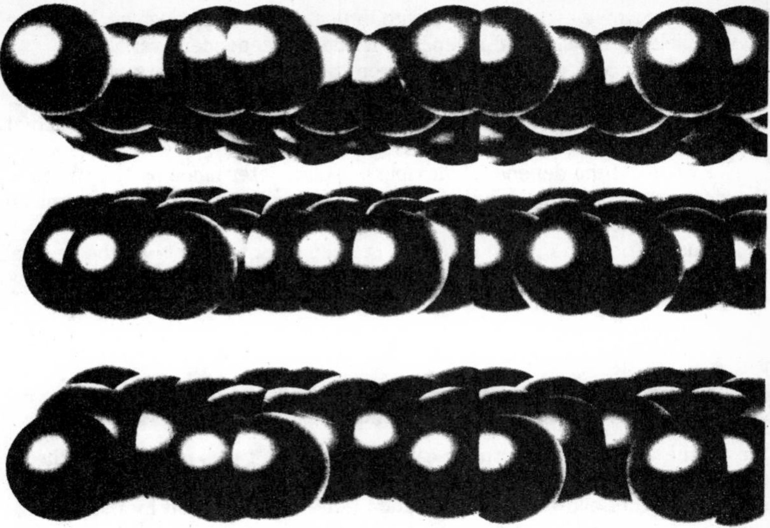

Fig. G.8 Graphite structure showing several layers

explains the use of graphite in pencil 'lead'. Mixtures of graphite and clay are baked to form the 'leads' in pencils which do not contain lead at all! The more graphite in the 'lead' the softer it is; the more clay the harder.

GRAPHS

Drawing graphs is a convenient way of displaying the results of experiments in which a change in one variable is being related to a change in another variable.

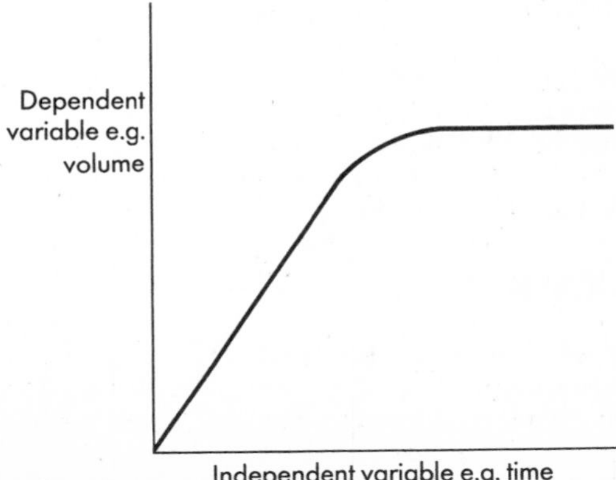

Fig. G.9 Graph axes

For example, the variation in mass with time for a decomposing chemical. The two variables are called the independent and the dependent variables.

The independent variable is plotted on the x-axis; it is the variable which changes in a way that is fixed by the experimenter. In the example above, time is the independent variable because the time interval is usually fixed at one minute, one hour or one day etc., as appropriate.

The values of the dependent variable are then determined by the values of the independent variable. The mass of a decomposing chemical is determined by the time interval chosen.

The usual form of a graph is to plot the dependent variable on the vertical (y) axis and the independent variable on the horizontal (x) axis, e.g. mass change vertically against time horizontally (see Fig. G.9.)

GREENHOUSE EFFECT

This is the atmospheric warming caused by certain gases in the atmosphere, e.g carbon dioxide and methane. They allow sunlight through to warm the earth but do not allow the heat radiation (infra-red) given off by the earth to escape. Heat is trapped in the layer of air near the surface of the earth. The effect is increasing as more **carbon dioxide** accumulates in the atmosphere. The planet Venus, whose atmosphere is mostly carbon dioxide, has a very high temperature as a result of this effect.

Any gas calculated to increase this effect is called a 'greenhouse gas'.

GROUPS OF THE PERIODIC TABLE

A group is a vertical column of elements in the periodic table. The elements in a group have similar physical and chemical properties which change in a predictable way from top to bottom in the group. This change is called a trend in the properties. There are eight groups in the periodic table.
Some groups have names as well as numbers.
Group 1 is called the **Alkali metals**
Group 2 is called the **Alkaline earth metals**
Group 7 is called the **Halogens**
Group 0 is called the **Noble gases**

GROUP NUMBER

The group number of an element is related to the number of electrons in the outer shell of the atom.

For the first seven groups, the group number equals the number of outer electrons.

Group 0 elements have eight (two for helium) outer electrons but are not now called group 8.

GROUP TRENDS

Some group trends are common to all groups. For example, from top to bottom of each group

- the atoms get gradually larger as the number of shells of electrons increases; Fig. G.10 shows the first three alkali metals.

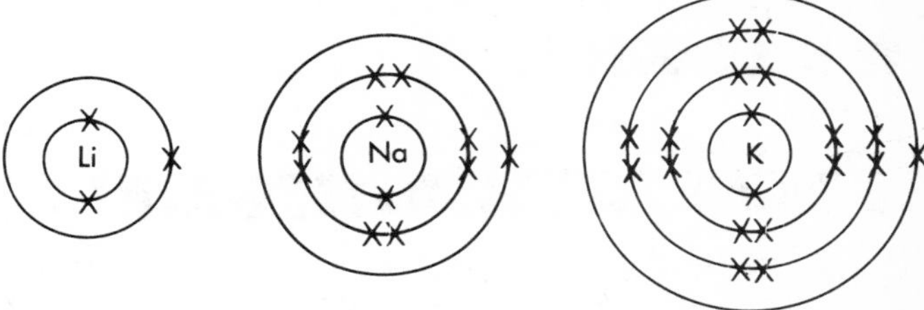

Fig. G.10 Increasing size of alkali metals down the group

- The number of electrons in the outer shell always equals the group number for elements in the same group; Table G.2 shows this for group 2 elements.

Element	*Electron arrangement*
beryllium	2 2
magnesium	2 8 2
calcium	2 8 8 2

Table G.2 Electron arrangement in the first three group 2 elements

- The atoms lose their outer electron(s) more easily; the further away from the positively charged nucleus the outer electrons are, the smaller is the attraction keeping them in the atom.
- The density of the elements increase: for example, the three alkali metals at the top of the group float on water, the two at the bottom of the group sink in water.

HABER, FRITZ (1868–1934)

In 1896, the president of the British Association, Sir William Crookes, stated that 'the fixation of atmospheric nitrogen is one of the great discoveries awaiting the ingenuity of chemists'. Fritz Haber of Germany made that discovery in 1908 and received the Nobel prize for it in 1918.

Among his many other chemical investigations was an attempt to recover gold from sea water. He found it uneconomic to extract and so his efforts to help his country repay its First World War debts came to nothing.

HABER PROCESS

Two elements are needed to synthesise **ammonia** – **nitrogen** and **hydrogen**, they are obtained from the cheapest sources at the time of manufacture. In the UK at present, the cheapest source of hydrogen is natural gas; it has not always been so.

THE ORIGINAL HABER PROCESS

At various times hydrogen has been made from:

- Water by electrolysis: this was used by Haber in the pilot plant

$$2H_2O(l) \xrightarrow{\text{electricity}} 2H_2(g) + O_2(g)$$

- Steam by reaction with coke:

coke	+	steam	→	carbon monoxide	+	hydrogen
$C(s)$	+	$H_2O(g)$	→	$CO(g)$	+	$H_2(g)$

$$\underbrace{CO(g) + H_2(g)}_{\text{water gas}}$$

This process is **endothermic** so the coke gets cooler. The mixture of gases formed is called **water-gas**. This reaction cooled down the coke, so air was passed in to burn some of the coke in order to re-heat it. This produced a gas mixture called producer-gas.

coke	+	air	→	carbon monoxide	+	nitrogen
$2C(s)$	+	$O_2/4N_2(g)$	→	$2CO(g)$	+	$4N_2(g)$
				producer gas		

These two processes were alternated to produce a steady stream of gas containing hydrogen, nitrogen and carbon monoxide.

A further reaction with steam converted the carbon monoxide into carbon dioxide and produced more hydrogen.

carbon monoxide	+	steam	→	carbon dioxide	+	hydrogen
$CO(g)$	+	$H_2O(g)$	→	$CO_2(g)$	+	$H_2(g)$

The Modern Haber Process

Today's process differs in two ways from the original process. (See Fig. H.1.)

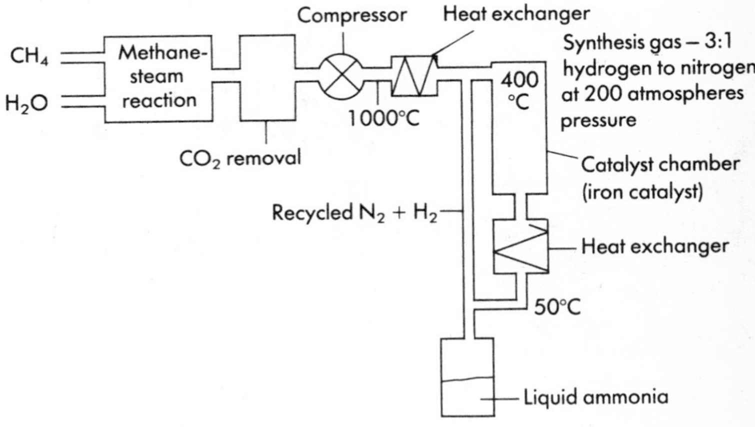

Fig. H.1 Haber process – flow diagram

- First, it is much more energy-efficient. Modern plant uses only about half the energy used by the first plants built.
- Secondly, the source of hydrogen is now methane reacted with steam; half the hydrogen comes from the steam and half from the methane.

methane	+	steam	→	carbon dioxide	+	hydrogen
$CH_4(g)$	+	$2H_2O(g)$	→	$CO_2(g)$	+	$4H_2(g)$

A mixture of hydrogen and nitrogen in the ratio of 3:1 is called 'synthesis gas'. This mixture is compressed to a pressure 200 times normal air pressure and is passed over an iron catalyst at about 450°C. Reaction occurs but only about

15% of the gas is converted into ammonia. The unconverted gas is recycled so that eventually 98% of the synthesis gas is converted into ammonia.

hydrogen	+	nitrogen	↔	ammonia	+	heat
$3H_2(g)$	+	$N_2(g)$	↔	$2NH_3(g)$		$\Delta H = -92 kJ mol^{-1}$

The economics of the process

- Natural gas comes through a national pipeline, so the size of the plant needed to make hydrogen is reduced. Modern ammonia plants are therefore smaller and cheaper to build than they were seventy years ago

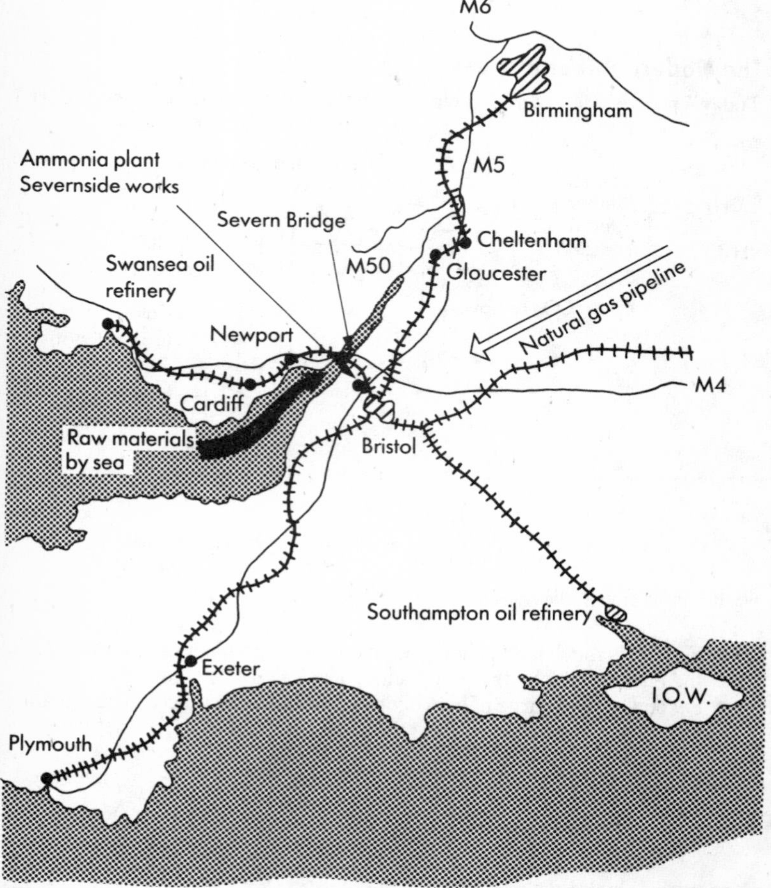

Fig. H.2 Severnside ammonia plant site Reproduced by kind permission from BP Educational Service

- The heat given out in the synthesis($\triangle H$ is negative) is not wasted; it is absorbed in heat exchangers and used to drive the compressors which pressurise the synthesis gas to 200 atmospheres before it enters the catalyst vessel
- A further economy of manufacture comes from the use of the by-product carbon dioxide (formed in the reaction that produces hydrogen for the process); some is reacted with ammonia on a nearby site to produce **urea**, the rest is sold, for example, as a coolant for nuclear reactors

Siting the ammonia plant

An important part of the process of making chemicals as cheaply as possible is choosing the best place to site the plant.

- Natural gas can be piped almost anywhere and nitrogen is freely available in the air
- The process uses large quantities of water as a reactant so the plant must be sited near a river
- The chosen site should be close to the means of transport – roads, rail and deep-water ports – that will distribute the product to customers at home and abroad
- Ammonia should be made close to other plants that will use it for making nitric acid and fertilisers
- The plant could be sited close to an oil refinery to make use of refinery gases in place of methane

Two major plants are at Billingham-on-Tees and at Severnside, Bristol; both are close to a port, a river, a supply of hydrocarbons and good transport systems (see Fig. H.2.)

HAEMATITE, Fe_2O_3

Haematite is a dull-red oxide of iron mined in many parts of the world for use in smelting. Its name derives from the same root as 'haemoglobin' and means 'blood-red ore'.

There are no longer any economically workable sources of haematite in Britain. Haematite ores used in the British iron and steel industry come from Australia, Sweden and the USA.

HALF-LIFE, $t_{1/2}$

This term applies to the decay or disintegration of atoms of radioactive elements. It is the time taken for half the atoms of the radioactive element to disintegrate. It is also the time taken for the radioactivity of a radioactive element to become half its original value.

Half-lives vary from microseconds to billions of years. For example, the half life of the carbon-14 isotope present in minute amounts in natural carbon dioxide is 5 700 years. In a period of 5 700 years, half of the C-14 atoms originally present will have disintegrated. This is shown in a nuclear equation as:

$$^{14}_{6}C \rightarrow ^{14}_{7}N + ^{0}_{-1}e \quad t_{1/2} = 5\,700y$$

The half life of uranium-238, however, is 4.5 billion years!

◀ Equations ▶

HALIDES

Compounds containing any of the halogen atoms are called halides. Sodium chloride, sodium bromide and sodium iodide are three halides of sodium. Halides can be made by reacting a metal or a non-metallic element with the chosen halogen, e.g.

copper	+	chlorine	→	copper(II)chloride
Cu(s)	+	$Cl_2(g)$	→	$CuCl_2(s)$
phosphorus	+	bromine	→	phosphorus(III) bromide
2P(s)	+	$3Br_2(l)$	→	$2PBr_3(l)$

Test for halides

The commonest halide is the chloride. The test for a chloride is given in the section on **anions**.
For example:

potassium chloride	+	silver nitrate	→	silver chloride	+	potassium nitrate

If a bromide is present the silver nitrate test will produce a very pale yellow precipitate of silver bromide. If an iodide is present a deeper yellow precipitate of silver iodide forms.

HALOGENS – GROUP 7

The name halogens is derived from the Greek words *halos*; salt or sea; *genes*; forming. The group consists of four naturally occurring non-metallic elements, fluorine, chlorine, bromine and iodine. The fifth member, astatine, is a synthetic element.

Properties

- All the elements have diatomic molecules, F_2, Cl_2, Br_2 and I_2
- All are coloured
- Fluorine and chlorine are gases at room temperature, bromine is a liquid and iodine a solid

STRUCTURE

The electronic structure of the group members is shown in Table H.1.

Halogen	*Electron arrangement*
fluorine	2 7
chlorine	2 8 7
bromine	2 8 18 7
iodine	2 8 18 18 7

Table H.1 The electron arrangement of the halogens

- Each atom contains seven outer electrons – the same as the group number
- The more shells the larger the atom

REACTIONS

When halogen atoms react, they do so by attracting one electron from another atom. The positively charged nucleus attracts the electron into the outer shell of electrons giving the shell its maximum number of electrons – eight. The smaller the atom the greater is this attraction. Chlorine atoms have a stronger attraction for electrons than iodine atoms and therefore are more reactive. The reactivity of the elements decreases down the group, fluorine being extremely reactive and iodine being weakly reactive. The relative reactivity of the halogens is,

fluorine > chlorine > bromine > iodine
(the symbol > means greater than).

Halogens are reactive elements, they react with most metallic and non-metallic elements and with water. Usually, the reactions give out large amounts of heat. Copper powder will ignite without heating in chlorine and even gold reacts with chlorine! The following reactions are of special importance.

Reactions of halogens with water

All react to form acidic bleaching solutions. For example, chlorine:

chlorine	+	water	→	hydrochloric acid	+	chloric(I) acid (bleach)
$Cl_2(g)$	+	$H_2O(l)$	→	$HCl(aq)$	+	$HOCl(aq)$

Reactions of halogens with metals forming ionic compounds

- Metal atoms react by losing electrons from their outer electron shell.
- Halogen atoms accept these electrons into their outer shell.
- The reaction is called 'electron transfer'. For example, when lithium reacts with chlorine, atoms of each element react:

lithium atom	+	chlorine atom	→	lithium ion	+	chloride ion
Li	+	Cl	→	Li^+	+	Cl^-

Diagramatically this is shown as in Fig. H.3.
In reactions which result in the formation of ions, the ions formed always have full outer shells of electrons – eight electrons.

Li
Lithium atom
Cl
Chlorine atom

Li^+
Lithium ion
Cl^-
Chloride ion

Fig. H.3 Reaction of lithium and chlorine atoms

Reactions with non-metals forming covalent/molecular compounds

- Non-metal atoms always react with other non-metal atoms by sharing electrons to give each a full outer electron shell. For example, when hydrogen and chlorine react, atoms of each element first form. Then:

hydrogen atom	+	chlorine atom	→	hydrogen chloride molecule
H	+	Cl	→	HCl

Diagramatically this is shown as in Fig. H.4

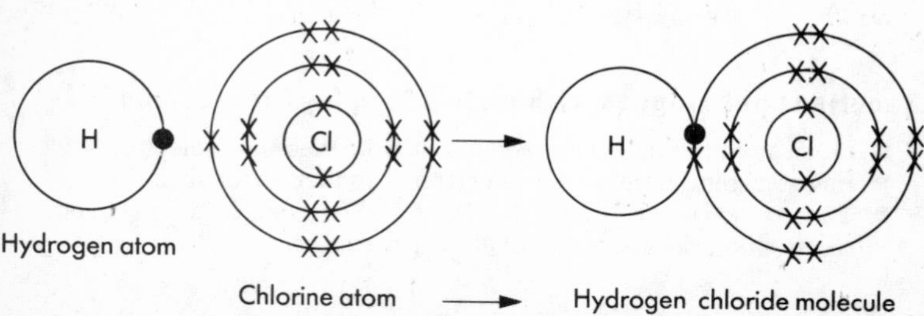

Fig. H.4 Reaction of hydrogen and chlorine atoms

Reactions of halogens with other halide solutions

The order of reactivity of the halogens: chlorine, bromine and iodine is easily shown by the following series of reactions:

- Chlorine will displace bromine from any bromide
- Chlorine will displace iodine from any iodide
- Bromine will displace iodine from any iodide
- Iodine will not displace any halogen from any halide

The reactions are:

$$Cl_2(g) + 2KBr(aq) \rightarrow 2KCl(aq) + Br_2(aq)$$
$$Cl_2(g) + 2KI(aq) \rightarrow 2KCl(aq) + I_2(aq)$$

and

$$Br_2(aq) + 2KI(aq) \rightarrow 2KBr(aq) + I_2(aq)$$

- Fluorine will displace all three halogens from their salts. However, it cannot be used safely in school and college laboratories and so is not studied practically in GCSE courses. Its properties and reactions are easily predicted from an understanding of the trends in properties of the other halogens.

HARD WATER

Hard water is water that will not lather easily with soap. It is natural river, spring or aquifer water containing dissolved calcium or magnesium compounds. Water will be hard in those areas of the country where the underlying rock contains magnesium carbonate or gypsum, calcium sulphate. (See Fig. C.2.) There are two types of hardness, **temporary hardness** or' carbonate hardness' and **permanent hardness** or 'non-carbonate hardness'.

(Magnesium compounds are not common in the British Isles. Small areas of magnesium containing limestone called dolomite occur in Yorkshire and Nottinghamshire and magnesium sulphate is present in some spa waters – Epsom salts is magnesium sulphate. The hardness effects of magnesium compounds are exactly the same as those of calcium compounds. For simplicity and to save repetition, the name magnesium can be substituted for calcium in all that follows.)

Causes of hardness in water

The cause of both types of hardness is the presence of calcium or magnesium ions in water.

Temporary hardness

Temporary-hard water is hard water that can be softened by boiling. It contains dissolved calcium hydrogencarbonate. The limestone and chalk that cause temporary hardness are not very soluble in water. Ground-water, however, contains dissolved carbon dioxide which reacts with them.

calcium carbonate	+	water	+	carbon dioxide	→	calcium hydrogencarbonate solution
$CaCO_3(s)$	+	$H_2O(l)$	+	$CO_2(g)$	→	$Ca(HCO_3)_2(aq)$

Very little reaction occurs and the calcium hydrogencarbonate content of natural waters is low. It is measured in parts per million (ppm).

What happens when soap is added?

Soaps are sodium salts of long chain **fatty acids** such as stearic acid. Soap reacts with the calcium ions in the water:

calcium ions	+	sodium stearate (soap)	→	calcium stearate (scum)	+	sodium ions

Calcium stearate is not soluble in water and forms a floating precipitate called scum. Scum sticks to baths, washbasins and clothes and is unsightly. It is for this reason that soap is not used for washing clothes in hard-water areas of the country.

What happens when the water is heated?

Heating temporary-hard water decomposes the calcium hydrogencarbonate. Insoluble calcium carbonate forms and the water becomes soft – it no longer contains dissolved calcium compounds.

calcium hydrogencarbonate solution	→	calcium carbonate (scale or fur)	+	carbon dioxide	+	water
$Ca(HCO_3)_2(aq)$	→	$CaCO_3(s)$	+	$CO_2(g)$	+	$H_2O(l)$

This is an exact reversal of the reaction which produced the hard water in the ground. The result is that a solid deposit forms on heated surfaces in contact with temporary hard water. In electric kettles it forms on the element and is called 'kettle-fur'. In domestic and industrial water boilers it is called 'boiler-scale'. In both cases its presence can reduce the heat-efficiency of the process. In boilers it can lead to blocked pipes and boiler explosions.

Permanent hardness

Permanent-hard water cannot be softened by boiling. In all other properties it is the same as temporary-hard water. Permanent hardness is caused by the presence of calcium sulphate, $CaSO_4$, dissolved in the water. Natural processes produce very dilute solutions, measured in ppm, of this compound. Permanent hardness has the same effect on soap as temporary hardness. Both effects are caused by calcium ions in the water.

The differences between temporary and permanent hardness arise from the different effects of heat on hydrogencarbonates and sulphates. Calcium sulphates do not decompose on heating, but calcium hydrogencarbonates do.

On heating permanently hard water in a kettle or boiler, no deposit of fur or scale is formed.

Avoiding the effects of hardness

If soapless detergents are used for washing, no scum forms and there is no disadvantage to using hard water. Modern washing powders contain soapless detergent or soap or a mixture of the two. They are blended to suit the water in the customer's home area. Soap is still excellent for washing clothes where there is no hardness in the water.

To avoid fur or scale, the ions responsible for hardness must be removed. Heating will not remove both forms of hardness and is expensive. The commonest method makes use of the ion-exchange process. When hard-water is passed through an ion-exchange resin all the calcium ions are exchanged for sodium ions. The resulting soft-water contains no compounds capable of reacting with soap or of depositing in boilers or kettles.

◀ Ion exchange, zeolites ▶

HAZARD WARNING SYMBOLS

Many chemicals are hazardous in one way or another. Hazard warning symbols are placed on containers of harmful chemicals to warn the user of the possible danger in their use. These symbols are shown in Fig. H.5.

Fig. H.5 Hazard labels

HEALTH SALTS

These are usually so-called because when dissolved in water they produce a liquid which resembles the spa water from natural springs popular in the last century as Health Spas. Epsom had such a spring which gave its name to

Epsom salts, magnesium sulphate, a laxative. Modern 'Health Salts' are mainly a mixture of sodium hydrogencarbonate and a solid acid such as citric acid. On mixing with water, the acid and sodium hydrogencarbonate react producing an effervescence of carbon dioxide gas:

sodium hydrogencarbonate + citric acid → sodium citrate + water + carbon dioxide

Some of these mixtures contain pain-killers, laxatives or both.

HEAT EXCHANGERS

Heat exchangers were first developed by Carl Bosch for the **Haber process.** A heat exchanger is a piece of equipment for transferring heat from one material to another without allowing them to come into contact with each other. For instance, most central heating systems have a heat exchanger that transfers heat from the hot water tank to the central heating pipes. In industry, 'waste heat' can be made to heat-up cold liquids or gases before reaction.

Examples of the use of heat exchangers in industry

- In the smelting of iron, the hot waste gases from the blast furnace are used to heat-up the incoming air 'blast' to save fuel in the heating of the furnace.
- In the Contact process, heat from the exothermic oxidation of sulphur is used to produce steam to run an electricity generator to supply the plant's needs.
- In the Haber process, the heat of reaction of nitrogen and hydrogen is used to heat up the incoming mixture to about 450°C in preparation for reaction on the catalyst.

HELIUM, He

Helium is the first member of the **noble gases.** It is named after the Greek word for sun – *helios.*

Helium was discovered to be present on the Sun before it was found on earth, by Pierre Janssen. Janssen observed the Sun's spectrum during the solar eclipse of 1868. The spectrum contained a yellow line that did not belong to any known element. Helium was discovered on Earth in 1895 by **William Ramsay.**

Sources

Helium is found in some natural gas deposits, mainly in the USA. There are no sources in the UK.

Uses

Because helium is non-flammable and less dense than air it is used in place of the dangerously flammable hydrogen in the new series of airships and in aeroplane tyres. Toy balloons now contain helium.

A mixture of helium and air is breathed by deep-sea divers and deep tunnellers to avoid the 'bends'. If a diver breathing air surfaces quickly, nitrogen from the blood forms bubbles in the blood vessels. These become blocked, especially at the joints. The 'bends' is a very painful and sometimes fatal condition.

HOMOLOGOUS SERIES

This is a series of organic compounds of similar chemical properties. The compounds in the series can be represented by a general molecular formula. Examples of homologous series are:

- alkanes – saturated hydrocarbons – general formula C_nH_{2n+2}
- alkenes – unsaturated hydrocarbons – general formula C_nH_{2n}
- alcohols – contain an $-OH$ group – general formula $C_nH_{2n+1}OH$

HYDRATION

Hydration occurs when water reacts with a compound producing a single chemical product. For example, ethene is hydrated to ethanol by reaction with steam in the presence of a catalyst.

ethene	+	steam	→	ethanol
$C_2H_4(g)$	+	$H_2O(g)$	→	$C_2H_5OH(g)$

HYDROCHLORIC ACID, HCl (aq)

Hydrochloric acid is a mineral acid. The concentrated acid is a 35% by weight solution of hydrogen chloride in water. It is a typical strong acid. It reacts with metals, alkalis and bases, carbonates and indicators in the same way that all strong **acids** do.

MANUFACTURE

Hydrochloric acid is made industrially by burning hydrogen in **chlorine**. It is also a valuable by-product of many processes in which chlorine is reacted with organic compounds.

Uses

In the laboratory, concentrated hydrochloric acid will produce chlorine if added to potassium permanganate crystals.

hydrochloric acid	+	oxygen atoms from potassium permanganate	$\rightarrow$	chlorine	+	water
$2HCl(aq)$	+	$[O]$	$\rightarrow$	$Cl_2(g)$	+	$H_2O(l)$

One of its common industrial uses is to 'pickle' steel. Pickling is the process of dissolving rust from steel articles. The bodies of cars, cookers and refrigerators are all pickled before painting.

$$Fe_2O_3(s) + 6HCl(aq) \rightarrow 2FeCl_3(aq) + 3H_2O(l)$$

HYDROGEN, H_2

Hydrogen is a colourless, odourless gas. It is the lightest element and the least dense gas known. It is not soluble in water and does not affect indicators. Hydrogen is highly flammable and explosive when mixed with air. Natural hydrogen contains three different types of hydrogen atom – three **isotopes:**
hydrogen–1, normal hydrogen has one proton only in its nucleus
hydrogen–2, deuterium has one proton and one neutron in its nucleus
hydrogen–3, tritium has one proton and two neutrons in its nucleus.

LABORATORY PREPARATION

In the laboratory, hydrogen is made by the reaction of zinc and dilute sulphuric acid. (See Fig. H.6.) Hydrogen is collected over water or by upward delivery into a gas jar.

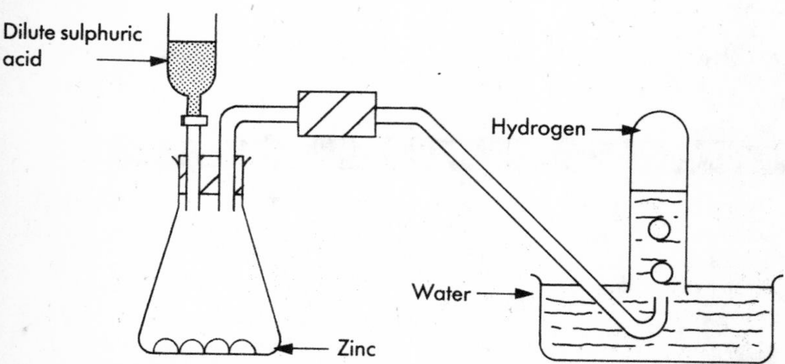

Fig. H.6 Preparation of hydrogen

zinc	+	sulphuric acid	$\rightarrow$	zinc sulphate	+	hydrogen
$Zn(s)$	+	$H_2SO_4(aq)$	$\rightarrow$	$ZnSO_4(aq)$	+	$H_2(g)$

Hydrogen also forms when reactive metals such as those in groups 1 and 2 react with water. It is also produced at the cathode in the electrolysis of any dilute aqueous solution of an electrolyte.

Test for hydrogen

Hydrogen is best known for its explosive nature. It burns in a test tube with a squeaky pop.

Reducing properties

Hydrogen is a powerful reducing agent. It will reduce the oxides of all metals below zinc in the reactivity series, e.g.

copper oxide	+	hydrogen	→	copper	+	water
$CuO(s)$	+	$H_2(g)$	→	$Cu(s)$	+	$H_2O(l)$

Hydrogen burns in chlorine to form hydrogen chloride:

hydrogen	+	chlorine	→	hydrogen chloride
$H_2(g)$	+	$Cl_2(g)$	→	$2HCl(g)$

Structure of the hydrogen molecule

Hydrogen is diatomic – its molecule contains two atoms joined together by a single covalent bond. (See Fig. H.7.)

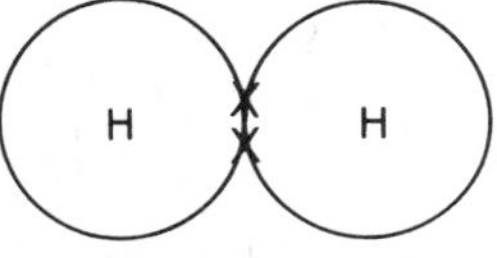

Fig. H.7 Hydrogen molecule

Uses

Hydrogen is used in the laboratory for reducing metal oxides.

In industry, it is used to make ammonia in the **Haber process**. Margarine is made by **hydrogenation** of fats.

HYDROGENATION

This is the chemical process of adding **hydrogen** to a molecule.

The most common example is the addition of hydrogen to unsaturated fatty acids in the manufacture of margarine. This process is called 'hardening'.

It is carried out by passing hydrogen into a mixture of heated vegetable oils with a nickel catalyst. This process converts liquid **fatty acids** into solid fatty acids. Some of the unsaturated fatty acids are left unhydrogenated so that

- the final product is softer than butter
- the presence of unsaturated fatty acids makes the product healthier to eat

HYDROGEN CHLORIDE

Hydrogen chloride is a colourless gas that fumes in moist air. It is very soluble in water, forming hydrochloric acid and so the gas will turn damp indicator paper red. It has a sharp smell, forming an acidic solution in the nose which attacks the nose lining. It affects the eyes in a similar way. For these reasons the gas must be treated with care and used only in a well-ventilated laboratory.

LABORATORY PREPARATION

The reaction between sodium chloride and concentrated sulphuric acid produces hydrogen chloride gas. (See Fig. H.8.)

sodium chloride	+	concentrated sulphuric acid	→	sodium hydrogen sulphate	+	hydrogen chloride
NaCl(s)	+	$H_2SO_4(l)$	→	$NaHSO_4(s)$	+	HCl(g)

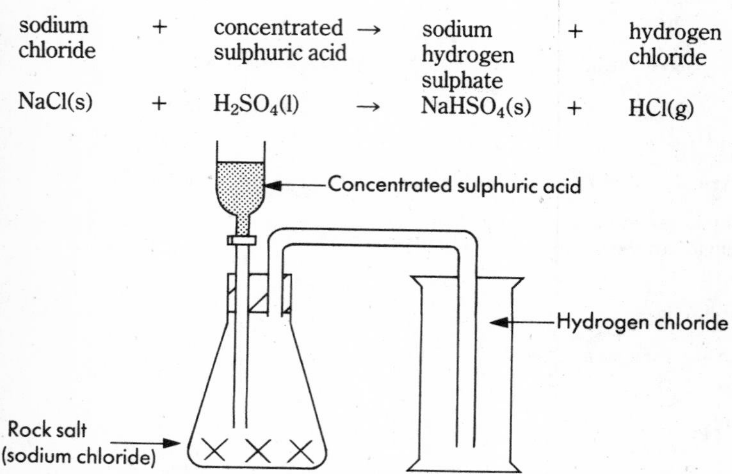

Fig. H.8 Preparation of hydrogen chloride

Test for hydrogen chloride

- Hydrogen chloride forms misty fumes in moist air. It can readily be recognised by this behaviour.
- When mixed with ammonia a white smoke is formed. This is the usual chemical test for the gas.

hydrogen chloride	+	ammonia	→	solid ammonium chloride
HCl(g)	+	$NH_3(g)$	→	$NH_4Cl(s)$

HYDROGEN IONS, H^+

The hydrogen atom consists of a single electron orbiting a nucleus containing one proton. Removing the electron produces a gaseous hydrogen ion which is therefore a proton. Hydrogen ions in solution are always attached to one or more water molecules. They are usually called hydrated hydrogen ions or oxonium ions, H_3O^+. They are found in all acid solutions. In common use the term hydrogen ion may be used for the hydrated ion, H_3O^+, or H^+ (aq) as well as the proton, H^+.

HYDROGEN PEROXIDE, H_2O_2

Hydrogen peroxide is a colourless liquid used only in dilute solutions in school laboratories. It is a powerful oxidising agent.

It decomposes in the presence of catalysts such as maganese (IV) oxide or platinum:

hydrogen peroxide solution	→	water	+	oxygen
$2H_2O_2(aq)$	→	$2H_2O(l)$	+	$O_2(g)$

Oxygen gas can be prepared in the laboratory by this reaction. (See Fig. H.9)

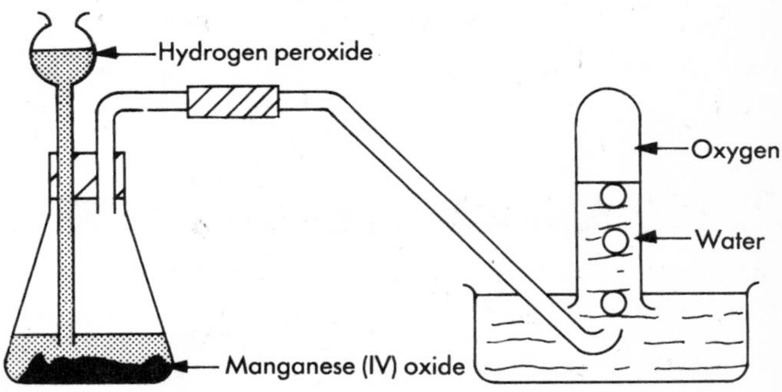

Fig. H.9 Preparation of oxygen from hydrogen peroxide

The concentration of hydrogen peroxide solutions are usually quoted in 'volume strengths'. For example, '20 volume' hydrogen peroxide will produce 20 cm^3 of oxygen gas for every 1 cm^3 of solution decomposed.

Uses

Dilute solutions are used to bleach hair and delicate fabrics.

HYDROLYSIS

The term hydrolysis is derived from two Greek words, *hydros*, water; *lusis*, loosening. It is the process of splitting up a compound using water, for example, the hydrolysis of starch to glucose splits up the polymer, starch into the monomer, glucose. It occurs by the action of water molecules on starch molecules in the presence of an acid catalyst.

			acid catalyst	
starch	+	water	$\rightarrow$	glucose
			H^+ (aq)	
$(C_6H_{10}O_5)_n(aq)$	+	$nH_2O(l)$	$\rightarrow$	$nC_6H_{12}O_6(aq)$

HYDROXIDE IONS, OH^-

The hydroxide ion, also called the hydroxyl ion, is found in all alkaline solutions. It is the ion responsible for alkalinity. Hydroxide ions turn indicators blue.

Reactions

The reaction of alkalis are the reactions of the hydroxide ion. Hydroxide ions form precipitates with most metal ions.

The concentration of hydroxide ions in water is equal to the concentration of hydrogen ions. This is the reason water is neutral to indicators.

water	$\leftrightarrow$	hydrogen ions	+	hydroxide ions
$H_2O(l)$	$\leftrightarrow$	$H^+(aq)$	+	$OH^-(aq)$

HYGROSCOPIC

Substances which absorb water from the air, without dissolving in it are said to be hygroscopic, Gr, *hygros*; wet. Wool, glass, sea-salt and many anhydrous salts are hygroscopic. These substances become heavier by absorbing water without any very obvious change in appearance occurring. Table salt contains small amounts of hygroscopic magnesium chloride from the salt deposits that give us our salt supplies. To stop salt absorbing moisture and 'caking', magnesium carbonate is added, as it counteracts this effect.

IMMISCIBLE

This is a term used to describe liquids that do not mix with each other. Oil and water are immiscible.

INDICATORS

These are dyes or mixtures of dyes which respond to acids and alkalis by changing colour. Litmus is a blue dye which turns red in acids. **Universal indicator** is a mixture of dyes which changes through the colours of the spectrum from strongly acidic to strongly alkaline. Universal indicator will detect neutral solutions and distinguish between weak and strong acids and alkalis. For these reasons it is more useful than litmus.

INDIGESTION TABLETS

These are mixtures of weak bases used to neutralise excess acidity in the stomach.

◄ Antacids ►

INDUSTRIAL PLANT LOCATION

Chemical plant has always been located where the greatest economy of operation is possible. Generally, chemical plant needs to have easy i.e. cheap access to:

raw materials for the manufacturing processes
energy for heating – coal, electricity, oil
water for cooling
waste disposal sites
skilled workers
good transport
deep water port

- If large amounts of electricity are needed the plant may have to build its own station, e.g. plant for electrolysis of brine or alumina.

- If large amounts of water are needed as a reactant, e.g. in ammonia production, the plant would be close to a river.
- If large quantities of waste were produced, e.g. in bauxite purification, waste disposal areas would have to be close by. Plant sited near rivers or the sea do not dispose of their harmful waste into them – except in error.
- If large amounts of coal were needed for electricity production, the site would need to be close to a coal mine. Examples of site choice in Britain based on these principles are seen in the chemical industry concentrated around
  Teesside in the North East
  Runcorn in the North West
  Bristol in the South West

These areas have access to mineral deposits (raw materials), coal, river water, deep water ports, labour supply and good transport links. The South East has all of these except the raw materials and coal, there are therefore fewer chemical plants there. Fig. I.1 shows the position of the ICI works at Runcorn showing the resources available to it.

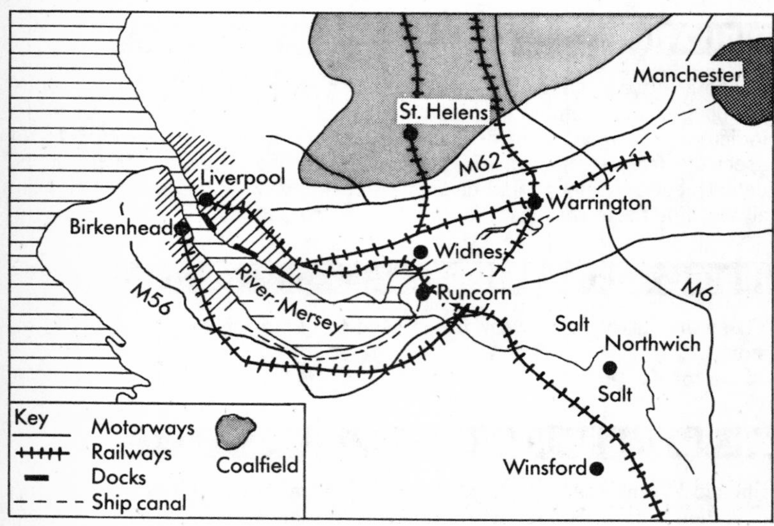

Fig. I.1 Centre of chemical industry – Runcorn

How changes alter the needs of a site

The sources of raw materials are ever-changing and the places where particular industries were sited in the past are not necessarily the best sites for today's industry. For example, in the iron industry of the mid-eighteenth century, coke was replacing wood charcoal as the fuel and reducing agent used. This caused a movement to new sites which were close to both coalfields and iron ore deposits. In the last decade, iron ore deposits in this country have been worked out, and the ore has to be imported. A modern iron works would now be built near a deep-water port and a coalfield.

◀ Haber process ▶

INERT GASES

The group of elements now called **noble gases** were once called the inert gases. Inert means totally unreactive. Until 1962, none of these gases had been known to react at all. When xenon became the first 'inert gas' to form a compound – with platinum fluoride – and later krypton fluorides were made, the gases could no longer be called 'inert'. The term noble can be interpreted as 'less reactive than any other elements'.

INSULATORS

◀ Non-conductors ▶

IODIDES

These are compounds of iodine. Iodine can form covalent or ionic bonds with other elements.

Ionic iodides are easily oxidised to iodine.

Test for an iodide

Ionic iodides react with silver nitrate solution to form a yellow precipitate of silver iodide. The test is carried out in the same way as the test for **chlorides**.

silver nitrate + metal iodide → solid silver iodide + metal nitrate

IODINE, I_2

Iodine is a grey solid which forms a purple vapour on heating. It was discovered by accident in 1811 by Courtois whilst extracting sodium and potassium salts from sea-weed ash. The name is derived from the Greek word for violet, *iodes,* after the purple vapour that first caught the eye of its discoverer.

Iodine is the least reactive of the halogens. It is a powerful germicide, like chlorine and bromine, but less harmful to the flesh and less easily evaporated than either. For these reasons a solution of iodine in ethanol was once in common use as an antiseptic on cuts and wounds. This solution was called 'tincture of iodine'

ION EXCHANGE

Ion exchange is now a common technique for removing unwanted ions from water. It uses natural rocks called **zeolites** or synthetic resins (cross-linked polystyrene) which match the properties of the natural zeolites.

Water can be treated to remove the calcium or magnesium ions which cause hardness using an ion exchange column. It is likely that ion exchange will be used to reduce the nitrate levels in drinking water to meet new EEC limits in the next few years.

Cation exchangers

Cation exchange resins are polymers with a negatively charged end. When soaked in sodium chloride, sodium ions become attached to the negatively charged end of the resin molecules. When hard-water is passed through the column, the sodium ions are replaced by doubly charged calcium or magnesium ions. Calcium or magnesium ions stick to the resin and sodium ions enter the water supply. Sodium ions do not make water hard, so the cation exchange resin has effectively softened the water. (See Fig. I.2)

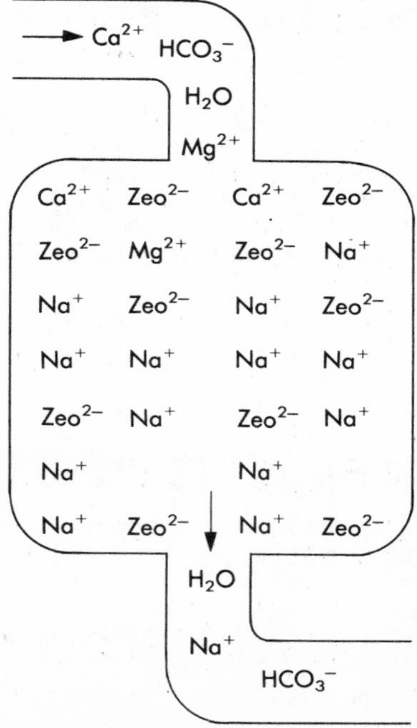

Fig. I.2 Cation exchange

sodium resin	+	calcium ions	→	calcium resin	+	sodium ions
resin	+	(hard water)	→	spent resin	+	(soft water)

When the resin ceases to work it is regenerated by adding a concentrated solution of common salt:

calcium resin	+	sodium chloride	→	sodium resin	+	calcium ions

Ion exchange resins such as these are used in dishwashers to ensure soft-water for washing. The resin is automatically regenerated provided the reservoir of salt is refilled from time to time.

Anion exchangers

Anion exchange resins are polymers with a positively charged end. When soaked in sodium chloride, chloride ions become attached to the ends. If water containing nitrate ions, NO_3^-, is passed through the resin, the nitrate ions exchange for the chloride ions. The water which comes out of the resin contains chloride ions instead of nitrate ions.

chloride resin	+	nitrate ions	→	nitrate resin	+	chloride ions

The resin is regenerated using salt solution in the same way as cation exchange resins.

A mixed anion/cation exchange resin will remove both unwanted cations and anions. These are sold in water filters and water de-ionisers.

- Water 'filters'. The cation exchange resins will remove metal ions such as calcium (hardness), aluminium, copper, lead and zinc. The anion exchange resin removes nitrate and sulphate. In addition, water 'filters' contain activated charcoal to absorb chlorine and organic chlorine-containing compounds which give water an unpleasant taste if present.

  Water 'filters' are not strictly filters at all. **Filtration** is a process of separating solids from liquids.
- Water de-ionisers. These will produce pure water for use in steam irons or car batteries. The resin exchanges cations for hydrogen ions and anions for hydroxide ions. These ions combine to form water and so there are no chloride or sodium ions produced to make the water impure. De-ionisers are common in industry where ions in cooling water and boiler feed cause corrosion.

IONIC BONDS

An ionic bond forms when one or more electrons are exchanged between two atoms leading to the formation of ions with full outer electron shells. The formation of sodium chloride by reaction between sodium and chlorine atoms shows this clearly. (See Fig. I.3)

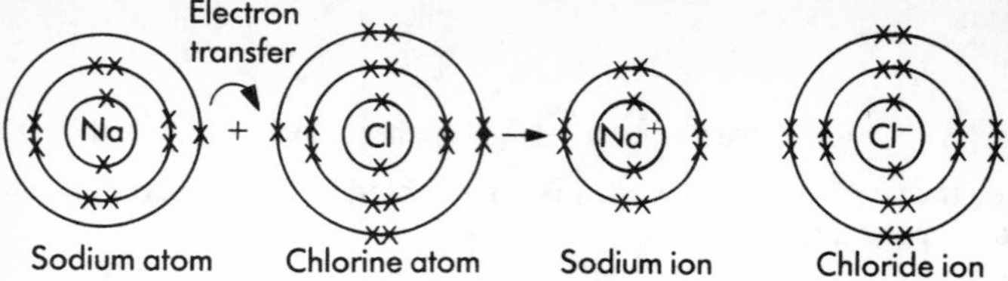

Fig. I.3 Formation of an ionic bond

sodium	+	chlorine	→	sodium chloride
2Na(s)	+	Cl_2(g)	→	2NaCl(s)

The reaction is between a chlorine atom and a sodium atom. During the reaction, the sodium atom makes contact with a chlorine atom, a single electron is given up by the sodium atom and accepted by the chlorine atom. Sodium and chloride ions form. These ions are then strongly attracted together by the force of attraction between opposite charges. Billions of such processes occur during the reaction and crystalline solid sodium chloride forms. (See Fig. G.6)

IONS FORMED BY OTHER ELEMENTS

- Group two metals transfer two electrons per atom, group three metals transfer three.
- Group seven non-metals accept one electron per atom, group six non-metals accept two.

PROPERTIES OF IONIC COMPOUNDS

Properties characteristic of ionic compounds are:

- high melting and boiling points – always solids at room temperature
- can be electrolysed when molten
- usually soluble in water
- usually not soluble in organic solvents like 1, 1, 1 – trichloroethane

IONS

Ions are charged atoms or charged groups of atoms. Atoms form ions by accepting or giving up enough electrons to achieve a full outer shell.

Atoms in charged groups also have full outer shells. Table I.1 shows the symbols and charges on common ions.

Charged atoms	*Name of ion*	*Charged groups of atoms*	*Name of ion*
H^+	hydrogen	NH_4^+	ammonium
Cl^-	chloride	OH^-	hydroxide
Br^-	bromide	NO_3^-	nitrate
I^-	iodide	CO_3^{2-}	carbonate
O^{2-}	oxide	SO_4^{2-}	sulphate
Na^+	sodium	PO_4^{3-}	phosphate
Mg^{2+}	magnesium	$CH_3CO_2^-$	ethanoate

Table I.1 Symbols and charges on common ions

IRON, Fe

From the Iron Age, some 3,000 years ago, to the present day the chemistry of the production of iron has changed little but the technology used in the process has developed greatly. The world is more dependent on iron than ever as a constructional material in spite of its corrodibility. Iron is the second most abundant metallic element in the earth's crust. Its main ores are oxides such as **haematite**, Fe_2O_3. The main reason why iron and not the more abundant aluminium is the most widely used metal lies in the cost of production.

Workable deposits of iron ore are more abundant and the smelting process uses less energy. Both factors lead to a cheaper end product. The process of iron extraction is called smelting. It is done in a **blast furnace** (see Fig. B.1).

THE REDUCTION OF IRON ORE

The furnace is charged from the top with coke, limestone and iron ore. A blast of hot air enters at the bottom.

Coke is a fuel and burns in the hot-air blast

			2000°C		
carbon	+	oxygen	→	carbon monoxide + heat	
(coke)		(air)		(reducing agent)	
$2C(s)$	+	$O_2(g)$	→	$2CO(g)$	ΔH negative

Carbon monoxide reduces the iron oxide to iron

carbon		iron		molten		carbon	
monoxide	+	oxide	→	iron	+	dioxide	+ heat
$3CO(g)$	+	$Fe_2O_3(s)$	→	$2Fe(l)$	+	$3CO_2(g)$	ΔH negative

Both processes are exothermic and heat the furnace contents causing the iron formed to melt. Liquid iron flows to the bottom of the furnace and is tapped off twice daily.

THE ACTION OF THE LIMESTONE FLUX

The term 'flux' means 'a substance which creates a fluid'. The limestone converts the silica (sand) into a liquid 'slag'. This is important; the two products of the process must be liquids so that the furnace contents can be removed without stopping the reaction.
The limestone is decomposed by the heat of the furnace:

calcium carbonate	→	calcium oxide	+	carbon dioxide
	heat			
$CaCO_3(s)$	→	$CaO(s)$	+	$CO_2(g)$

The calcium oxide formed, a basic oxide, neutralises the silica impurity in the ore:

calcium oxide	+	silicon dioxide (silica)	→	calcium silicate (slag)
$CaO(s)$	+	$SiO_2(s)$	→	$CaSiO_3(l)$

The slag floats on the molten iron and is tapped off first.

CAST OR PIG IRON

The liquid iron from the furnace contains about 4% dissolved carbon. If allowed to solidify in moulds it is called 'cast iron' or 'pig iron'. Most iron is taken quickly to a nearby plant for conversion to the many alloys of iron that we call steel.

USES

Iron is mainly made into **steel**. The uses of iron are therefore the uses of steel. The strength, hardness, toughness and corrosion resistance of iron can be altered by alloying it with other elements. The existence of a wide range of steels accounts for the widespread use of steel in homes and buildings.

Steelmaking

To make steel from blast furnace iron, the carbon impurity first has to be removed. A blast of oxygen is passed through the molten iron. The carbon in the iron burns away in the oxygen. When the carbon has been removed, measured quantities of other elements are added. Hundreds of different alloy steels are in use.

IRON COMPOUNDS

Iron forms two different ions, Fe^{2+} and Fe^{3+}. They are present in iron(II) and iron(III) compounds respectively. For example, iron(II) chloride is $FeCl_2$ and iron(III) chloride is $FeCl_3$. The chemical name for **haematite**, Fe_2O_3, is iron(III) oxide.

Iron(II) and iron(III) compounds can be identified and distinguished by their reaction with sodium hydroxide solution.

◀ Cation tests ▶

ISOMERS

These are different compounds with the same molecular formula. For example, there are two isomers of butane (See Fig. I.4).

```
                                      H
                                      |
                                    H-C-H
     H  H  H  H                     H |  H
     |  |  |  |                     | |  |
   H-C--C--C--C-H                 H-C-C--C-H
     |  |  |  |                     | |  |
     H  H  H  H                     H H  H

       butane                   2-methylpropane
```

Fig. I.4 The isomers of butane

ISOTOPES

An element may have atoms which are chemically the same but they have different mass numbers: these are called isotopes. Isotopes are atoms with the same number of protons but different numbers of neutrons.

Uranium has two natural isotopes, U-235 and U-238. Table I.2 shows the compositions of their nuclei.

Particles	*U-235*	*U-238*
protons	92	92
neutrons	143 (235-92)	146 (238-92)

Table I.2 The isotopes of uranium

KETTLE-FUR

Temporary hard water produces a solid deposit in kettles known as 'kettle fur'. Kettle-fur is calcium carbonate, $CaCO_3$. In electric kettles the fur is deposited on the heating element. In flame-heated kettles it forms on the heated surface – the base. Kettle-fur, being a carbonate, will dissolve in acids. The acids used in fur-removers must dissolve the fur without attacking the metal parts of the kettle. Commercial products usually contain phosphoric, formic or sulphamic acids.

The scale formed in boilers is identical in chemical nature to kettle-fur.

◄ Boiler scale ►

KINETIC THEORY OF GASES

We explain the behaviour of gases by regarding them as being made up of molecules continually colliding with each other as they move about at random. The temperature of the gas is proportional to the kinetic energy of the molecules. Pressure in a gas is caused by the collision of its molecules with the sides of the container. This is the kinetic theory. The term kinetic means *motion.*

KINETIC THEORY OF CHEMICAL REACTION

The theory explains chemical reaction by assuming that when colliding molecules have between them a certain minimum energy, they will react with each other. This minimum energy for reaction is called the activation energy. The first step in the reaction involves breaking the bonds in the reactants. The atoms formed then rearrange themselves into molecules of products by making new bonds.

- If extra energy is required for this to happen it is taken from the surroundings (endothermic reaction).
- If there is a surplus of energy when the bonds reform, the excess is given out (exothermic reaction).

◄ Bonds, collisions theory ►

KRYPTON, Kr

Krypton is a noble gas. It gets its name from the Greek word for hidden; *kryptos*. It was discovered in 1898 by William Ramsay. It is used in high-efficiency lamps such as miners' lamps and aircraft lights. It allows the lamp filament to run hotter than in normal argon–filled lamps, with a corresponding increase in light output for the same energy input. Modern tungsten-iodine car headlamps are also krypton-filled.

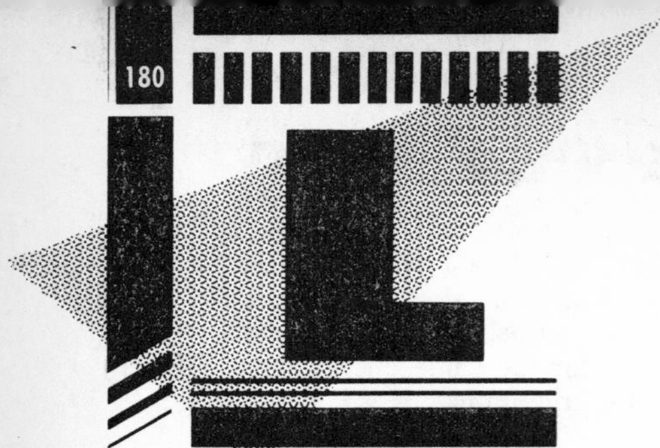

LARGE MOLECULES

Polymer molecules and natural fats are often classed as large molecules. However, large molecules and giant molecules are often classified together as macromolecules. Some idea of the sizes of the three classes of molecules can be gained from Table L.1.

Molecules	*Macromolecules*	
small molecule	*large molecule*	*giant molecule*
glucose $C_6H_{12}O_6$	poly(ethene) $\left(C_2H_4 \right)_{20\,000}$	pin-head sized diamond C_{billions}

Table L.1 Molecules, large molecules and giant molecules

The larger the molecule, the higher the melting and boiling point. Large molecules will therefore have melting points of 200–500°C, compared with figures generally below this for small molecules and values often over 1000°C for giant molecules.

Like all molecular substances, large molecules will not conduct electricity.

LEAD, Pb

Lead is of ancient origin. Its symbol is derived from the Latin *plumbum*; its name from Anglo-Saxon *lead*.

Lead is a very dense, grey metal. It is very soft and easily shaped. It is very resistant to corrosion and chemical attack. Lead pipes made in Roman times are still intact today. Sulphuric acid was once made in lead chambers.

Alloys of lead such as solder, type-metal and pewter are in common use. Lead-acid batteries in cars, lead flashings on houses and lead radiation shields are examples of some of the uses of pure lead. Lead oxides are used in anti-corrosion paints and lead crystal glass. Lead and its compounds are toxic and accumulate in the body. Care should be taken not to ingest them.

LEAD(II) BROMIDE, $PbBr_2$

Lead (II) bromide is a white solid ionic compound. Its low melting point (375°C) allows it to be electrolysed in its molten state more easily than most ionic compounds.

Electrolysis produces molten lead at the cathode (m.p. of lead 328°C) and bromine gas at the anode (b.p. of bromine 59°C):

At the cathode:	$Pb^{2+}(l)$	+	$2e^-$	→	$Pb(l)$
At the anode:	$2Br^-(l)$	−	$2e^-$	→	$Br_2(g)$

LIEBIG CONDENSER

This is the common water-cooled condenser invented by **Justus von Liebig** (1803–1873) who was also one of the first chemists to suggest using potassium and phosphorus minerals as fertilisers.

LIME KILN

Lime 'burning', the term used for heating limestone in kilns, is a centuries-old process. It involves heating limestone to over 1000°C in a lime kiln to decompose it. (See Fig. L.1) The type of reaction occurring is called **thermal decomposition.**

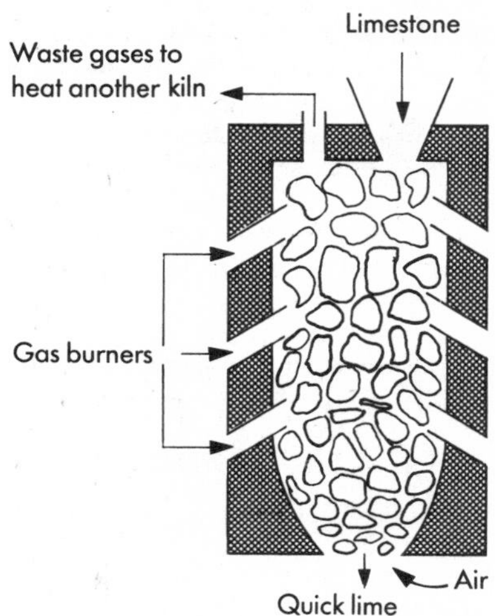

Fig. L.1 Lime kiln

calcium carbonate (limestone)	→	calcium oxide (quicklime)	+	carbon dioxide
$CaCO_3(s)$	→	$CaO(s)$	+	$CO_2(g)$

The high temperature is achieved by burning coal mixed with the limestone or by heating with burning natural gas – whichever is cheaper. Waste heat from the kilns is used to pre-heat the ingoing limestone, so saving energy.

MAIN USES OF QUICKLIME

- Most quicklime is used in steelmaking; it reacts with the acidic oxides of phosphorus and silicon converting them into slag and removing them from the steel
- It is hydrated to make **slaked lime** or hydrated lime and used to reduce the acidity of agricultural land

LIMELIGHT

To be in the 'limelight' is an expression that means to be the centre of public attention. It refers to the early stage spotlight which used a lump of **quicklime** heated to white-heat by an acetylene or a coal gas flame; the very bright light produced was called limelight.

LIME SCRUBBER

A suggested method for the reduction of '**acid-rain**' would be to reduce the amount of sulphur dioxide coming from power station chimneys – the main source of this pollutant. The favoured method for achieving this would be to react the acidic gas with a limestone/water slurry in a lime-scrubber. (See Fig. L.2)

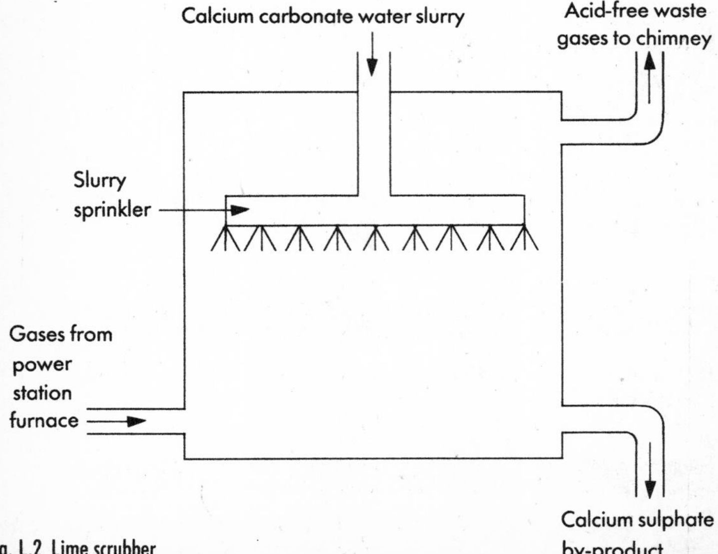

Fig. L.2 Lime scrubber

LIMESTONE, $CaCO_3$

Limestone is one of several natural forms of calcium carbonate. Others are chalk, marble and calcite. A pure form of limestone is quarried in Derbyshire. These deposits were formed about 300 million years ago and extend to 3,000 feet in depth.

QUARRYING FOR LIMESTONE

The large limestone quarry at Tunstead covers about 3 square miles in area and produces six million tonnes of limestone annually. One third of this limestone feeds ICI chemical plants in the North West, a third is made into lime for other industries and the rest is used as roadstone.

USES

When limestone is the main rock of a region, acid rain falling there is neutralised and has no harmful effects. Limestone and its products have many uses. They are used

- in the production of
  quicklime and slaked lime
  iron and **steel**
  glass
  washing soda
  cement and mortar
  plasters and polishes
- in the processing of
  sugar
  household water
- as a soil neutraliser in agriculture
- as a road-making stone; to make **asphalt**
- as a reagent to remove sulphur dioxide from power station flue-gases (Huge amounts will be needed if the electricity industry decides to fit '**lime-scrubbers**' to its main power stations).

LIMEWATER, $Ca(OH)_2(aq)$

A solution of calcium hydroxide (slaked lime) in water is called limewater. It is used in laboratories to test for **carbon dioxide**.

LIQUIDS

A liquid is a state of matter in which the molecules or ions present are close together, strongly attracted to each other but free to move about at random.

This attraction causes the particles to have a fixed volume, unlike the particles of a gas which have almost no attraction and so fill any space available. The state symbol (l) is added to the formulae of liquids in chemical equations.

LITHIUM, Li

Lithium is the lightest-known metal and a member of the alkali metals. It is a silvery metal which floats on water. It is very reactive to water and most non-metallic elements. Its reactions are similar to those of sodium but less vigorous. The name is derived from the Greek for stone; *lithos*. Lithium forms a very light, strong alloy with aluminium which is used in aircraft parts. It is a component of lithium-iodine batteries which are now fitted to power heart pacemakers and lithium-chlorine batteries which are in modern cameras; these batteries have long lives.

MACROMOLECULES

Macromolecules as their name suggests are very large molecules or giant molecules. Some macromolecules are man–made, others are found naturally. **Polymers** are examples of man–made macromolecules whilst starch and protein are examples of natural macromolecules. All polymers have large molecules e.g **poly(ethene), starch** and **proteins.** Large molecules contain thousands of atoms per molecule. (See Fig. M.1) Large molecules have lower melting points than giant molecules, do not conduct electricity and are not very soluble in water.

Giant molecules have billions of atoms per molecule. Examples of giant molecules are **diamond, graphite, silicon** and **silicon dioxide.** (See Fig. C.3. and C.4.) Giant molecules are usually hard solids with high melting points and boiling points, they are insoluble in water and (except for graphite) do not conduct electricity.

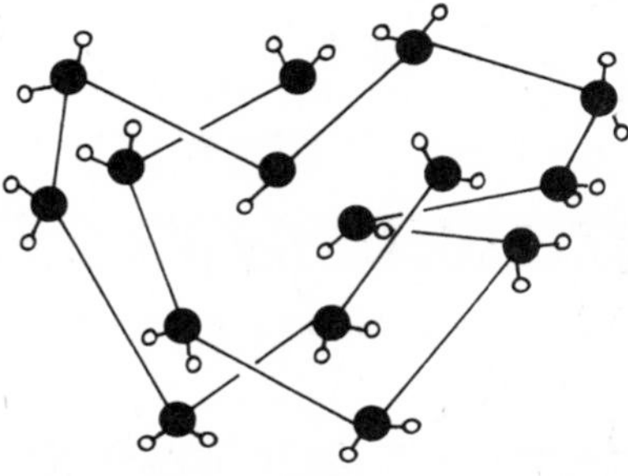

Fig. M.1 Part of a large molecule – poly(ethene)

MAGNESIUM, Mg

Magnesium was discovered in 1808 by **Humphry Davy.** Its name is derived from 'Magnesia' a district in Thessaly, Greece. It is an alkaline earth metal – a member of Group 2 of the periodic table. It is a whitish metal slightly denser than water. It is normally found in the laboratory as a thin coiled strip known as magnesium ribbon.

Properties

Magnesium is stable in air but burns with a very bright flame in the presence of air to give a mixture of magnesium oxide and magnesium nitride. It burns with an even brighter light in pure oxygen. It was used in flash photography because of this property.

magnesium	+	oxygen	→	magnesium oxide
$2Mg(s)$	+	$O_2(g)$	→	$2MgO(s)$

Magnesium is a typical **metal**. It is used in a number of light alloys. (See Table M.1.)

Alloy	*Elements*			
duralium	0.5% Mg	95% Al	4% Cu	0.5% Mn
magnalium	5% Mg	95% Al		
Y-metal	90% Al	10% Cu. Ni and Mg		

Table M.1 Magnesium alloys

MAGNESIUM CARBONATE, $MgCO_3$

Magnesium carbonate occurs naturally as magnesite. It is insoluble in water, but dissolves slowly in rain water (carbonic acid) to form magnesium hydrogencarbonate which causes **temporary hardness** in water.

MAGNESIUM HYDROXIDE, $Mg(OH)_2$

Magnesium hydroxide is slightly soluble in water forming an alkaline solution. It is a typical **base**.

MAGNESIUM OXIDE, MgO

Magnesium oxide is a typical **base**. It has a very high melting point and is therefore used as a lining for furnaces. It is slightly soluble in water forming magnesium hydroxide.

MAGNESIUM SULPHATE, $MgSO_4$

Magnesium sulphate occurs naturally as Epsom Salts. ($MgSO_4 7H_2O$). It is used as a laxative.

MALTOSE, $C_{12}H_{22}O_{11}$

Maltose is a carbohydrate. It is formed when starch is hydrolysed by the enzymes, amylase and ptyalin, present in saliva.

$$\text{starch} + \text{water} \rightarrow \text{maltose}$$
$$2(C_6H_{10}O_5)_n(s) + nH_2O(l) \rightarrow nC_{12}H_{22}O_{11}(aq)$$

MANGANESE, Mn

Manganese was discovered in 1774 by J.G.Gahn. Its name derives from the Latin *magnes* meaning magnet. It is a typical **transition metal**. Manganese is used to make ferromanganese steels and other alloys such as manganese bronze, manganin and duralumin.

MANGANESE (IV) OXIDE, MnO_2

Manganese(IV) oxide occurs naturally as pyrolusite. It is the compound that causes the purple colour in amethyst. Manganese(IV) oxide is a black powder, insoluble in water.

Reactions

Manganese(IV) oxide can act as an **oxidising agent** and a **catalyst**. It oxidises concentrated hydrochloric acid to chlorine.

manganese (IV) oxide	+ hydrochloric acid	→	chlorine	+ manganese (II) chloride	+ water
$MnO_2(s)$	+ $4HCl(aq)$	→	$Cl_2(g)$	+ $MnCl_2(aq)$	+ $2H_2O(l)$

Manganese(IV) oxide is the catalyst used in the preparation of oxygen from hydrogen peroxide.

hydrogen peroxide	→	oxygen	+	water
$2H_2O_2(aq)$	→	$O_2(g)$	+	$2H_2O(l)$

Manganese(IV) oxide is used for making dry Leclanche cells and as a catalyst in linseed oil paints.

MAN-MADE ELEMENTS

◀ Elements ▶

MARBLE

Marble (calcium carbonate) occurs naturally. **Limestone** under the effect of both heat and pressure changes into this very hard metamorphic rock.

Marble chips are used in the laboratory together with dilute hydrochloric acid for the preparation of carbon dioxide.

calcium carbonate		hydrochloric acid		carbon dioxide		calcium chloride		water
	+		→		+		+	
$CaCO_3(s)$	+	$2HCl(aq)$	→	$CO_2(g)$	+	$CaCl_2(aq)$	+	$H_2O(l)$

Marble can be polished, producing a smooth shining surface which is used in buildings and for carving into statues.

MASS NUMBER

Mass number is the sum of the number of protons and neutrons in an atom. It is usually shown as a number at the top left of the symbol of an element. Thus ^{12}C has a mass number of 12 i.e. it has 6 protons and 6 neutrons.

◀ Atomic number, isotopes ▶

MELTING

Melting is the term used to describe the change of state from solid to liquid. Melting can be explained by the **kinetic theory**. When a solid is heated, vibrations of the particles in the solid increase but the forces within the particles are sufficient to hold the structure together. Eventually a point is reached when the vibrations are so great that the forces between the particles cannot hold the structure together and the particles start to move. At this point we say a liquid has been formed and the temperature at which this occurs is called the **melting point**.

MELTING POINT

Melting point is the temperature at which a substance turns from a solid to a liquid.

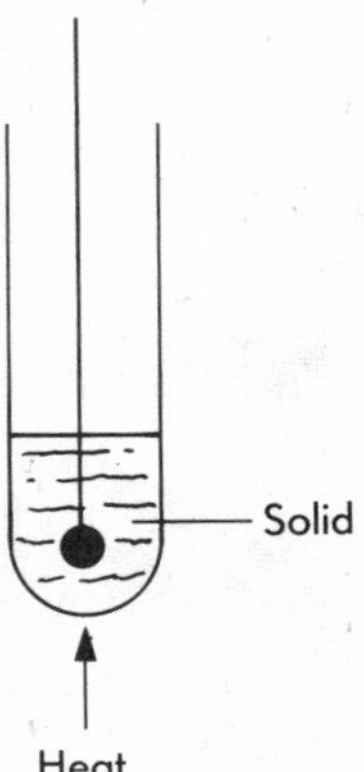

Fig. M.2 Measuring melting points

Chemists measure melting points for two primary reasons:

- To test the purity of a substance – a pure chemical melts at a definite temperature (which is the same as its freezing point)
- To identify unknown chemicals – pure chemicals have unique melting points e.g. water 0°C

Molecular compounds such as carbon dioxide and trichloromethane have *low* melting points; giant molecular and ionic compounds have ***high*** melting points. If the melting point of a substance is above room temperature (about 25°C) then it will be a solid.

Melting points can be found using the apparatus shown in Fig. M.2.

MENDELEEV, DIMITRI (1839–1907)

Mendeleev was a Russian chemist and the originator of the **periodic table.** His idea was to arrange the elements in order according to their atomic masses whilst placing elements with similar properties in the same vertical columns. In order to do this he had to leave gaps for elements that had not at that time (1869) been discovered. He listed separately some 'odd' elements such as iron, cobalt and nickel which did not fit into the main columns. Part of the table devised by Mendeleev is shown below.

The most important feature of Mendeleev's work was that he was able to predict the properties of the missing elements in his table and later, when the elements were discovered, very strong proof was provided that his ideas had been correct.

Group 1	*Group 2*	*Group 3*	*Group 4*	*Group 5*	*Group 6*	*Group 7*	*Group 8*
H							
Li	Be	B	C	N	O	F	
Na	Mg	Al	Si	P	S	Cl	
K	Ca	?	Ti	V	Cr	Mn	Fe. Co .Ni
Cu	Zn	?	?	As	Se	Br	
Rb	Sr	Yt	Zr	Nb	Mo	?	Ru. Rh. Pd. Ag

(? = elements not yet discovered)

MERCURY, Hg

Mercury has been known since about 1600 BC. It was named after the latin word for the god of the occult, Mercurius. Mercury is the only liquid metal. It is a dense liquid with a silvery lustre. It is **volatile** and its vapour, like the liquid, is very poisonous. For this reason, you should take care if you accidentally break a mercury thermometer.

METAL EXTRACTION

The **reactivity series** is a good guide when choosing which method for the extraction of metals. Metals high in the reactivity series such as sodium and potassium are extracted by **electrolysis** of their molten chlorides. Metals lower in the series such as zinc, iron and lead are made by reduction of their oxides with carbon. Metals at the bottom of the reactivity series such as gold, silver and platinum occur in the free state.

METAL OXIDES

Most metal oxides are **basic** although some such as lead, tin and zinc are **amphoteric**.

◀ Oxides ▶

METALS

The essential difference between a metal and a non-metal is its ability to gain or lose electrons. A metal is an element which forms positive ions by losing electrons.

PROPERTIES

Physical properties

Metals tend to have the following physical properties; they

- are lustrous (can be polished)
- are sonorous (make a metallic sound when hit)
- are strong and tough (high tensile strength)
- are malleable (can be made into sheets of metal)
- are ductile (can be drawn into wires)
- are solids with high melting points
- have relatively high densities
- are good conductors of heat and electricity

Chemical properties

- their oxides are basic
- their chlorides are ionic
- tend to be reducing agents
- react with acids to give hydrogen

Mercury is classified as a metal although it is a liquid because it forms positive ions by losing electrons.

◀ Reactivity series ▶

METHANE, CH_4

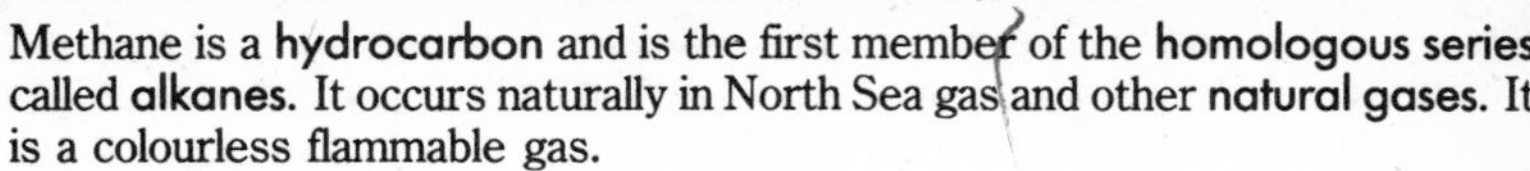

Methane is a **hydrocarbon** and is the first member of the **homologous series** called **alkanes.** It occurs naturally in North Sea gas and other **natural gases.** It is a colourless flammable gas.

Its structural formula is:

```
     H
     |
  H—C—H
     |
     H
```

METHANOIC ACID, HCO_2H

Methanoic acid is an **acid** and is the first member of the **homologous series** called **carboxylic acids.** It used to be called *formic acid* because it was obtained by distilling red ants. ('Formica' is the Latin word for ants.)

The structure of methanoic acid is:

```
     H
     |
  H—C—O—H
     |
     H
```

METHANOL, CH_3OH

Methanol is an alcohol and is the first member of the **homologous series** called **alcohols.** It is used in the manufacture of methanal which is used to make **bakelite,** and is also used as a solvent for varnishes and paints.

The structure of methanol is:

```
     H
     |   O
     |  //
  H—C
     |  \
     |   O—H
     H
```

METHYLATED SPIRITS

Methylated spirits is **ethanol** that has had **methanol** added to it plus a small amount of paraffin oil to make it unpalatable. It is dyed a purple colour to distinguish it from water. Pyridine, which has a distinctive smell, is added to make it recognisable by blind people.

◄ Ethanol ►

METHYL ORANGE

Methyl orange is a synthetic dye which is used as an **indicator**. It is yellow in solutions with a pH above 4 and red in solutions with a pH below 3.

MIDGLEY, THOMAS (1889–1944)

Midgley was an American chemist who made two remarkable discoveries that were very much acclaimed during his lifetime. In 1921 he discovered how to improve the fuel economy of motor car engines by adding a lead compound called **'anti-knock'**. In 1930 he discovered a non-toxic, non-flammable, and therefore, a safe substitute for the refrigerants used at that time. This compound is CFC−12. Sadly, both these discoveries, although great achievements in their day, are now at the centre of concern about the growing atmospheric **pollution**.

MILK OF LIME

Milk of lime is formed when **calcium hydroxide** (slaked lime) is made into a thin paste with water. In industry it is used as a cheap alkali to remove acidic waste.

MILK OF MAGNESIA

Milk of magnesia is a suspension of magnesium hydroxide in water. It is used as an **antacid**.

MINERALS

Minerals are naturally occuring inorganic compounds. If metals are extracted from the mineral then it is called an **ore**. Examples of minerals are bauxite, (aluminium oxide), haematite, (iron(III) oxide) and rock salt, (sodium chloride).

MIXTURES

A mixture is a substance which consists of two or more elements or compounds **not** chemically combined together. Examples of mixtures are air, ink and sea-water.

Mixtures:

- can be separated by physical means e.g. filtration or distillation.

- have properties which are the average of those substances in it
- have variable compositions

MOLARITY

The concentration of a solution expressed in **moles** per litre is known as its molarity.

Example

Thus, if a solution contains 80 g of sodium hydroxide in one litre of solution, it has a molarity of 2 mol per litre.

- 0.1 mol per litre sulphuric acid contains 0.1 moles or 9.8 g of sulphuric acid in one litre of solution
- 0.01 mol per litre potassium hydroxide contains 0.01 moles or 0.56g of potassium hydroxide in one litre of solution.

MOLAR SOLUTION

If a solution contains one mole of a substance dissolved in one litre of a solution it is referred to as a molar solution.

Molar solutions have a **molarity** of 1 mole per litre.

Examples of molar solutions

- one litre of solution containing 40 g of sodium hydroxide
- one litre of solution containing 98 g of sulphuric acid
- one litre of solution containing 46 g of ethanol

MOLAR VOLUME

The molar volume of a gas is the volume occupied by 1 mole of the gas at standard temperature (0°C) and standard pressure (1 atmosphere). The volume for all gases is approximately 22.4 litres under standard conditions. At room temperature (25°C) and pressure (1 atmosphere) the molar volume is 24 litres.

Example

Thus 1 mole of any gas e.g. 17 g of ammonia, 44 g of carbon dioxide, 28 g of nitrogen, all occupy 24 litres at room temperature and pressure.

MOLECULAR FORMULA

Molecular formula shows how many of each type of atom there are in a molecule. Thus, hydrogen peroxide, H_2O_2 contains 2 atoms of hydrogen and 2 atoms of oxygen.

◀ **Formula** ▶

MOLECULAR WEIGHT

◀ Relative molecular mass ▶

MOLECULES

A molecule is the smallest particle of an element or compound that can exist in a free and separate state. The theory of molecules was developed by Amaddeo Avogadro. Most non-metals are molecular e.g. oxygen O_2, phosphorus P_4, sulphur S_8. Most compounds of non-metals are also molecular e.g. ammonia, NH_3, carbon dioxide CO_2, water H_2O.

◀ Molar volume ▶

MOLES

The mole is the amount of substance that contains the same number of particles as there are atoms in 12.00 grams of the carbon isotope carbon−12. This number of atoms is 6×10^{23} and is called the Avogadro number. Since relative atomic mass and relative molecular mass are based on carbon–12 then the relative atomic mass of an element and the relative molecular mass of an element or compound must contain Avogadro's number of particles. Thus, the following all contain the same number of particles:

- 44 grams of carbon dioxide (molecules)
- 18 grams of water (molecules)
- 23 grams of sodium (atoms)
- 100 grams of calcium carbonate

100 grams of calcium carbonate contains 1 mole of calcium atoms (40 grams), 1 mole of carbon atoms (12 grams) and 3 moles of oxygen atoms (48 grams).

You must make sure that you state the type of particles you are talking about, thus, 1 mole of oxygen atoms has a mass of 16 grams and the mass of 1 mole of oxygen molecules is 32 grams.

A mole of *electrons* is called a **Faraday**.

MOLYBDENUM, Mo

Molybdenum was discovered by P.J. Hielm in 1781. Its name is derived from the Greek word; '*molybdos*' meaning 'lead'. Molybdenum is added to steels to prevent brittleness.

MONOCLINIC SULPHUR

◀ Sulphur ▶

MONOMERS

A monomer is a small molecule that can be **polymerised** to make a large molecule.

Examples of monomers and their polymers are shown in Table M.2.

Monomer	*Polymer*
chloroethene	poly(chloroethene) (PVC)
ethene	poly(ethene)
propene	poly(propene)
styrene	poly(styrene)
tetrafluoroethene	polytetrafluoroethene (PTFE)

Table M.2 Monomers and their polymers

MORTAR

Mortar is a mixture of sand and slaked lime (calcium hydroxide). Water is added to this mixture and as the water evaporates it leaves a hard mass. The sand helps to make the mixture porous. Mortar is used to stick bricks together. As time goes by, the calcium hydroxide reacts with the carbon dioxide in the air to form calcium carbonate which helps the mortar to set hard. Mortar dissolves in rain water and therefore in old buildings the mortar gradually wears away. Nowadays, cement is added to the mixture.

MOSELEY, HENRY (1887–1915)

Moseley, an English chemist, showed by investigating X-ray spectra of elements that the positive charge on the nucleus in an atom was a whole number. This positive charge is called the **atomic number** of the element. Moseley also showed that if elements were arranged in the order of their atomic numbers then the elements fell into a regular periodic pattern. This idea helped to clear up anomalies that existed in Mendeleev's table, and since 1913 elements have been arranged in atomic number order and not in atomic mass order. Moseley was killed in the First World War at the age of 28.

◀ Mendeleev, Dimitri ▶

NAPHTHALENE, $C_{10}H_8$

Naphthalene is a molecular compound. It is a white soft solid with a melting point of 80°C. It has a typical smell referred to as, 'moth balls'; these are a naphthalene product sometimes used to protect materials in the home from attack by moth larvae.

NATIVE ELEMENTS

Native elements are elements that occur uncombined in nature – they are in their free state. Examples of native elements are the unreactive metals such as silver, gold and platinum. Examples of native non-metals are carbon, nitrogen, oxygen and sulphur.

NATURAL GAS

Natural gas is mainly methane, CH_4. It is a fossil fuel and is found trapped in rocks usually with **petroleum**. Other gases such as ethane, propane, butane, helium and hydrogen sulphide are found in natural gas depending on its location.

Natural gases from France and Canada contain up to 25% of hydrogen sulphide. This is removed and used as a supply of sulphur in the manufacture of **sulphuric acid**.

Table N.1 shows the percentage composition of natural gas samples from various locations; **North Sea Gas** is almost entirely methane.

	Algeria	*France*	*Italy*	*The Netherlands*	*UK*	*USA*
carbon dioxide	0.2	9.6	–	0.8	0.5	0.1
ethane	10.2	5.5	3.7	8.3	4.0	11.1
hydrogen sulphide	–	15.3	–	–	–	–
methane	83.5	69.6	95.9	81.8	94.4	80.9
nitrogen	6.1	–	0.4	14.1	1.1	7.9

Table N.1 Percentage composition of natural gas samples from different countries

Uses

One of the uses of methane is the manufacture of hydrogen for the **Haber process**. Methane is reacted with steam:

methane	+	steam	→	carbon monoxide	+	hydrogen
CH_4 (g)	+	H_2O (g)	→	CO (g)	+	$3H_2$ (g)

The mixture is then reacted with more steam to form carbon dioxide and hydrogen. Carbon monoxide is removed either by liquefaction or by dissolving it in an alkali.

NEON, Ne

Neon is one of the **noble gases**. It was discovered in 1898 by Ramsay and Travers and its name is derived from the Greek word *neos* meaning 'new'.

Uses

It is used to fill red advertising strip lights, and is the starter gas in sodium street lamps. The electric current conducted by the neon warms up the lamp which vaporises the solid sodium; the light is red until it warms up sufficiently to vaporise the sodium. When the sodium is fully vaporised it conducts electricity giving a yellow glow which when mixed with the red from the neon gives the sodium street lamps their characteristic orange light.

NEUTRALISATION

Neutralisation is used to describe the reaction between the oxide ions or the hydroxyl ions of a **base** or **alkali** with the hydrogen ions of an **acid** to form water. A salt is also formed in the reaction.

Example of a neutralisation reaction

acid	+	base	→	salt	+	water
e.g.						
hydrochloric acid	+	sodium hydroxide	→	sodium chloride	+	water
HCl(aq)	+	NaOH(aq)	→	NaCl(aq)	+	H_2O(l)

If this is written ionically we get:

H^+(aq)	+	OH^-(aq)	→	H_2O(l)

NEUTRAL OXIDE

These oxides have neither acidic properties nor basic properties. They are oxides of non-metals. There are very few neutral oxides. Examples are water, H_2O; carbon monoxide, CO; nitrogen monoxide, NO and dinitrogen oxide, N_2O.

NEUTRON

The symbol for a neutron is n. It is a subatomic particle found in the **nucleus** of an atom. It has a relative atomic mass of 1 unit and has no electric charge.

◀ Sub-atomic particles ▶

NEWLANDS, JOHN (1837–1898)

Newlands was an English scientist. In 1863, he found that when the elements were arranged in the order of their atomic masses, every eighth element was similar. He called this the 'Law of Octaves' comparing this similarity with the eighth note in an octave of music. This periodic trend forms the basis of the **periodic table**. The law only applied to the first sixteen elements and, unfortunately, his idea was ridiculed. Indeed, a member of the Royal Society asked Newlands if he had considered arranging the elements in alphabetical order. In 1883 his contribution to chemistry was recognised, he was presented the award of the Davy Medal by the Royal Society.

NICHROME

Nichrome is an alloy containing 60% nickel, 26% iron and 14% chromium. It has a resistance to electricity, is resistant to atmospheric corrosion at high temperatures and has a high melting point. It is therefore used as wire or ribbons for electric heating elements. It is also used as a substitute for platinum in the **flame test**.

NICKEL, Ni

Nickel was first discovered in 1751 by Cronstadt. It is found as the ore pentandite deep in the ground and was named nickel after the German word meaning 'the devil'. It is found as the free element in meteorites. Its main use is in the manufacture of **nickel alloys**. It is also used as a catalyst for the addition of hydrogen across a carbon – carbon double bond e.g. in the manufacture of margarine from vegetable oils.

NICKEL ALLOYS

There are a number of nickel alloys, as shown in Table N.2.

Alloy	*Composition*	*Use*
nichrome	60% Ni, 26% Fe, 14% Cr	electric heating elements
monel metal	70% Ni, 30% Cu	chemical industry
cupro-nickel	75% Cu, 25% Ni	British silver coins
German silver	80% Cu, 10% Zn, 10% Ni	silver plated table-ware
manganin	84% Cu, 12% Mn, 4% Ni	standard resistance coils

Table N.2 Nickel alloys

◀ Unsaturated fatty acids ▶

NITRATES

Properties

All nitrates are soluble in water. Sodium nitrate and potassium nitrate when heated decompose to give oxygen and a nitrite, e.g.

potassium nitrate	→	oxygen	+	potassium nitrite
$2KNO_3(s)$	→	$O_2(g)$	+	$2KNO_2(s)$

Most other metal nitrates decompose to give the metal oxide, nitrogen dioxide and oxygen, e.g.

lead(II) nitrate	→	lead(II) oxide	+	nitrogen dioxide	+	oxygen
$2Pb(NO_3)_2(s)$	→	$2PbO(s)$	+	$4NO_2(g)$	+	$O_2(g)$

Ammonium nitrate decomposes into dinitrogen oxide and water

ammonium nitrate	→	dinitrogen oxide	+	water
NH_4NO_3	→	N_2O	+	H_2O

Tests for nitrates

The tests for a nitrate group are:

- Addition of an equal volume of freshly prepared iron(II) sulphate to an aqueous solution of the suspected nitrate. Slope the tube and carefully pour concentrated sulphuric acid down its side. The presence of a nitrate is confirmed when a brown ring forms between the two layers.
- Addition of aluminium foil to the suspected nitrate and a small amount of sodium hydroxide solution. Warm the mixture gently. The presence of a nitrate is confirmed if ammonia gas is given off.

Uses

Potassium nitrate and ammonium nitrate are used as **fertilisers**. Gunpowder is a mixture of sulphur, charcoal and potassium nitrate.

NITRIC ACID, HNO_3

MANUFACTURE

Nitric acid is made by the catalytic oxidation of ammonia. A mixture of air and ammonia is passed over a platinum catalyst at about 850°C:

ammonia	+	oxygen	→	nitrogen monoxide	+	water
$4NH_3(g)$	+	$5O_2(g)$	→	$4NO(g)$	+	$6H_2O(g)$

The nitrogen monoxide readily oxidises further to form nitrogen dioxide:

nitrogen monoxide + oxygen → nitrogen dioxide

$$2NO(g) + O_2(g) \rightarrow 2NO_2(g)$$

The nitrogen dioxide is reacted with water and more oxygen:

nitrogen dioxide + water + oxygen → nitric acid

$$4NO_2(g) + 2H_2O(l) + O_2(g) \rightarrow 4HNO_3(l)$$

The overall reaction is:

ammonia + oxygen → nitric acid + water

$$NH_3(g) + 2O_2(g) \rightarrow HNO_3(l) + H_2O(l)$$

Properties

Dilute nitric acid is a typical acid except that it is also an **oxidising agent.** It does not react with metals to give hydrogen because the hydrogen is readily oxidised to water and the nitric acid is reduced to nitrogen dioxide.

Concentrated nitric acid is a very powerful oxidising agent.

Uses

The main use of nitric acid is in the manufacture of **ammonium nitrate** and dynamite.

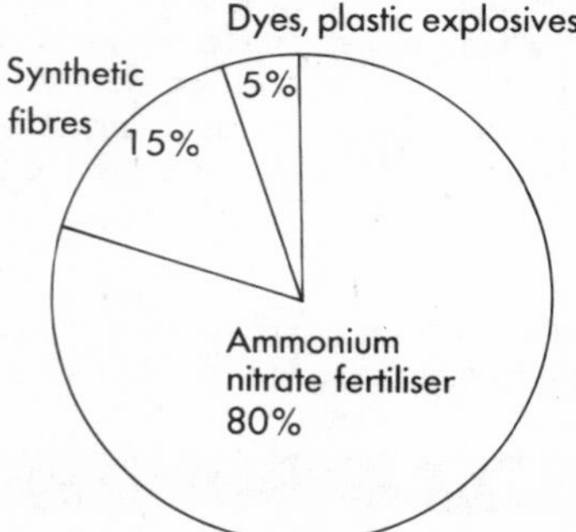

Fig. N.1 Uses of nitric acid

NITRITES

The nitrite ion is NO_2^-. Sodium nitrate and potassium nitrate are the only two solid nitrites. Acidified solutions of nitrites are **reducing agents.**

Nitrites can be distinguished from nitrates by adding dilute hydrochloric acid. Nitrites give off brown fumes of nitrogen dioxide; nitrates do not react with the dilute acid. Nitrites are used in the manufacture of dyes.

NITROGEN, N_2

Nitrogen was discovered in 1772 by Rutherford. About 78% of the air by volume is nitrogen. Nitrogen occurs mainly as saltpetre which is crude sodium nitrate. Nitrogen compounds are present in all fertile soil. Nitrogen is an essential element in all plant and animal tissues, it is found in compounds called **proteins.**

MANUFACTURE

Nitrogen is manufactured by the **fractional distillation** of liquid air.

In the laboratory

It is made by heating ammonium nitrite.

ammonium nitrite	→	nitrogen	+	water
$NH_4NO_2(g)$	→	$N_2(g)$	+	$2H_2O(g)$

Properties

It is a colourless, tasteless, odourless and neutral gas. It is non-poisonous, does not support burning, and is relatively unreactive. Certain elements e.g. magnesium and calcium, will continue to burn in nitrogen to form nitrides. At high temperatures, nitrogen will react with oxygen to form oxides of nitrogen. This reaction can take place in the internal combustion engine producing one of the atmospheric pollutants.

Uses

The main use of nitrogen is in the manufacture of ammonia. It is also used as an inert atmosphere in 'food storage'. Liquid nitrogen (boiling point – 196°C) is used to freeze fruits that do not freeze well by normal methods e.g. strawberries and to 'freeze-dry' coffee to make instant coffee granules.

NITROGEN CYCLE

This cycle shows how nitrogen is used and re-used. The conversion of nitrogen into compounds of nitrogen is called the fixation of nitrogen. This can take place in three ways:

- Lightning causes nitrogen and oxygen to react together to form nitrogen monoxide
- Bacteria *(bacillus radiciola)* in root nodules of certain plants e.g. peas and clover can absorb nitrogen direct from the air; these types of plants are called leguminous plants
- Free living nitrifying bacteria in the soil convert nitrogen into nitrogen compounds

About 60% of nitrogen is fixed naturally, 30% artificially by the **Haber process** and 10% by combustion processes.

Nitrogen enters the soil from the death and decay of plants and animals. Denitrifying bacteria convert nitrates back into nitrogen: a process known as denitrification. (See Fig. N.2)

◀ Air ▶

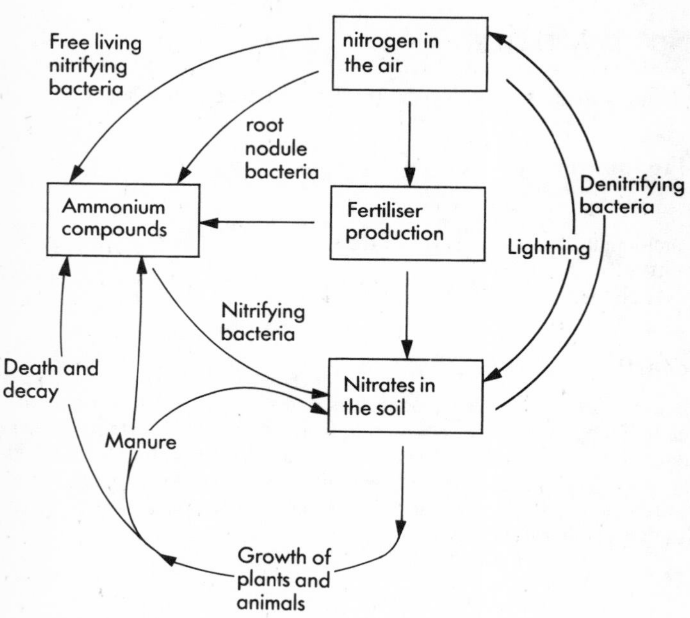

Fig. N.2 The nitrogen cycle

NITROGEN DIOXIDE, NO_2

Nitrogen dioxide is a brown gas with a pungent smell. It is very poisonous, denser than air and soluble in water. It is an **acidic oxide**.

It can be made by heating certain **nitrates** e.g. lead(II) nitrate:

lead(II) nitrate	→	nitrogen dioxide	+	lead(II) oxide	+	oxygen
$2Pb(NO_3)_2(s)$	→	$4NO_2(g)$	+	$2PbO(s)$	+	$O_2(g)$

It is formed in internal combustion engines. The electric spark and subsequent explosion of the petrol/air mixture causes nitrogen and oxygen to combine to form nitrogen monoxide which then reacts with air to form nitrogen dioxide.

NITROGEN MONOXIDE, NO

Nitrogen monoxide is formed in internal combustion engines. The electric spark and subsequent explosion of the petrol/air mixture causes nitrogen and oxygen to combine to form nitrogen monoxide, which is poisonous. The exhaust systems of some cars are fitted with special catalysts which convert the poisonous gases in the fumes to safer gases.

nitrogen monoxide	+	carbon monoxide	→	nitrogen	+	carbon dioxide
$2NO(g)$	+	$2CO(g)$	→	$N_2(g)$	+	$2CO_2(g)$

◀ Catalytic converters ▶

NITROGENOUS FERTILISERS

As the name suggests, these are fertilisers containing nitrogen. The nitrogen in these compounds is converted within the plants into proteins. Nitrogenous fertilisers replace the nitrogen in the soil removed by plants. Failure to do this would result in poor yields in future years. However, the addition of too much fertiliser can also cause problems. Excess fertiliser will dissolve in rain water which finds its way into rivers. This causes river plants to grow rapidly, using up oxygen; it also prevents sunlight from entering the water. The lack of oxygen causes fish to die.

◀ Eutrophication ▶

NOBEL, ALFRED (1833–1896)

Alfred Nobel discovered dynamite in 1866 and blasting gelatin (used for blasting rocks) in 1875. He died in 1896 and in his will he left the interest from his large estate to be given annually as prizes for the furtherance of Peace, Literature, Chemistry, Physics, Physiology and Medicine. The prizes were first awarded in 1901. Nobel prizes are regarded as the highest honour an individual can receive in these fields.

NOBLE GASES

These used to be called the 'rare gases' because they were thought, when they were first discovered, to be uncommon. (See Table N.3.)

Noble gas	*Year of discovery*	*Discoverers*
argon	1894	W. Ramsay Lord Rayleigh
helium	1868	J.N. Lockyer P.J.C. Jannsen
krypton	1898	W. Ramsay M.W. Travers
neon	1898	W. Ramsay M.W. Travers
radon	1900	F.E. Dorn
xenon	1898	W. Ramsay M.W. Travers

Table N.3 Noble gases – discovery

Noble gases can now be obtained by **fractional distillation** of liquid air, but helium is usually obtained from **natural gas**. They were then known as the 'inert gases' because they were thought to be unreactive. However, in 1962 it was shown that xenon formed compounds and since that date various compounds of krypton and xenon have been isolated. Today, they are known as the noble gases because, like the noble metals, they are relatively unreactive. (See Table N.4.) All the gases are **monatomic**.

Element	*Symbol*	*Atomic number*	*Atomic mass*	*Melting point °C*	*Boiling point °C*
helium	He	2	4	−272	−269
neon	Ne	10	20	−249	−246
argon	Ar	18	40	−189	−186
krypton	Kr	36	84	−157	−152
xenon	Xe	54	131	−112	−107
radon	Rn	86	222	− 71	− 62

Table N.4 Noble gases – properties

NON-CONDUCTORS

These are substances such as plastic coverings that do not conduct electricity. If they are used to cover a wire carrying an electric current they are called insulators.

As a general rule all non-metals, except **graphite**, and compounds in the solid state are non-conductors.

NON-ELECTROLYTES

This term is used to describe compounds which do not conduct electricity when in the liquid form or when dissolved in water. Many organic compounds are non-electrolytes e.g. ethanol and sugar.

NON-METAL OXIDES

Non-metal oxides are covalent compounds. The oxides usually react with water to give acids, e.g. sulphur trioxide reacts to give sulphuric acid and carbon dioxide reacts to give carbonic acid. A few non-metal oxides are neutral e.g. water and carbon monoxide.

NON-METALS

The essential difference between metals and non-metals is their ability to lose or gain electrons. A non-metal is an element which forms negative ions by gaining electrons.

PROPERTIES

Physical properties

- dull in appearance
- easily break if they are solids
- either gases, liquids or solids with low melting points and boiling points
- have a low density, are poor conductors of heat and electricity

Chemical properties

- their oxides are usually acidic
- their chlorides are covalent
- they form stable compounds with hydrogen
- they tend to be oxidizing agents
- they do not react with dilute acids

NORTH SEA GAS

North Sea Gas is almost entirely methane CH_4. In Britain the domestic gas supply is provided by gas obtained from wells in the North Sea. It does not contain any carbon monoxide and therefore it is not poisonous. It has no smell and therefore a chemical with a characteristic smell is added so that leaks can be detected.

◀ Natural gas ▶

NPK FERTILISERS

These are fertilisers which contain the three elements nitrogen, phosphorus and potassium essential for soil fertility. They usually contain ammonium nitrate, ammonium phosphate and potassium chloride in varying proportions. The proportion of nitrogen, phosphorus and potassium in the mixture is usually quoted on the container, e.g; 9% N, 9% P and 9% K.

NUCLEAR FISSION

Nuclear fission occurs when atoms split releasing large amounts of energy. This is the principle of nuclear power stations where the radioactive nucleus of uranium – 235 splits into fragments and releases a large amount of energy.

$$^{235}U \rightarrow {}^{90}Sr + {}^{142}Xe + 3\,{}^{1}n$$

NUCLEAR FUSION

Nuclear fusion is the joining together of small atomic nuclei to form larger nuclei so releasing large amounts of energy. This type of reaction is thought to happen continuously on the sun; the source of the sun's energy, and the earth's. In this reaction four hydrogen atoms join together to form helium and release a positron and energy.

$$4\,{}^{1}H \rightarrow {}^{4}He + 2\,{}^{0}e^{+} + \text{energy}$$

NUCLEONS

The term nucleons refers to both the protons and neutrons in the nucleus of an atom.

NUCLEUS

This is the small part in the centre of an atom. The nucleus of hydrogen consists of a single proton whereas for other elements the nucleus contains both protons and neutrons.

NYLON

Nylon was discovered in 1934 by the American chemist W. H. Carothers and made by a reaction known as **condensation polymerisation.** It is made by reacting together 1,6–diaminohexane and hexan–1,6–dioyl chloride. (See Fig. N.3). Nylon is used for making the bristles on toothbrushes, fibres for ropes, carpets and clothing, combs and gear wheels.

$$nH_2N-\text{▨}-NH_2 + nClOC-\text{▧}-COCl \rightarrow \left[HN-\text{▨}-\overset{H}{\overset{|}{N}}-\underset{\underset{O}{\|}}{C}-\text{▧}-CO \right]_n + nHCl(aq)$$

Fig. N.3 Nylon manufacture

The reaction can be easily shown in a laboratory by an experiment known as the 'nylon rope trick'. (See Fig. N.4)

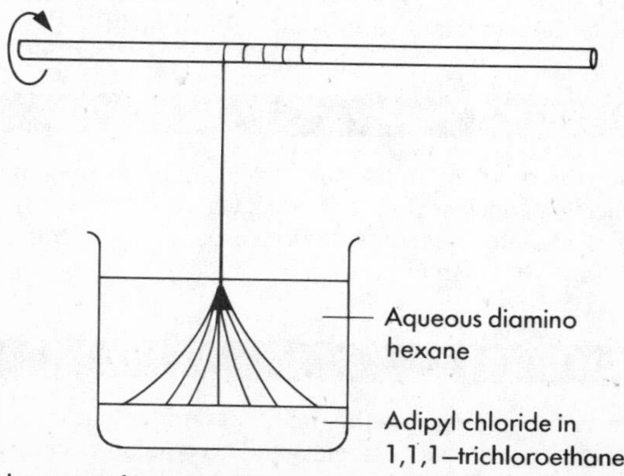

Fig. N.4 The 'nylon rope trick'

OCTANE, C_8H_{18}

Octane is the eighth member of the **homologous series** of alkanes. It is the main constituent of petrol and it is from an isomer of this alkane that the term 'octane number' is derived. Petrol that burns with the same efficiency as this isomer is given an octane number of 100. Nowadays petrol with an octane number between 97 and 100 is called 4 star petrol.

OIL

Oil was formed many millions of years ago from tiny sea creatures dying and sinking to the bottom of the sea. Over a period of time they became covered with mud and sand, this sediment exerted a pressure and heat that led to the formation of oil which seeped upwards through porous rock until it came into contact with non-porous rock. Here the oil and gas remain trapped until they are tapped by man and his drilling equipment. Oil is a mixture of many hydrocarbons which can be separated into various fractions by **fractional distillation.**

ORE

Metals are usually found as compounds such as carbonates, chlorides, sulphides and oxides. These compounds are often mixed with unwanted

Metal	*Ore*	*Main metal compound*
aluminium	bauxite	aluminium oxide
calcium	chalk	calcium carbonate
copper	malachite	copper carbonate
iron	haematite	iron(III) oxide
lead	galena	lead(II) sulphide
magnesium	dolomite	mixture of calcium carbonate and magnesium carbonate
sodium	rock salt	sodium chloride
zinc	zinc blende	zinc sulphide

Table 0.1 Ores

compounds in rocks. If the metal is to be extracted from this rock, the rock is referred to as the ore of the metal. Hence an ore is a rock from which a metal can be economically extracted. (See Table O.1.)

ORGANIC CHEMISTRY

Organic chemistry studies only the chemistry of compounds containing carbon, which in most cases also contain hydrogen. (Organic compounds can contain other elements such as the halogens, oxygen, nitrogen, phosphorus and sulphur). The number of compounds containing only carbon and hydrogen is far greater than all the compounds of all the other elements. This is because carbon can both covalently bond to four other atoms and join up with itself to form either chains of atoms of varying lengths or rings of atoms of various size. This property is known as **catenation.**

Organic chemistry was used to describe compounds that were found in living organisms such as plants and animals. In 1828 the German scientist, Wohler, made **urea** (an organic compound found in our bodies) from an inorganic compound: ammonium cyanate.

Note: carbon monoxide, carbon dioxide and metal carbonates are **NOT** classified as organic compounds.

Organic compounds tend to be gases, volatile liquids or low melting solids. They tend to be insoluble in water and on burning in excess oxygen they form carbon dioxide and water.

OXIDATION

Oxidation is brought about by **oxidising agents**, and can be either the:

- addition of oxygen
- removal of hydrogen
- loss of electrons
- increase in **oxidation number**

Example

An example of oxidation is:

iron(II) oxide	+	oxygen	→	iron(III) oxide
$4FeO(s)$	+	$O_2(g)$	→	$2Fe_2O_3(s)$

This is oxidation either because:

- iron(II) oxide has gained oxygen
- the iron(II) ion has lost electrons,

$$Fe^{2+} - e \rightarrow Fe^{3+}$$

- the oxidation number of iron(II) has been increased from +2 to 3. Oxygen is the oxidising agent

OXIDATION NUMBER

The oxidation number of an atom shows the number of electrons over which it has lost or gained control as a result of its bonding. A positive number shows loss of control; a negative number shows gain of control. This system was invented by Johnson in 1880.

Ionic compounds

The oxidation number of elements in ionic compounds is equal to the charge on the ions in that compound.

Iron is Fe^{3+} therefore iron has an oxidation number of +3 and the chloride ion is Cl^{-}, so chlorine has an oxidation of −1.

Elements

The oxidation number of elements is zero.

Rules

Oxidation numbers can be given to elements in all compounds if the following rules are obeyed;

i) The total oxidation number in a neutral compound is zero.
ii) The total oxidation number on a charge ion equals the charge on the ion.
iii) Fluorine in compounds containing fluorine always has an oxidation number of −1.
iv) The oxidation number of oxygen in most compounds is −2, the exceptions are compounds with fluorine where it is +2 and in peroxides when it is − 1.
v) The oxidation number of hydrogen in most compounds is +1, the exceptions are hydrides of Group I and Group II metals when it is −1.

Example

Thus in sulphuric acid H_2SO_4, the oxidation numbers are for hydrogen +1, for sulphur +6 and for oxygen −2; for the nitrate(V) ion $NO^{-}{}_3$, nitrogen is +5 and oxygen −2.

Advantages

- They can be used to classify elements in compounds and are used in the systematic naming of compounds e.g. sulphate(IV) $SO_3{}^{2-}$ and sulphate(VI) $SO_4{}^{2-}$. In these ions the oxidation number of sulphur is +4 and +6 respectively.
- They can be used to balance redox equations.

OXIDES

Oxides are compounds containing oxygen and one other element. Oxides can be made by burning or heating the element in oxygen.

Classification of oxides is difficult because some oxides can be in more than one group.

CLASSIFICATION

Acidic oxides

These are usually the oxides of non-metals; they react with **bases** to form salts plus water.

sulphur trioxide	+	potassium hydroxide	→	potassium sulphate	+	water
$SO_3(g)$	+	$2KOH(aq)$	→	$K_2SO_4(aq)$	+	$H_2O(l)$

Basic oxides

These are usually the oxides of metals, they react with **acids** to form salts plus water.

magnesium oxide	+	sulphuric acid	→	magnesium sulphate	+	water
$MgO(s)$	+	$H_2SO_4(aq)$	→	$MgSO_4(aq)$	+	$H_2O(l)$

Amphoteric oxides

These are oxides of elements that fall on the dividing line between metals and non-metals in the periodic table. Oxides of elements such as tin, aluminium, zinc, lead and antimony are amphoteric. Amphoteric oxides react with acids to form a salt plus water and they react with alkalis to form a salt plus water.

zinc oxide	+	hydrochloric acid	→	zinc chloride	+	water
$ZnO(s)$	+	$2HCl(aq)$	→	$ZnCl_2(aq)$	+	$H_2O(l)$
zinc oxide	+	sodium hydroxide	→	sodium zincate	+	water
$ZnO(s)$	+	$2NaOH(aq)$	→	$Na_2ZnO_2(aq)$	+	$H_2O(l)$

Neutral oxides

These oxides are neither acidic nor basic nor amphoteric. Carbon monoxide, dinitrogen oxide, nitrogen monoxide and water are neutral.

Higher oxides

These oxides contain more oxygen than is suggested from the oxides of other elements in the same Group in the periodic table. Peroxides are examples of higher oxides. Higher oxides are good oxidising agents which tend to give off oxygen when heated.

Mixed oxides

These oxides behave as a mixture of two simpler oxides. The two best known examples are iron(II) iron(III) oxide Fe_3O_4 which is a mixture of FeO and Fe_2O_3 and dilead(II) lead(IV) oxide (red lead) Pb_3O_4 which is a mixture of 2 moles of lead(II) oxide (PbO) and 1 mole of lead(IV) oxide PbO_2.

◀ Acidic oxides, amphoteric oxides, basic oxides ▶

OXIDISING AGENTS

In a **redox reaction**, the substance which is reduced does the oxidising. It is known as the oxidising agent. Examples of strong oxidising agents are oxygen, nitric acid, concentrated sulphuric acid, potassium dichromate(VI) and potassium manganate(VII).

Test for an oxidising agent

The test for an oxidising agent is to add a substance that is easily reduced (a reducing agent) where an obvious change takes place.

- Add to potassium iodide, acidified with dilute sulphuric acid – the solution turns brown showing that iodine is formed. The formation of iodine can be confirmed by adding 1, 1, 1–trichloroethane; the organic layer turns purple.
- Add to a freshly made solution of iron(II) sulphate acidified with dilute sulphuric acid. The pale green colour of iron(II) sulphate turns yellow showing that iron(III) ions have been formed. The formation of iron(III) ions can be confirmed by adding sodium hydroxide solution; a reddish brown precipitate is formed.

OXYACETYLENE

Acetylene is nowadays called **ethyne**. The combustion of acetylene in oxygen is used to produce very high temperatures in order to weld together or to cut metals. When a mixture of acetylene and oxygen burn the temperature exceeds 3 000 °C. The supply of the gases is from cylinders which are fed into a blow-pipe; the gases are then burnt at the jet.

acetylene (ethyne)	+	oxygen	→	carbon dioxide	+	water
$2C_2H_2(g)$	+	$5O_2(g)$	→	$4CO_2(g)$	+	$2H_2O(g)$

OXYGEN, O_2

Oxygen is the most abundant element in the earth's crust. It forms nearly 50% of the earth's crust by mass where it is found mainly in compounds such as carbonates and silicates. It occurs as the free element in air. It forms about 21% of the atmosphere by volume (about 23% by mass). It was discovered independently by **Scheele** in 1772 and **Priestley** in 1774. It was given the name 'oxygen' by Lavoisier. Oxygen means 'acid producer'. Lavoisier thought that all acids contained oxygen.

Test for oxygen

The test for oxygen is that it relights a glowing splint.

MANUFACTURE

Oxygen is manufactured by the **fractional distillation** of liquid air. It is most readily made in the laboratory by the catalytic decomposition of **hydrogen peroxide** using manganese (IV) oxide. (See Fig. H.9)

hydrogen peroxide	→	oxygen	+	water
$2H_2O_2(aq)$	→	$O_2(g)$	+	$2H_2O(l)$

Properties

Oxygen is a colourless, odourless, tasteless gas which is slightly soluble in water. It is neutral to indicators. It reacts to form many different types of **oxides**. Oxygen is a very powerful oxidising agent. (One of the definitions of oxidation is 'the addition of oxygen'.)

Uses

Oxygen is used in **steel** making, in oxygen tents in hospitals, in **oxy-acetylene** flames and as a rocket fuel.

OXYHAEMOGLOBIN

Oxyhaemoglobin is formed when haemoglobin in the blood reacts with oxygen.

haemoglobin + oxygen ⇌ oxyhaemoglobin

This travels round the body in the blood giving up its oxygen where it is required.

OZONE, O_3

Ozone is an **allotrope** of oxygen. Its name is derived from the Greek word; *ozein* meaning 'to smell'. It was discovered by Schonbein in 1839.

Ozone is a pale blue gas which is poisonous. However, in small quantities it is used to freshen up the atmosphere in crowded places such as theatres and underground railways because it rapidly destroys many organic compounds. Drinking water and surgical instruments can be sterilised using ozone.

Ozone is a powerful **oxidising agent**.

Ozone is formed at high altitudes by a process in which oxygen absorbs high energy rays (ultra violet radiation) from the sun.

oxygen	⇌	ozone
$3O_2(s)$	⇌	$2O_3(g)$

This ozone layer has the useful property of filtering out some of the high energy radiation from the sun. This radiation can cause damage to the eyes and skin cancer. The ozone layer can be destroyed by CFCs (**Chlorofluorocarbons**) released from aerosols.

◀ **Disinfectant** ▶

PAPER

Paper is made from the cellulose fibres of wood. Paper is bleached using **sulphur dioxide.**

◀ **Bleach** ▶

PARAFFIN

Paraffin is obtained by the **fractional distillation** of **crude oil.** It is a mixture of liquids with a boiling range of about 170 – 250°C. It is used as a fuel for heating. Another name for paraffin is *kerosene.*

PEPTIDE LINK

The linkage between amino acids that polymerise to form **proteins** is called the peptide link. Its structure is:

```
        H
        |
  —C—N—
   ||
   O
```

The same linkage is found in **nylon,** where it is called an amide link.

PERCENTAGE COMPOSITION

The percentage composition of a compound can be calculated from its formula. For example, if you wanted to find the percentage of nitrogen in:

(a) ammonium nitrate NH_4NO_3
(b) ammonium sulphate $(NH_4)_2SO_4$
(c) urea $CO(NH_2)_2$

you would use the following method:

(a) Mass of one mole of ammonium nitrate = 80
Mass of nitrogen = 28
% of nitrogen = 28/80 × 100 = 35%

(b) Mass of 1 mole of ammonium sulphate = 132
Mass of nitrogen = 14
% of nitrogen = 14/132 × 100
= 10.6%

(c) Mass of 1 mole of urea = 60
Mass of nitrogen = 28
% of nitrogen = 28/60 × 100
= 47%

What is the percentage of:
(d) potassium in potassium chloride (KCl)
(e) carbon in methane (CH_4)?

(d) Mass of 1 mole of potassium chloride = 74.5
Mass of potassium = 39
% of potassium = 39/74.5 × 100
= 52.3%

(e) Mass of 1 mole of methane = 16
Mass of 1 mole of carbon = 12
% of carbon = 12/16 × 100
= 75%

PERCENTAGE YIELD

Some reactions do not go to completion; they are **reversible**. The following method can be used to calculate % yield:

28 g of calcium oxide is obtained when 200 g of calcium carbonate is heated. The % yield of calcium oxide is as follows:

calcium carbonate	⇌	calcium oxide	+	carbon dioxide
$CaCO_3(s)$	⇌	$CaO(s)$	+	$CO_2(g)$

1 mole of calcium carbonate should give 1 mole of calcium oxide
100 g of calcium carbonate should give 56 g of calcium oxide
Hence 200 g of calcium carbonate should give 112 g of calcium oxide. If only 28 g was formed then:
% yield = 28/112 × 100 = 25%

PERIODIC TABLE

In the periodic table the elements are arranged in order of their **atomic numbers** in horizontal rows. Each row is called a **period**. Elements with similar properties appear above one another in vertical columns called groups. There are eight groups and seven periods. The periodic table is very useful as it will help you to remember the properties of elements and their compounds. (See Fig. P.1)

◀ Mendeleev, Moseley ▶

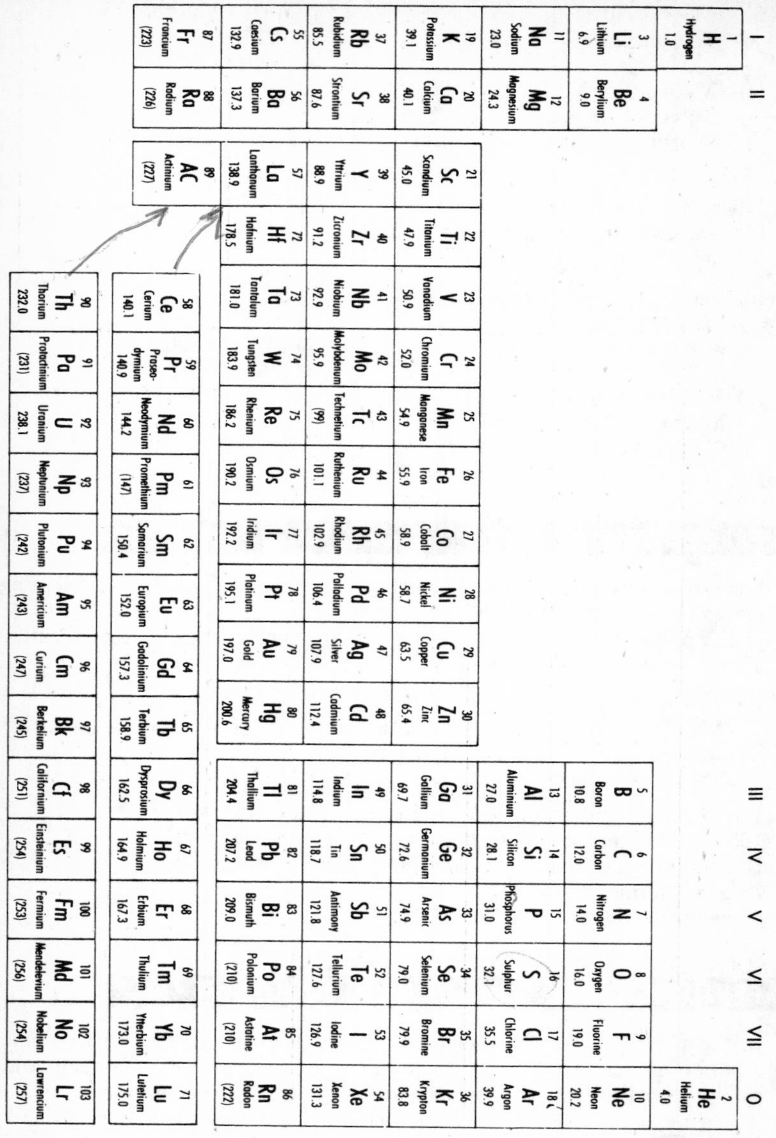

I	II											III	IV	V	VI	VII	0
1 H Hydrogen 1.0																	2 He Helium 4.0
3 Li Lithium 6.9	4 Be Beryllium 9.0											5 B Boron 10.8	6 C Carbon 12.0	7 N Nitrogen 14.0	8 O Oxygen 16.0	9 F Fluorine 19.0	10 Ne Neon 20.2
11 Na Sodium 23.0	12 Mg Magnesium 24.3											13 Al Aluminium 27.0	14 Si Silicon 28.1	15 P Phosphorus 31.0	16 S Sulphur 32.1	17 Cl Chlorine 35.5	18 Ar Argon 39.9
19 K Potassium 39.1	20 Ca Calcium 40.1	21 Sc Scandium 45.0	22 Ti Titanium 47.9	23 V Vanadium 50.9	24 Cr Chromium 52.0	25 Mn Manganese 54.9	26 Fe Iron 55.9	27 Co Cobalt 58.9	28 Ni Nickel 58.7	29 Cu Copper 63.5	30 Zn Zinc 65.4	31 Ga Gallium 69.7	32 Ge Germanium 72.6	33 As Arsenic 74.9	34 Se Selenium 79.0	35 Br Bromine 79.9	36 Kr Krypton 83.8
37 Rb Rubidium 85.5	38 Sr Strontium 87.6	39 Y Yttrium 88.9	40 Zr Zirconium 91.2	41 Nb Niobium 92.9	42 Mo Molybdenum 95.9	43 Tc Technetium (99)	44 Ru Ruthenium 101.1	45 Rh Rhodium 102.9	46 Pd Palladium 106.4	47 Ag Silver 107.9	48 Cd Cadmium 112.4	49 In Indium 114.8	50 Sn Tin 118.7	51 Sb Antimony 121.8	52 Te Tellurium 127.6	53 I Iodine 126.9	54 Xe Xenon 131.3
55 Cs Caesium 132.9	56 Ba Barium 137.3	57 La Lanthanum 138.9	72 Hf Hafnium 178.5	73 Ta Tantalum 181.0	74 W Tungsten 183.9	75 Re Rhenium 186.2	76 Os Osmium 190.2	77 Ir Iridium 192.2	78 Pt Platinum 195.1	79 Au Gold 197.0	80 Hg Mercury 200.6	81 Tl Thallium 204.4	82 Pb Lead 207.2	83 Bi Bismuth 209.0	84 Po Polonium (210)	85 At Astatine (210)	86 Rn Radon (222)
87 Fr Francium (223)	88 Ra Radium (226)	89 AC Actinium (227)															

58 Ce Cerium 140.1	59 Pr Praseo-dymium 140.9	60 Nd Neodymium 144.2	61 Pm Promethium (147)	62 Sm Samarium 150.4	63 Eu Europium 152.0	64 Gd Gadolinium 157.3	65 Tb Terbium 158.9	66 Dy Dysprosium 162.5	67 Ho Holmium 164.9	68 Er Erbium 167.3	69 Tm Thulium	70 Yb Ytterbium 173.0	71 Lu Lutetium 175.0
90 Th Thorium 232.0	91 Pa Protactinium (231)	92 U Uranium 238.1	93 Np Neptunium (237)	94 Pu Plutonium (242)	95 Am Americium (243)	96 Cm Curium (247)	97 Bk Berkelium (245)	98 Cf Californium (251)	99 Es Einsteinium (254)	100 Fm Fermium (253)	101 Md Mendelevium (256)	102 No Nobelium (254)	103 Lr Lawrencium (257)

Fig. P.1 Periodic table

PERIODS

There are seven periods in the **periodic table.**
Period 1 – two elements: hydrogen and helium
Period 2 – eight elements; lithium to neon
Period 3 – eight elements: sodium to argon
Period 4 – eighteen elements: potassium to krypton
Period 5 – eighteen elements: rubidium to xenon
Period 6 – thirty-two elements: caesium to radon
Period 7 – probably thirty-two elements: francium to the 'island of stability'

◄ Trends in the periodic table ►

PERMANENT HARDNESS

Permanent hardness in water is caused by soluble compounds such as calcium sulphate and magnesium sulphate. These compounds cannot be removed by boiling. Pure water can be obtained from permanently hard water by either **distillation** or **ion-exchange.**

◄ Temporary hardness ►

PERSPEX

Perspex is a **polymer** made from the **monomer**, methyl methacrylate. Perspex has similar properties to glass but it is much harder to break. It is used to make aircraft windows, camera lenses and motorcycle windshields.

PETROL

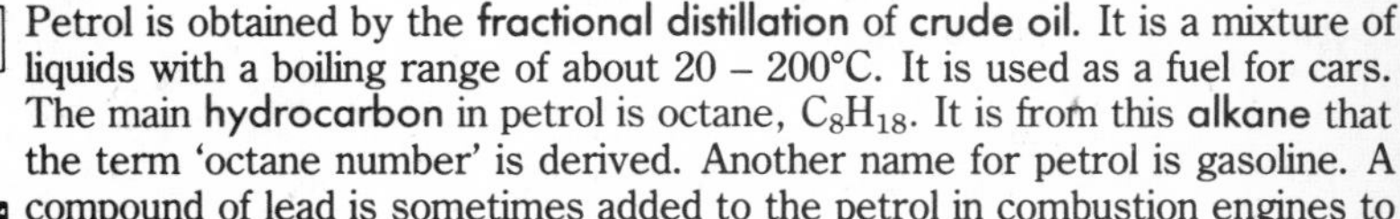

Petrol is obtained by the **fractional distillation** of **crude oil.** It is a mixture of liquids with a boiling range of about 20 – 200°C. It is used as a fuel for cars. The main **hydrocarbon** in petrol is octane, C_8H_{18}. It is from this **alkane** that the term 'octane number' is derived. Another name for petrol is gasoline. A compound of lead is sometimes added to the petrol in combustion engines to prevent knocking.

PETROLEUM

Petroleum or crude oil is a **fossil fuel.** Its name is derived from *petra* meaning 'rock' and *oleum* meaning 'oil', i.e. oil obtained from rock because petroleum is found trapped in pockets between porous and non-porous rocks underground. It is a mixture of a large number of **hydrocarbons.**

PHENOLPHTHALEIN

Phenolphthalein is an **indicator.** It is colourless in acidic and neutral solutions and red in alkaline solutions. Phenolphthalein can be used to distinguish between solutions of sodium hydrogencarbonate, in which it is colourless, and sodium carbonate in which it is red.

PHOSPHORUS

Phosphorus has the property of shining in the dark – hence its name. It is not found free in nature, but it is found in a large number of widely occurring compounds such as phosphates. About three-fifths of your bone mass is calcium phosphate. Phosphorus is one of the major plant nutrients and so it is added to **fertilisers** usually as either calcium superphosphate or ammonium phosphate. Phosphorus aids the growth of roots in plants and speeds up the ripening of fruit.

Phosphorus has two **allotropes**, white phosphorus and yellow phosphorus.

PHOTOSYNTHESIS

Photosynthesis is the process whereby green plants *synthesise carbohydrate* foods from carbon dixoide and water in the presence of sunlight and a **catalyst** of **chlorophyll**. It is an **endothermic reaction**.

carbon dioxide + water → glucose + oxygen

$$6CO_2(g) + 6H_2O(l) \rightarrow C_6H_{12}O_6(s) + 6O_2(g)$$

The glucose molecules polymerise to make long chain carbohydrates such as cellulose and starch.

◀ **Carbohydrates, polymerisation** ▶

pH SCALE

The pH scale is a number scale which shows the acidity and alkalinity of a substance dissolved in water. Most aqueous solutions have pH values between 1 and 14. (See Fig. P.2.)

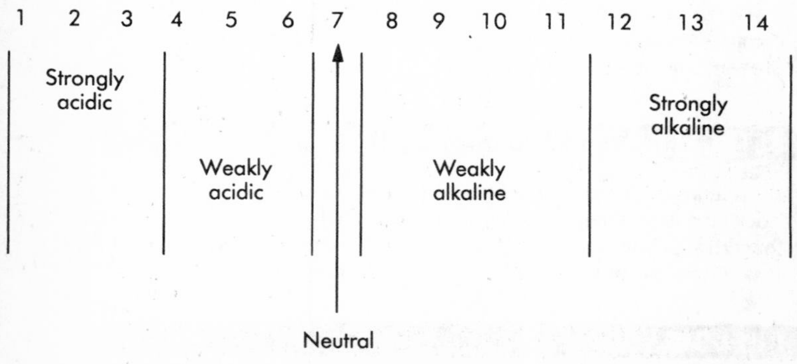

Fig. P.2 pH scale

If a solution has a pH less than 7, it is acidic. The smaller the number, the stronger the acid. 0.1 M hydrochloric acid has a pH of 1 – it is a **strong acid**; 0.1 M ethanoic acid has a pH of 4 – it is a **weak acid**.

If a solution has a pH greater than 7, it is alkaline. The larger the number the stronger the alkali. 0.1 M sodium hydroxide has a pH of 13 – it is a **strong alkali**; 0.1 M ammonia solution has a pH of 9 – it is a **weak alkali**.

Pure water and solutions of many salts in water have a pH of 7; they are neutral. (See Fig. P.3.)

The easiest way to measure pH is to use an indicator such as **universal indicator** or pH paper.

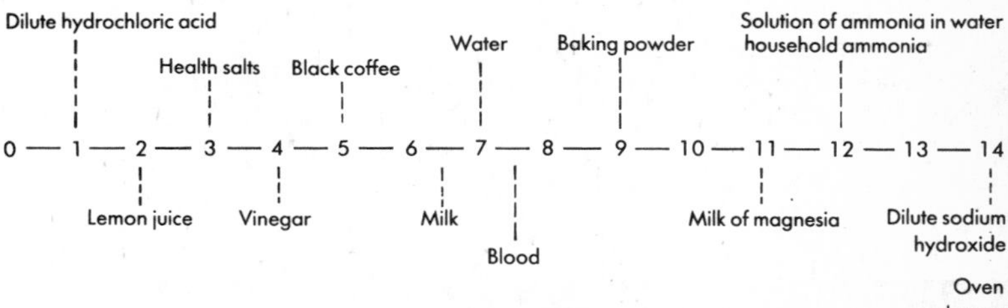

Fig. P.3 pH of some common solutions

pH measures the hydrogen ion concentration. p is from the German word *potenz* meaning 'power' and H is the symbol for hydrogen. Those of you familiar with logarithms will understand that:

$pH = 1/\log_{10}[H^+]$

or;

$pH = -\log_{10}[H^+]$

The sign [ ] is used to represent the concentration in mol/dm^3.

e.g. What is the pH of 0.01 mol/dm^3 hydrochloric acid?

$pH = -\log_{10}[0.01]$
$= -[-2]$
$= 2$

Hence pH of 0.01 M hydrochloric acid is 2.

What is the pH of 0.0005 M hydrochloric acid?

$pH = -\log_{10}[0.0005]$
$= -(-3.30)$
$= 3.30$

PICKLING

Pickling is the term used to describe the removal of rust from sheets of steel before they are painted.

PIPETTE

A pipette is used in titrations to measure fixed volumes of liquids very accurately. Pipettes are made in different sizes; the common volumes measured are 5 cm^3, 10 cm^3, 25 cm^3 and 50 cm^3. It is much safer to fill a pipette with liquids using a pipette filler. This is a special device that draws the liquid into the pipette thus avoiding using one's mouth to suck up the liquid.
◀ Titration ▶

PLASTER OF PARIS

Calcium sulphate occurs naturally as gypsum, $CaSO_4.2H_2O$. When it is heated gently, it loses water to form plaster of paris $(CaSO_4)_2.H_2O$, so called because it was first made on a large scale in Montmartre, a district of Paris. When plaster of paris is mixed with water, it gets warm and then sets solid. It expands slightly when it sets and thus can be used to reproduce details of moulds which are known as plaster casts.

POLLUTION

Pollution destroys the natural purity of a substance.

POLLUTION OF THE AIR

One of the causes of pollution is **acid rain** formed by the burning of fossil fuels which contain sulphur or the emission of oxides of nitrogen from the exhausts of motor vehicles. Acid rain causes stonework to decay and metals to corrode. It also causes diseases of the lungs.

Sulphur dioxide, a major pollutant, is also formed during the manufacture of **steel**, and manufacture of sulphuric acid by the **contact process**. Exhaust fumes contain unburnt **hydrocarbons, carbon monoxide** and lead compounds, as well as oxides of nitrogen. The manufacture of **aluminium** produces waste gases from the process that contain fluorides which have to be removed.

The purity of air can be judged by studying lichens which are found as crust-like growths on plants – if the air is pure, they are found in plenty, if the air is polluted there are very few.

POLLUTION OF WATER

Fertilisers

If too much fertiliser is put on the land, the excess dissolves in water and finally finds its way into the rivers. In rivers it encourages algae and plants to grow very large. The rivers become choked with plants and starve the water of oxygen, causing animal life to die.

Manufacturing processes

In the manufacturing processes that require large volumes of water for cooling, the warm water is pumped back into rivers. This also encourages the growth of plants. Some fishes cannot survive at these higher temperatures because of lack of oxygen.

Detergents

Synthetic **detergents** also cause pollution problems; less oxygen will dissolve in the water, a foam or lather may be formed and many detergents contain phosphates which again encourage the growth of algae and river plants.

Shipping accidents

Shipping accidents frequently cause large oil spills. One way to break down the oil spilt is to spray on a detergent, but this can also be damaging.

POLLUTION BY NON-BIODEGRADABLE PLASTICS

Many plastics are very stable; they do not rot and hence they are difficult to destroy. Polyvinylchloride, for example, does not decompose; when burnt it gives off hydrogen chloride gas which is poisonous and which dissolves in water to form hydrochloric acid.

POLY(ETHENE) OR POLYTHENE

Low density polythene is made from the monomer ethene. When ethene gas is put under very high pressure, the ethene molecules join together in very long chains. Using this method the chains are not straight but have side branches. The main disadvantage of low density polythene is that it softens at around 100°C. If you look at the structure of poly(ethene) you can see that it is an **alkane** with a very long chain. It is saturated, and this accounts for its unreactivity. It does not react with acids or alkalis.

In 1953 Professor Ziegler discovered another method of polymerising ethene. This method takes place at temperatures up to 150°C and pressures up to 200 atmospheres in the presence of special catalysts (called Ziegler catalysts). The large molecules of polythene are unbranched and can pack together closely. This type of polythene is called high density polythene; it does not soften in boiling water. High density polythene is used for making plastic bags.

◀ Polymerisation ▶

POLYMER

A polymer is a long chain molecule made by **polymerisation**.

Examples of polymers are shown in Table P.1.

Polymer	*Use*	*Monomer*
poly(acrylonitrile)	fibres	acrylonitrile
poly(ethene)	plastic bags	ethene
poly(methylmethacrylate)	glass substitute	methyl methacrylate
poly(propene)	washing-up bowls, shaped chairs	propene
poly(styrene)	packaging	styrene
poly(tetrafluoroethene)	non-stick surfaces	tetrafluoroethene
poly(vinylchloride)	records	vinyl chloride

Table P.1 Examples of polymers

POLYMERISATION

This is a reaction in which a large number of small molecules or **monomers** join together to make a large molecule or **polymer**.

◀ **Addition polymerisation, condensation polymerisation** ▶

POLY(PROPENE)

Poly(propene) is made from the monomer **propene**.

POLY(STYRENE)

The correct chemical name for this chemical is poly(phenylethene). It is made by stirring the monomer, phenylethene, with a **catalyst** such as benzoyl peroxide. The viscous syrup formed is gently heated to complete the **polymerisation** process.

The main uses of polystyrene are as a packaging material and as a heat insulator.

POLY(TETRAFLUOROETHENE) OR PTFE

This **polymer** is made from the monomer tetrafluoroethene. PTFE is unaffected by everyday chemicals so is used to make a non-stick surface in cooking pans and frying pans.

POLY(VINYLCHLORIDE) OR PVC

This polymer should be called poly(monochloroethene). PVC is chemically unreactive and is used for upholstery, plastic mackintoshes, suitcase coverings and gramophone records.

POTASSIUM, K

The name potassium was derived from potash. Potash is potassium carbonate and is contained in wood-ash. Potassium was first extracted by **Sir Humphry Davy** in 1807 by the **electrolysis** of molten potassium hydroxide.

Potassium is in Group I of the **periodic table** and is more reactive than sodium.

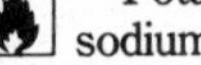

POTASSIUM DICHROMATE(VI), $K_2Cr_2O_7$

This is an orange-red solid which is soluble in water. It is a powerful oxidising agent. In the presence of dilute sulphuric acid it oxidises iron (II) compounds to iron (III) compounds, potassium iodide to iodine and ethanol to ethanoic acid. In these reactions potassium dichromate (VI) is reduced to chromium (III) compounds which are green in colour. Thus when potassium dichromate (VI) oxidises a compound there is a colour change of orange to green.

◀ **Breathalysers** ▶

POTASSIUM MANGANATE(VII), $KMnO_4$

This is also known as potassium permanganate(VII). It is a purple-black solid that is soluble in water forming an intense purple solution. It is a powerful oxidising agent. In the presence of dilute sulphuric acid it oxidises iron(II) compounds to iron(III) compounds, potassium iodide to iodine and ethanol to ethnoic acid. In these reactions potassium manganate(VII) is reduced to maganese(II) compounds which are colourless. Thus, when potassium manganate(VII) oxidises a compound there is a colour change from purple to colourless.

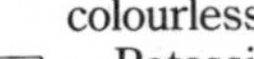

Potassium manganate(VII) cannot be used with hydrochloric acid because it will oxidise it to chlorine. (This is one of the methods of preparing **chlorine.**)

PRECIPITATE

A precipitate is an insoluble solid that separates out during a chemical reaction. **Precipitation** is the opposite of dissolving. Precipitation is used to make insoluble salts, e.g. when an aqueous solution of sodium carbonate is added to an aqueous solution of calcium nitrate a precipitate of calcium carbonate is formed.

sodium carbonate	+	calcium nitrate	→	calcium carbonate	+	sodium nitrate
$Na_2CO_3(aq)$	+	$Ca(NO_3)_2(aq)$	→	$CaCO_3(s)$	+	$2NaNO_3(aq)$

Precipitation reactions are used to recognise certain ions.

Precipitates can be separated from solutions by either **filtration** or centrifugation.

◀ **Qualitative analysis** ▶

PRECIPITATION

This is the term used to describe a reaction in which a precipitate is formed.

PRIESTLEY, JOSEPH (1733–1804)

Joseph Priestly studied theology and became a minister of the church. He made a number of important discoveries including the discovery of oxygen, nitrogen, nitrogen monoxide, dinitrogen oxide and soda-water; he also showed that water was a compound of hydrogen and oxygen.

PRODUCER GAS

Producer gas is a mixture of carbon monoxide and nitrogen. It is made by passing air over hot coke. The reaction is very **exothermic.**

air	+	coke	→	carbon monoxide	+	nitrogen
$O_2(g) + 4N_2(g)$	+	$2C(s)$	→	$2CO(g)$	+	$4N_2$

◀ **Water gas** ▶

PROPANOL, C_3H_7OH

Propanol is the third member of the **homologous** series of **alcohols.** There are two **isomers** of propanol, propan-1-ol and propan-2-ol; both have all the usual properties of alcohols.

PROPANONE

Propanone is used mainly in the laboratory as a solvent for organic compounds. It is used for washing residues after the residue has first been washed with water. Propanone removes water and any remaining propanone readily vaporises (it is volatile), leaving the residues clean and dry.

PROPENE, C_3H_6

Propene is the second member of the **homologous** series of **alkenes.** It polymerises to give **poly(propene).** It has all the usual properties of alkenes.
◀ **Ethene, polymerisation** ▶

PROTEINS

Protein makes up a large proportion of animal life e.g. about 15% of your body mass is protein. Protein is a vital constituent of living cells; it occurs in blood, muscles, hair, toe-nails, finger-nails and cartilage. It is essential that we eat plenty of protein. Foods that are rich in protein include milk, cheese, meat, fish, nuts and beans.

All proteins are **nitrogen** containing **polymers** of **amino acids**. This can be shown by heating protein with **soda-lime**; **ammonia** gas is given off. Proteins also contain hydrogen, carbon and oxygen and other elements. **Haemoglobin** is a protein, it colours the blood red.

All proteins have the **peptide link** between the amino-acids.

Proteins can be broken down by **hydrolysis**. If we eat meat this process of hydrolysis is speeded up by **enzymes** (proteases) in our digestive system. One way of tenderising meat is to sprinkle a small amount of such an enzyme on the meat. Enzymes are also proteins. Another way is to marinade the meat. The meat is left overnight in vinegar or wine and the proteins are slowly broken down. A more violent way of breaking down protein is to actually beat the meat with a wooden hammer – you may have seen a butcher or a cook beating steak before cooking it.

◀ Analysis ▶

PROTONS

Protons are one of the types of particles found in an **atom**. It has a mass of one unit and a charge of +1. The symbol for a proton is p. The hydrogen ion, H^+, is a proton. The number of protons in an atom gives its atomic number. Thus sodium, atomic number 11 has 11 protons in its nucleus. An acid can be defined as a proton donor. Thus, when hydrochloric acid is added to water, a proton is given by the acid to water:

$$HCl(aq) + H_2O(l) \rightarrow H_3O^+(aq) + Cl^-(aq)$$

Protons were discovered in 1919 by Geiger and Marsden by bombarding a very thin sheet of gold with **alpha particles**, although the significance of their work was explained later by Ernest Rutherford.

Rutherford subsequently obtained protons by bombarding nitrogen atoms with alpha particles. This was the first experiment in which one element had been transmuted into another – the nitrogen atom changes into an isotope of carbon.

PURITY

Chemists spend a great deal of time and effort purifying substances. A pure substance is a single **element** or **compound**. When a substance is pure it has a sharp boiling point and a sharp melting point, e.g. pure water always boils at 100° and melts at 0°C.

Most chemists test for purity by **analysis**. All pure samples of the same compound contain the elements combined in the same proportion by mass.

PVC

◀ Poly(vinyl chloride) ▶

PYROLYSIS

Pyrolysis is the heating of substances in the absence of air. It literally means 'splitting by fire'. Pyrolysis is used to dispose of plastic waste materials. The plastics are converted into re-usable hydrocarbons.

QUARTZ, SiO_2

Silicon dioxide occurs naturally in a crystalline form called quartz. It is a very hard substance. Quartz coloured by traces of iron compounds and manganese compounds is called amethyst.

QUICKLIME

Quicklime is the everyday name for **calcium oxide.**

Manufacture

It is manufactured by heating **limestone** (calcium carbonate) in **limekilns.** (See Fig. Q.1)

calcium carbonate	→	calcium oxide	+	carbon dioxide
$CaCO_3(s)$	→	$CaO(s)$	+	$CO_2(g)$

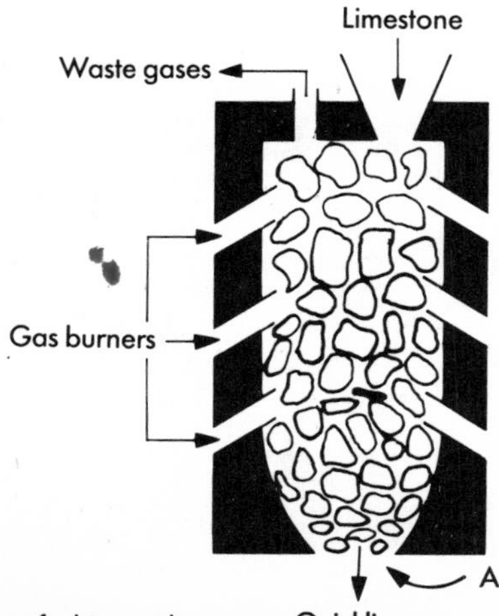

Fig. Q.1 Preparation of calcium oxide

Properties

Quicklime is usually found as hard, white, porous lumps. When heated to a very high temperature it gives off a vivid white light which was used for spot lights in the theatre. Hence the phrase 'being in the limelight'.

When it is left in air it absorbs water and carbon dioxide.

When water is added to quicklime, a great deal of heat is given out. This process is known as **slaking** and the product is **calcium hydroxide** or **slaked lime.**

Uses

- Quicklime is used in the laboratory for the preparation of **ammonia** and for drying **ethanol.** This method of drying ethanol produces absolute alcohol (pure ethanol)
- Industrially it is used for making **mortar, cement, soda-lime** and **steel.** It is also used to neutralise acid waste from industry.
- It is used by farmers to neutralise the soil if it is too acidic.

RADIOACTIVITY

The **nuclei** of some **atoms** are unstable and tend to split up with the emission of certain **alpha particles, beta particles** and gamma rays. When alpha and beta particles are emitted new elements are formed.

USES

Some of the uses of radioactivity include:

- treatment of cancer
- dating of plant and animals remains
- sterilising of surgical instruments and equipment
- controlling the thickness of paper and metal
- following the course of a process, e.g. The mechanism of a reaction by making one of the atoms radioactive or following the flow of blood through an artery by adding a radioactive dye
- treatment of certain foods to destroy bacteria

◀ **Equations (nuclear), nuclear fission, nuclear fusion** ▶

RATE OF REACTION

◀ **Speed of reaction** ▶

REACTIONS

When two or more substances react together to form a new product, a chemical reaction has occurred. There is usually a change in **energy**.

- **addition reactions**
- **cracking**
- **dehydration**
- **displacement**
- **hydration**
- **hydrolysis**
- **neutralisation**
- **precipitation**
- **redox**
- **reversible reactions**
- **thermal decomposition**
- **thermal dissociation**

See under appropriate headings for examples of these types of reactions.

REACTIVITY SERIES

Metallic elements

The reactivity series of metallic elements is a list in which the most reactive metal is placed at the top of the series and the least reactive is placed at the bottom. (See Fig. R.1) In general a more reactive metal can displace a less reactive metal from a solution of one of its salts:

iron	+	copper(II) sulphate	→	copper	+	iron(II) sulphate
Fe(s)	+	$CuSO_4$(aq)	→	Cu(s)	+	$FeSO_4$(aq)

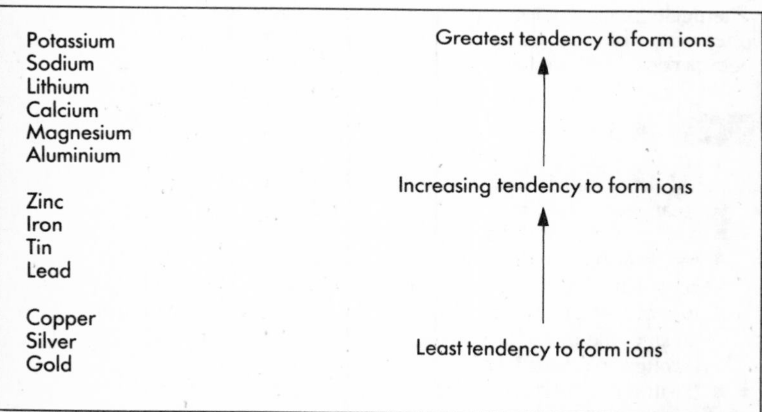

Fig. R.1

The reactivity series is a very useful way of remembering and understanding chemical reactions:

- Reactive metals such as sodium and potassium react with cold water.
- Metals above hydrogen react with dilute hydrochloric acid to form hydrogen and a salt.
- Metal compounds high in the reactivity series are stable to heat e.g. sodium carbonate does not break when heated, but copper(II) carbonate decomposes to give copper(II) oxide and carbon dioxide.
- Metals high in the series (those above aluminium) are manufactured by electrolysis.

Therefore the reactivity series is a very useful way of predicting reactions of metals.

Non-metals

It is also possible to make a list of reactivity for non-metals:
chlorine (most reactive)
bromine
oxygen
iodine
sulphur (least reactive)

Thus when chlorine is added to potassium iodide solution, iodine is formed together with potassium chloride.

◀ Displacement ▶

RECYCLING

The earth's resources will not last forever. The latest figures for the 'life time' of various metals suggests that the supply of some metals will run out unless some method can be found of recycling them. (See Table R.1)

Recycling makes metals cheaper and makes our resources last longer. The energy required to extract the metal from its ore has already been paid. Re-melting and refining scrap is only a small percentage of the original extraction costs.

Recycling is widely used in the manufacture of aluminium, iron, lead and zinc. (See Table R.2)

Metal	*Life*
copper	50 years
gold	20 years
lead	20 years
tin	20 years
zinc	20 years

Table R.1 Lifetime of some metals

Metal	*Scrap*
aluminium	drinking cans, milk bottle tops
iron	old cars
lead	lead-acid batteries
zinc	brass and other alloys

Table R.2 Uses of scrap

REDOX REACTIONS

A reaction involving **reduction** and **oxidation**. Examples of redox reactions are:

magnesium + carbon dioxide → magnesium oxide + carbon

$Mg(s) + CO_2(g) \rightarrow MgO(s) + C(s)$

Magnesium has been oxidised to magnesium oxide because it has gained oxygen, and carbon dioxide has been reduced to carbon because it has lost oxygen.

hydrogen + chlorine → hydrogen chloride

$H_2(g) + Cl_2(g) \rightarrow 2HCl(g)$

Hydrogen has been oxidised to hydrogen chloride because its oxidation number has increased from 0 to +1 and chlorine has been reduced to hydrogen chloride because it has gained hydrogen.

iron	+	copper(II) sulphate	→	copper	+	iron(II) sulphate
Fe	+	$CuSO_4$	→	Cu	+	$FeSO_4$

Iron has been oxidised to iron (II) ions in iron (II) sulphate because the oxidation number of iron has increased from 0 to +2 and the copper (II) ions in copper (II) sulphate have been reduced to copper because the oxidation number of copper has been reduced from +2 to 0.

In fact oxidation and reduction always occur together – it is impossible to have just an oxidation reaction or just a reduction reaction.

REDUCING AGENT

In a **redox reaction** the substance which is oxidised does the reducing. Examples of strong reducing agents are hydrogen, carbon, carbon monoxide, ammonia and metals.

Test for reducing agents

The test for a reducing agent is the addition of a substance that is easily oxidised (an oxidising agent) and reducing agents are present where an obvious change takes place:

- Add potassium manganate(VII) acidified with dilute sulphuric acid – the solution turns from purple to colourless.
- Add potassium dichromate(VI) acidified with dilute sulphuric acid – the solution changes from orange to green.

REDUCING SUGARS

◀ Benedict's solution, Fehling's solution ▶

REDUCTION

Reduction can be:

- the addition of hydrogen
- the removal of oxygen
- the gain of electrons
- the decrease in **oxidation number**

Reduction is brought about by **reducing agents.**

Example

iron(III) oxide	+	carbon monoxide	→	iron	+	carbon dioxide
$Fe_2O_3(s)$	+	$3CO(g)$	→	$2Fe(s)$	+	$3CO_2(g)$

This is reduction either because:

- iron (III) oxide has lost oxygen
- the iron (III) ion has gained electrons
  Fe^{3+} + $3e^-$ → Fe or
- the oxidation number of iron (III) has been reduced from +3 to zero

Carbon monoxide is the reducing agent.

RELATIVE ATOMIC MASS

The relative mass of an atom on a scale on which an atom of carbon−12 is 12.00

RELATIVE MOLECULAR MASS

The relative mass of a molecule on a scale on which an atom of carbon−12 is 12.00. Relative molecular mass is calculated by adding together the **relative atomic masses** of all the elements present, e.g. the relative molecular mass of ethanol C_2H_5OH is
$(12 \times 2) + (1 \times 5) + 16 + 1 = 46$

RESIDUE

When a solid is separated from a liquid by **filtration**, the solid remaining on the filter paper is called the residue.

RESPIRATION

Carbohydrates in our bodies are oxidised by oxygen in the air we breathe in to form carbon dioxide, water and energy. Some of this energy helps to keep us warm and move our muscles.

sugar	+	oxygen	→	carbon dioxide	+	water
$C_6H_{12}O_6(s)$	+	$6O_2(g)$	→	$6CO_2(g)$	+	$6H_2O(l)$

Oxygen is transported in our bodies by the haemoglobin in the blood.

REVERSIBLE REACTIONS

A reversible reaction is a reaction that can go either forwards or backwards depending on the conditions.

Examples

nitrogen	+	hydrogen	⇌	ammonia
$N_2(g)$	+	$3H_2$	⇌	$2NH_3(g)$

hydrated copper(II) sulphate	⇌	anhydrous copper(II) sulphate	+	water
$CuSO_4.5H_2O(s)$	⇌	$CuSO_4(s)$	+	$5H_2O(g)$

ammonium chloride	⇌	ammonia	+	hydrogen chloride
$NH_4Cl(s)$	⇌	$NH_3(g)$	+	$HCl(g)$

◀ Equilibrium ▶

RUBIDIUM, Rb

Rubidium is in Group I of the **periodic table**. It was discovered in 1861 by R.W. **Bunsen** and G.R.Kirchoff. Its name derives from the latin word; *rubidus* meaning 'red' taken from the colour it gives in the **flame test**.

RUSTING

Rust is the flaky brown solid which forms on iron and steel. Iron is the only metal that rusts. In order for rusting to take place both oxygen and water must be present. Other chemicals, such as sodium chloride dissolved in water, speed up the rusting process.

Rusting is an **oxidation** process. Rust is hydrated iron (III) oxide. Iron and steel objects can be protected by preventing air and water from reaching the surface. This can be done by painting, oiling, **galvanising**, covering with plastic, **electroplating** or **sacrificial protection**.

SACRIFICIAL PROTECTION

Sacrifical protection is a method used to prevent iron from **rusting**. A more reactive metal than iron, such as magnesium or zinc, is attached to the iron. The reactive metals are oxidised and dissolve in preference to iron. This method is used to protect the hulls of ships and underground pipes.

◀ Galvanising ▶

SAL AMMONIAC

Sal ammoniac is the common name for ammonium chloride.

◀ Ammonium chloride ▶

SALT

Salt is the common name given to sodium chloride ($NaCl$). Sodium chloride is also known as common salt.

Sodium chloride dissolved from underground deposits of rock salt is used to manufacture **sodium hydroxide, chlorine** and **hydrogen chloride.**

◀ Brine ▶

SALTS

Salts are formed by the **neutralisation** of **acids** by **bases.**

Acid + base $\rightarrow$ salt + water

Salts are ionic compounds. When the hydrogen ion of an acid is replaced by a metal ion or an ammonium ion, a salt is formed. Examples of salts formed from their parent acids are;

- sodium chloride ($NaCl$) from hydrochloric acid (HCl)
- potassium nitrate (KNO_3) from nitric acid (HNO_3)
- magnesium sulphate ($MgSO_4$) from sulphuric acid (H_2SO_4)
- sodium ethanoate (CH_3CO_2Na) from ethanoic acid (CH_3CO_2H)

Many of the compounds produced by the Inorganic Chemical Industry are salts. (See Table S.1)

Salt	*Use*
ammonium salts	fertilisers
barium sulphate	'barium meal' before stomach X-ray
calcium sulphate	plaster of Paris
copper(II) sulphate	fungicide
iron(II) sulphate	'iron tablets' for anaemia
magnesium sulphate	a laxative in some health salts
silver chloride	photographic film emulsion
sodium carbonate	washing soda
sodium nitrate	fertiliser
zinc chloride	flux in soldering
zinc carbonate	calamine lotion

Table S.1 Salts and their uses

Do not confuse *salts* with 'salt'! Salt (or common salt) is sodium chloride which is one of many salts!

SAPONIFICATION

Saponification is a term used to describe the **hydrolysis** reaction that occurs between fats and a concentrated solution of sodium hydroxide. The products are soap and glycerine. Oils are saponified in a similar reaction. Fats and oils are made up of large molecules. They are **esters**.

esters + water → acids + alcohols

Since saponification is carried out under alkaline conditions the acid is neutralised to form its sodium salt.

SATURATED FATTY ACIDS

Fatty acids are acids found in animal oils and fats or vegetable oils. They are also called **carboxylic acids**. The general formula of saturated fatty acids is $C_nH_{2n+1}CO_2H$. Examples of this type of acid are ethanoic acid, butyric acid and stearic acid.

◀ Fatty acids ▶

SATURATED HYDROCARBONS

Saturated hydrocarbons contain no double bonds. All the bonds are single bonds, so there is no spare bonding. **Alkanes** are saturated compounds.

SATURATED SOLUTIONS

A solution is saturated when it has dissolved as much of the solute as it can at a particular temperature. If any more solute is added to a saturated solution, the extra solute does not dissolve, unless the temperature is increased. Cooling hot saturated solutions gives crystals.

◄ Crystallisation ►

SCHEELE, KARL (1742–1786)

Scheele was a Swedish chemist who discovered **oxygen** in 1774 by heating potassium nitrate. In the same year he also discovered **chlorine** and **nitrogen.**

SEA WATER

Sea water contains at least 3.6% by mass of dissolved solids. About 2.8% is sodium chloride. Other salts present in sea water are calcium hydrogencarbonate, calcium sulphate, magnesium chloride, magnesium sulphate, potassium bromide, potassium chloride and potassium iodide. (See Fig. S.1.) Sea water plays an important part in the carbon cycle. The concentration of carbon dioxide in sea water is about 20 times by volume that in the atmosphere. Important chemicals that are extracted from the sea include bromine, iodine, magnesium and sodium chloride.

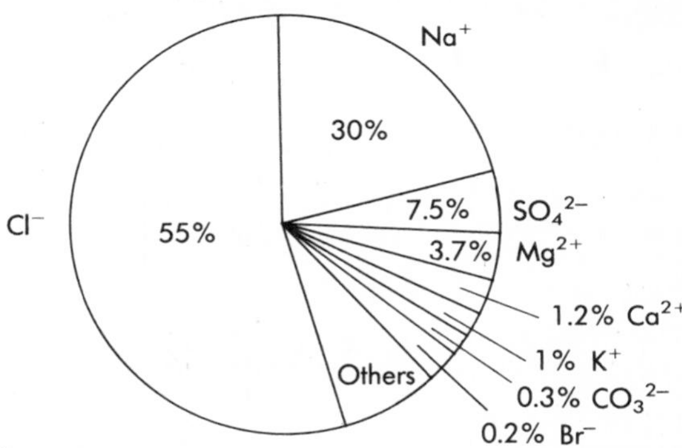

Fig. S.1 % of ions in sea water

SILICON, Si

The element silicon has a structure similar to **diamond** with atoms bonded in a giant molecular structure. (See Fig. S.2)

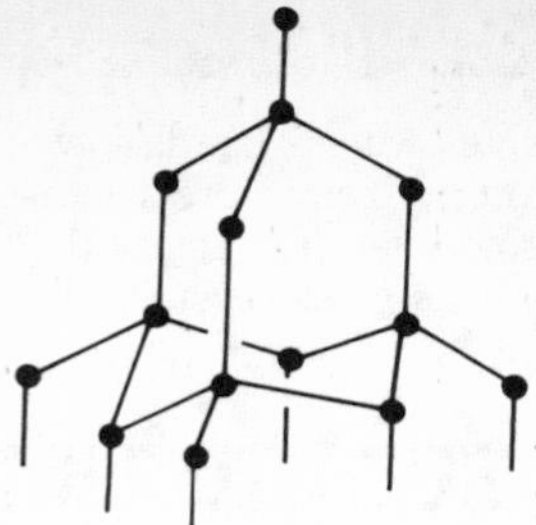

Fig. S.2 Silicon

MANUFACTURE

It can be made by heating silicon dioxide with magnesium, an example of competition for oxygen:

silicon dioxide	+	magnesium	→	silicon	+	magnesium oxide
$SiO_2(s)$	+	$2Mg(s)$	→	$Si(s)$	+	$2MgO(s)$

Use

It is used in microchips in computers.

SILICON DIOXIDE, SiO_2

Silicon dioxide or **quartz** is the main constituent of sand. It has a giant structure of silicon atoms and oxygen atoms. (See Fig. S.3.) Silicon dioxide is a solid which has a giant molecular structure; by comparison, carbon dioxide, its oxide which corresponds to silicon dioxide, is a gas because it has a simple molecular structure.

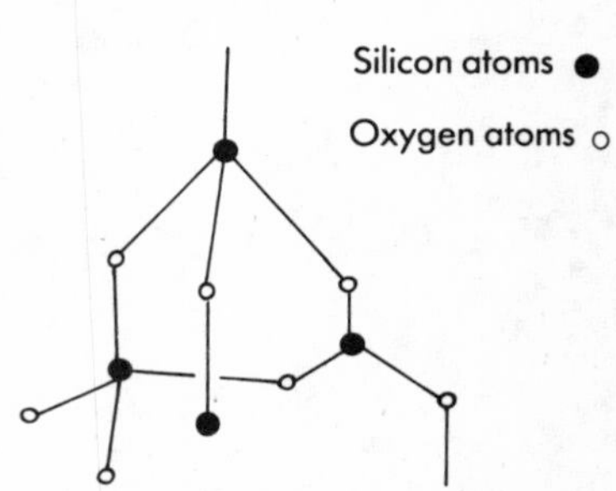

Fig. S.3 Silicon dioxide

SITING OF A CHEMICAL PLANT

The main factors to consider are:

- easy access to cheap raw materials; ores, water, fuel and power
- good transport; ships or rail for large tonnage; roads for smaller quantities
- a good supply of skilled labour nearby

Examples

For the manufacture of **ammonia** by the **Haber process** the site must be near to oil or a natural gas supply and by a river for a supply of water.

For the manufacture of **sulphuric acid** the site must be near to the major customers because the costs of transport are high; coastal sites are often chosen because sulphur has to be imported; there has to be easy access to customers who wish to buy the steam generated by the contact process.

◀ Industrial plant location ▶

SLAKED LIME

Slaked lime is the common name for **calcium hydroxide**. It is made by adding water to **calcium oxide** – a process known as **slaking**.

SLAKING

Slaking is the term used to describe the addition of water to lime (calcium oxide) to form **slaked lime** (calcium hydroxide).

SMELLING SALTS

A pungent mixture containing ammonium carbonate which is used to revive people who have fainted. The ammonium carbonate slowly decomposes to **ammonia** which helps to stimulate breathing.

ammonium carbonate	→	ammonia	+	water	+	carbon dioxide
$(NH_4)_2CO_3(s)$	→	$2NH_3(g)$	+	$H_2O(l)$	+	$CO_2(g)$

SMELTING

Smelting is the term used to describe the extraction of a metal from its ore by a process involving **melting**. Both **iron** and **zinc** are extracted from their respective ores by smelting processes.

SOAP

There are many different types of soap. Washing soaps are sodium or potassium salts of long-chain **fatty acids**. They are made by reacting animal fats or vegetable oils with **alkalis** by a process known as **saponification**.

Soap helps to get things clean by:

- reducing the surface tension of water which helps to wet the surfaces
- emulsifying oils and greases which converts them into minute droplets that can be rinsed away

Lithium soaps are used to make greases for machinery.

◀ Detergents ▶

SODA-LIME

Soda-lime is a mixture of sodium hydroxide, calcium oxide and calcium hydroxide. It is often used in place of sodium hydroxide because it is not deliquescent and it fuses at a much higher temperature.

SODIUM, Na

A reactive metal found in **Group 1** of the **periodic table**. It was discovered in 1807 by **Humphry Davy**. The name sodium is said to be derived from the Arabic word *soda* meaning 'headache metal'. The symbol Na is derived from its latin name: *natrium*.

MANUFACTURE

Because it is a reactive metal it has to be manufactured by **electrolysis** (of molten sodium chloride).

Uses

Sodium is used in sodium lamps giving them their characteristic yellow light. Liquid sodium is used to take heat from the core of some types of nuclear reactors. It is a very good conductor of heat and easily melted – melting point 98°C.

SODIUM CARBONATE, Na_2CO_3

Sodium carbonate is manufactured by the **Solvay process**.

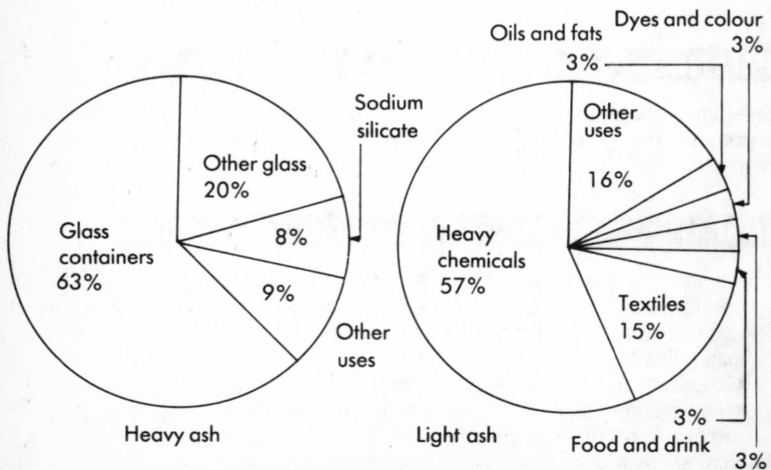

Fig. S.4 Uses of sodium carbonate

Uses

Sodium carbonate is used for the manufacture of glass, soap, sodium hydroxide and water glass. The crystalline form $Na_2CO_3, 10H_2O$ is sold under the name of **washing soda** and is used for softening water. It removes the calcium ions from hard water as insoluble calcium carbonate. (See Fig. S.4) If crystals of hydrated sodium carbonate are left exposed to the air they crumble into a white powder having formed the monohydrate.

$$Na_2CO_3.10H_2O(s) \rightarrow Na_2CO_3,H_2O\ (s) + 9H_2O\ (g)$$

SODIUM CHLORIDE, NaCl

Sodium chloride is a white crystalline solid, frequently called *common salt.* It contains equal numbers of Na^+ ions and Cl^- ions arranged in a face-centred cube type crystal lattice. It is fairly soluble in water. Sodium chloride is used to flavour food, as a preservative and for the manufacture of **chlorine, sodium hydroxide** and **sodium carbonate**.

SODIUM HYDROXIDE, NaOH

Sodium hydroxide is a white solid which is very soluble in water. In the solid state it is **deliquescent** and becomes very wet if it is left in the air. It is a typical strong **alkali** and is used in the manufacture of **soaps** and **aluminium.** (See Fig. S.5)

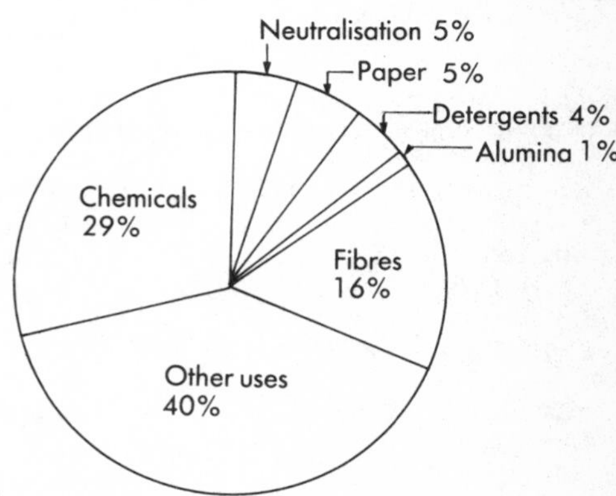

Fig. S.5 Uses of sodium hydroxide

SOFT WATER

Soft water is water that readily forms a lather with soap.

◀ **Hard water** ▶

SOLID

Solid is one of the three **states of matter**. A solid has a definite shape and a definite size (or volume). Ice is the solid state of water. All metals except **mercury** are solids.

SOLUTE

A solute is a substance that dissolves in a **solvent** to give a **solution**. In an aqueous solution of sodium chloride, the solute is sodium chloride and the solvent is water.

SOLUTION

A solution is a uniform mixture of two or more substances.

solute + solvent → solution

SOLVAY PROCESS

The Solvay process is used to manufacture **sodium carbonate**. The raw materials are sodium chloride, ammonia, water and calcium carbonate.

Ammonia dissolved in **brine** reacts with carbon dioxide made by heating calcium carbonate.

ammonia	+	carbon dioxide	+	water	→	ammonium hydrogencarbonate
$NH_3(g)$	+	$CO_2(g)$	+	$H_2O(l)$	→	$NH_4HCO_3(aq)$

The ammonium hydrogencarbonate reacts with the sodium chloride to form the slightly soluble sodium hydrogencarbonate.

ammonium hydrogen carbonate	+	sodium chloride	→	sodium hydrogen carbonate	+	ammonium chloride
$NH_4HCO_3(aq)$	+	$NaCl(aq)$	→	$NaHCO_3(s)$	+	$NH_4Cl(aq)$

The sodium hydrogencarbonate is filtered off and heated.

sodium hydrogen carbonate	→	sodium carbonate	+	water	+	carbon dioxide
$2NaHCO_3(s)$	→	$Na_2CO_3(s)$	+	$H_2O(g)$	+	$CO_2(g)$

Ammonia is recovered by heating the ammonium chloride formed with the calcium oxide.

ammonium chloride	+	calcium oxide	→	ammonia	+	calcium chloride	+	water
$2NH_4Cl(aq)$	+	$CaO(s)$	→	$2NH_3(g)$	+	$CaCl_2(aq)$	+	$H_2O(l)$

This process is very economical; the only waste product is calcium chloride.

SOLVENT

A solvent is a liquid that is used to dissolve substances. **Water** is the commonest solvent. Other solvents include **ethanol** and **propanone.**

Water is a solvent for many ionic substances and **ethanol** is a solvent for many molecular substances. Ionic compounds tend to be soluble in water; molecular compounds tend to be soluble in molecular liquids such as ethanol, trichloromethane and propanone. **Petrol** and tetrachloromethane are used to remove oil stains from clothes.

Other solvents in common use are shown in Table S.2.

Solvent	*Solute*	*Use*
amyl ethanoate	cellulose	nail varnish
1,1,1-trichloroethane	plastic	Tippex
benzene	rubber	mending rubber tyres
ethanol	iodine	tincture of iodine
ethanol	shellac	liquid polish
white spirit	pigments	paints

Table S.2 Solvents

SPECTATOR IONS

Spectator ions are ions that do not take part in a chemical reaction. They are present at the start of the reaction and at the end of a reaction. If we leave out the spectator ions in an equation, we are left with the *ionic equation*. Ionic equations balance in both the number of atoms and the number of charges in the reactants and the products. Consider the reaction between silver nitrate solution and sodium chloride solution:

silver nitrate	+	sodium chloride	→	silver chloride	+	sodium nitrate
$AgNO_3(aq)$	+	$NaCl(aq)$	→	$AgCl(s)$	+	$NaNO_3(aq)$

If we write this in terms of ions we get:

$Ag^+(aq) \quad + \quad NO_3^-(aq) \quad + \quad Na^+(aq) \quad + \quad Cl^-(aq)$

$\rightarrow \quad AgCl(s) \quad + \quad NO_3^-(aq) \quad + \quad Na^+(aq)$

$NO_3^-(aq)$ and $Na^+(aq)$ are spectator ions.

The ionic equation is:

$Ag^+(aq) \quad + \quad Cl^-(aq) \quad \rightarrow \quad AgCl(s)$

SPEED OF REACTIONS

The speed of a chemical reaction can be increased by:

- making the size of the reacting particles smaller

- increasing the concentration, or in the case of gases, increasing the pressure
- increasing the temperature
- adding a suitable catalyst
- light

◀ Kinetic theory, collision theory ▶

STALACTITES

◀ Calcium compounds ▶

STALAGMITES

◀ Calcium compounds ▶

STARCH

Starch is a **carbohydrate**, formed during **photosynthesis**. Sugar is first formed during photosynthesis and is then stored by converting the sugar into starch. The structure of starch can be represented as:

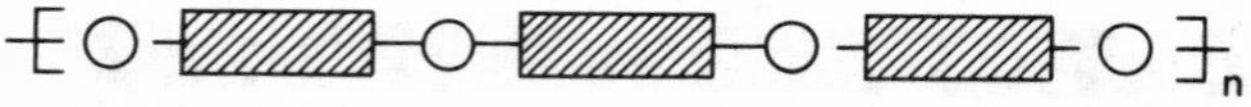

Test for starch

The test for starch is to add iodine solution - a dark blue coloured solution is formed if starch is present.

Starch can be broken down by **enzymes** into smaller molecules. There are enzymes (amylase) present in saliva that break down the large starch molecule into smaller molecules of maltose ($C_{12}H_{22}O_{11}$). This is one of the processes that takes place in digestion at body temperature. Starch can also be broken down into smaller molecules of glucose ($C_6H_{12}O_6$) by hot dilute hydrochloric acid. The reactions of starch with an enzyme and starch with dilute hydrochloric acid are both examples of **hydrolysis**.

STATES OF MATTER

There are three states of matter: solid, liquid and gas.

- A **solid** has a definite shape and a definite size (or volume).
- A **liquid** has no definite shape but has a definite volume.
- A **gas** has no definite shape and no definite size.

Fig. S.6 shows the words used to describe the changes from one state to another.

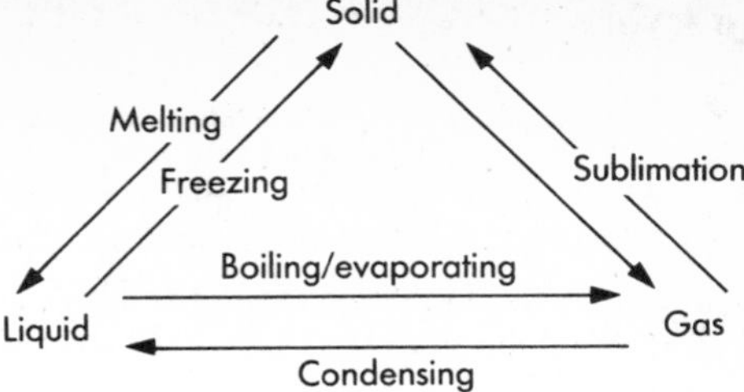

Fig. S.6 Terms describing changes in states of matter

STATE SYMBOLS

These are symbols which are included in equations to show the state of the reactants and the products:
(s) represents a solid
(l) represents a liquid
(g) represents a gas
(aq) represents a substance dissolved in water (aqueous solution)

Thus in the equation:

$CaCO_3(s) + H_2O(l) + CO_2(g) \rightleftharpoons Ca(HCO_3)_2(aq)$

shows that solid calcium carbonate reacts with liquid water and gaseous carbon dioxide to give an aqueous solution of calcium hydrogencarbonate.

STEAM

Steam is formed when **water** is heated to its **boiling point**. The molecules in water obtain sufficient energy to escape. The water molecules are further apart in steam than in water. (18g of water (1 mole) occupies 18 cm^3 but 18 g of steam occupies 30000 cm^3.) Steam at 100°C has much more energy than water at 100°C. **Metals**, such as **magnesium**, which only react slowly with cold water, react vigorously with steam.

STEARIC ACID

The systematic name for stearic acid is octadecanoic acid. The sodium salt of stearic acid, sodium stearate, is a typical **soap**. Stearic acid is named from the Greek word; *stear* meaning 'tallow'. Tallow is an animal fat containing an **ester** of stearic acid.

◀ Fatty acids ▶

STEEL

Steel is an **alloy** of iron and other elements.

MANUFACTURE

Steel is made from **blast furnace** iron by passing pure oxygen through the molten iron. This removes carbon and other non-metals as gaseous oxides. Solid, non-metallic, acidic oxides such as phosphorous oxide react with the special 'basic' lining. The resulting iron is mixed with the calculated amounts of alloying elements to make the appropriate steels. There are various types of steel. (See Fig. S.7.)

Steel	*Use*	*Constituents*	*Important properties*
spring steel	Suspension springs	iron 0.3a–0.6a carbon	contains sufficient carbon that will produce a springy metal
stainless steel	surgical instruments; cutlery	iron < 1a carbon 18a chromium	resistant to corrosion
chromium-vanadium steel	axles and wrenches	iron chromium vanadium and carbon	very strong, great resistance to strain
high-speed tungsten steels	cutting metal, drills etc.	iron with up to 20a tungsten	maintains sharp edge at high temperatures

Fig. S.7 Types of steel

STRONG ACIDS

◀ Acids ▶

STRONG ALKALIS

◀ Alkalis ▶

SUB-ATOMIC PARTICLES

The sub-atomic particles are **protons, neutrons** and **electrons** (See Table S.3)

Particle	*Mass*	*Charge*
electron	approx 0	−1
neutron	1	0
proton	1	+1

Table S.3 Sub-atomic particles

SUBLIMATION

Sublimation is the term used to describe the process whereby a solid turns into a vapour when it is heated without first melting and, on cooling, the vapour turns back directly into a solid. (See Fig. S.8.) An example of a substance that sublimes is iodine.

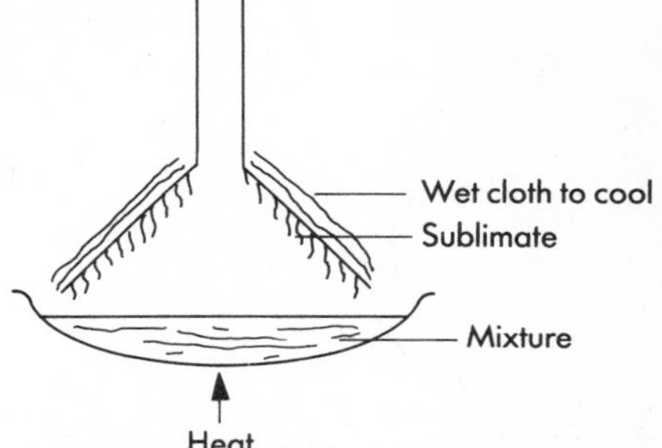

Fig. S.8 Sublimation

Note: Ammonium chloride does not sublime although it appears to. It undergoes **thermal dissociation** into two gases which recombine on cooling to reform ammonium chloride.

SUBSTITUTION REACTION

A substitution reaction is a reaction in which a reactive atom or group of atoms in a molecule is replaced by another atom or group of atoms.

Examples of substitution reaction

methane	+	chlorine	→	chloromethane	+	hydrogen chloride
$CH_4(g)$	+	$Cl_2(g)$	→	$CH_3Cl(g)$	+	$HCl(g)$

Replacement of a hydrogen atom by a chlorine atom.

chloroethane	+	sodium hydroxide	→	ethanol	+	sodium chloride
$C_2H_5Cl(l)$	+	$NaOH(aq)$	→	$C_2H_5OH(l)$	+	$NaCl(aq)$

Replacement of a chlorine atom by an hydroxyl group.

SULPHUR, S

Sulphur has been known since prehistoric times. It is a yellow solid, and is non-metallic. It has no taste or smell and is insoluble in water. Together with salt (sodium chloride), limestone (calcium carbonate), coal and oil, it is one of the five basic raw materials in the chemical industry.

Properties

Sulphur is a typical **non-metal**. It has two **allotropes**, rhombic sulphur and monoclinic sulphur. They are both made up of S_8 molecules but they are packed together differently so they have different melting points and different densities. (See Fig. S.9.)

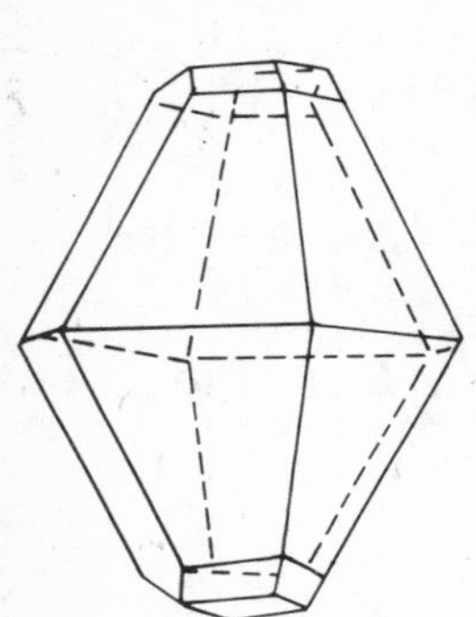

Fig. S.9a) Rhombic sulphur

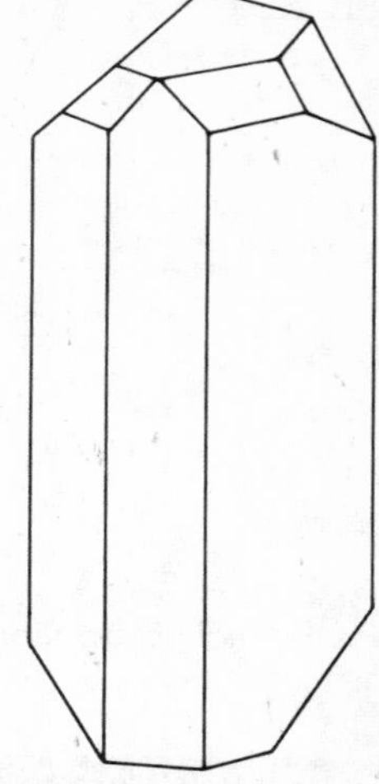

Fig. S.9b) Monoclinic sulphur

Sulphur is found as the free element in volcanoes and in underground deposits. It is found in compounds such as gypsum (calcium sulphate), Epsom salts (magnesium sulphate), and zinc blende (zinc sulphide).

It is extracted from undergound deposits by the **Frasch process**. It is also obtained as a by-product when sulphur compounds are removed from **natural gas**.

Uses

Sulphur is used for the manufacture of sulphuric acid (**Contact process**), as a fungicide and for **vulcanising** rubber.

SULPHUR DIOXIDE, SO_2 (g)

Sulphur dioxide is a common pollutant in the atmosphere. It is formed when **fossil fuels** such as coal, oil and some natural gases burn. It is formed in the manufacture of **zinc** but it is converted into sulphuric acid to prevent pollution of the atmosphere. It dissolves in water to form **acid rain**. Acid rain causes brickwork, and metal objects to corrode. If rivers and streams contain too much sulphur dioxide, the water becomes so acidic it prevents the growth of plants and also causes fish to die. Sulphur dioxide is not the only atmospheric pollutant. The pollutants from car exhausts are carbon monoxide, oxides of nitrogen and lead compounds – not sulphur dioxide!

Sulphur dioxide is formed when sulphur burns in air or oxygen.

sulphur	+	oxygen	→	sulphur dioxide
S(s)	+	$O_2(g)$	→	$SO_2(g)$

Sulphur dioxide is a colourless gas with a choking smell. It can be detected with a solution of acidified potassium dichromate(VI). Sulphur dioxide turns the colour of this solution from orange to green.

Sulphurous acid

Sulphur dioxide dissolves in water to form sulphurous acid, which is used for bleaching wood pulp and as a preservative in foods.

sulphur dioxide	+	water	→	sulphurous acid
$SO_2(g)$	+	$H_2O(l)$	→	$H_2SO_3(aq)$

SULPHURIC ACID

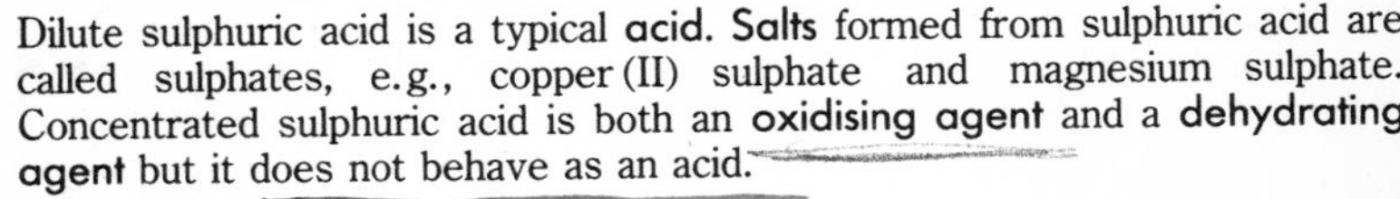

Dilute sulphuric acid is a typical **acid. Salts** formed from sulphuric acid are called sulphates, e.g., copper (II) sulphate and magnesium sulphate. Concentrated sulphuric acid is both an **oxidising agent** and a **dehydrating agent** but it does not behave as an acid.

MANUFACTURE

Sulphuric acid is made by the **Contact process.**

Uses

- Dilute sulphuric acid is used in the laboratory for the preparation of **hydrogen.**
- Concentrated sulphuric acid is used in the laboratory for the preparation of **ethene** and for drying gases such as chlorine, oxygen and nitrogen. Concentrated sulphuric acid cannot be used to dry gases that react with it e.g. the alkaline gas ammonia.
- Sulphuric acid is used in the manufacture of fertilisers, paints and detergents.
- It is the acid used in car batteries, so care must be taken when handling them.
- Industrially it is used to dry chlorine gas before it is liquified. (See Fig. S.10.)

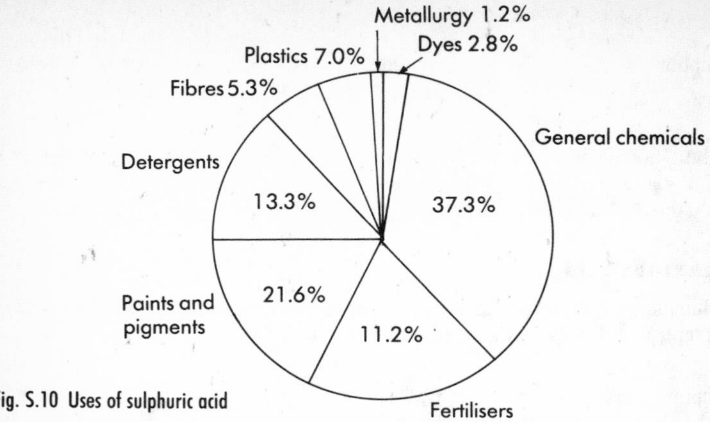

Fig. S.10 Uses of sulphuric acid

SULPHUR TRIOXIDE

Sulphur trioxide is made in the **Contact process.** It is made from sulphur dioxide and oxygen at 400°C in the presence of vanadium(V) oxide as a catalyst. The reaction is reversible:

sulphur dioxide	+	oxygen	⇌	sulphur trioxide
$2SO_2(g)$	+	$O_2(g)$	⇌	$2SO_3(g)$

Sulphur trioxide reacts violently with water to form a mist of sulphuric acid which prevents a solution being made. In order to avoid this problem, sulphur trioxide is dissolved in concentrated sulphuric acid.

SUPERPHOSPHATE

Superphosphate is a valuable **fertiliser.** It is made by heating calcium phosphate (which occurs naturally as either phosphate rock or phosphorite) with 70% concentrated sulphuric acid under a pressure of 6 atmospheres.

calcium phosphate	+	sulphuric acid	→	calcium hydrogen phosphate	+	calcium sulphate
$Ca_3(PO_4)_2(s)$	+	$2H_2SO_4(aq)$	→	$Ca(H_2PO_4)_2(s)$ calcium superphosphate	+	$2CaSO_4(s)$

Calcium superphosphate is a valuable source of phosphorus because, unlike calcium phosphate, it is soluble in water and is therefore available to plants when added to the soil.

SUSPENSION

This is dispersion of fine solid particles in a liquid which settles on standing. Milk of magnesia is a suspension of magnesium hydroxide in water.

A suspension differs from a solution of a solute in a solvent in the following ways:

- the solid particles settle on standing
- the solid particles can be seen
- it can be separated into the solid and liquid by filtration

SYMBOL

Each **element** is represented by a symbol. It is either one or two letters based mainly on either its English or its Latin name. When a symbol has two letters, the first one is written in upper case and the second in lower case. Some examples of symbols are:

- hydrogen H
- oxygen O
- chlorine Cl
- iron Fe
- silver Ag
- sodium Na

'Problem' symbols

The following symbols sometimes cause problems:

magnesium	Mg	manganese	Mn	fluorine	F	
copper	Cu	chromium	Cr	phosphorus	P	
argon	Ar	tin	Sn	lead	Pb	sodium Na

SYNTHESIS

Synthesis is the term used to describe a reaction in which a compound is made from its elements. Examples of synthesis reactions are:

sulphur	+	oxygen	→	sulphur dioxide
$S(s)$	+	$O_2(g)$	→	$SO_2(g)$
iron	+	sulphur	→	iron(II) sulphide
$Fe(s)$	+	$S(s)$	→	$FeS(s)$

Compounds made in this way usually have '**-ide**' endings, e.g., magnesium oxide is synthesised from magnesium and oxygen and hydrogen chloride from hydrogen and chlorine.

Exceptions to the **-ide** ending when compounds are synthesised are:

water (hydrogen oxide):

hydrogen	+	oxygen	→	water
$2H_2(g)$	+	$O_2(g)$	→	$2H_2O(l)$

ammonia (nitrogen hydride):

nitrogen	+	hydrogen	→	ammonia
$N_2(g)$	+	$3H_2(g)$	→	$2NH_3(g)$

SYSTEMATIC NAMES OF ORGANIC COMPOUNDS

Organic compounds are named systematically.

- The first part of the name indicates the number of **carbon** atoms in the compound. (See Table S.4.)

Number of carbon atoms	*Start of name*
1	meth–
2	eth–
3	prop–
4	but–
5	pent–

Table S.4

Functional group	*Name ending*	*Homologous series*
C–C	–ane	alkane
C=C	–ene	alkene
C–O–H	–ol	alcohol
CO_2H	acid	acids

Table S.5

- The name ending shows the **homologous** series of the compound. Compounds in the same homologous series contain the same functional group. (See Table S.5)
- Methane is an alkane with one carbon atom.
- Ethene is an alkene with two carbon atoms.
- Propanol is an alcohol with three carbon atoms.
- Butanoic acid is an acid with four carbon atoms.
- If a compund has **isomers**, the carbon atoms are numbered sequentially from 1. The carbon atoms are numbered in such a way that the smallest possible number appears in the name.

```
    Br  H
    |   |
Br—C—C—H
    |   |
    H   H
```

1,1-dibromoethene

```
   H   H
   |   |
H—C—C—H
   |   |
   Br  Br
```

1,2–dibromoethane

```
   H   H   H
   |   |   |
H—C—C—C—H
   |   |   |
   H   O   H
        \
         H
```

propan–l–ol

```
   H   H   H
   |   |   |
H—C—C—C—O—H
   |   |   |
   H   H   H
```

propan-2-ol

TEFLON

This is the common name for the polymer **poly(tetrafluoroethene)**. This **polymer** is very hard, resistant to heat and chemicals and has a high softening point. These properties make it suitable for making seals and gaskets. Its non-stick properties make it useful as a surface for cooking equipment.

TEMPORARY HARDNESS

Temporary hardness in water can be removed by boiling. It is caused by calcium hydrogencarbonate and magnesium hydrogencarbonate dissolved in water. When water containing these salts is boiled, the hydrogencarbonates decompose and precipitate the insoluble carbonates.

calcium hydrogen carbonate	→	calcium carbonate	+	water	+	carbon dioxide
$Ca(HCO_3)_2(aq)$	→	$CaCO_3(s)$	+	$H_2O(l)$	+	$CO_2(g)$

TERYLENE

Terylene is a polymer made by a **condensation polymerisation** reaction from benzene–1, 4–dicarboxylic acid (terephthalic acid) with ethane–1, 2–diol (ethylene glycol).

Uses

It is used as a fibre in cloth. It is also made into video and audio tapes and the familiar plastic lemonade and cola bottles.

TETRACHLOROMETHANE, CCl_4

This compound is commonly known as carbon tetrachloride. It is an important solvent for covalent compounds. It was used in certain types of fire extinguishers and as a refrigerant. It is sometimes used as a solvent for dry cleaning.

THERMAL DECOMPOSITION

Thermal decompostion occurs when a compound is heated and it breaks down into simpler substances. Thermal decomposition does not require air or oxygen and hence this is not written in the equation.

Examples of thermal decomposition

copper(II) carbonate	→	copper(II) oxide	+	carbon dioxide
$CuCO_3(s)$	→	$CuO(s)$	+	$CO_2(g)$
aluminium hydroxide	→	aluminium oxide	+	water
$2Al(OH)_3(s)$	→	$Al_2O_3(s)$	+	$3H_2O(g)$

Note: Group I metal carbonates and metal hydroxides do not break down when heated.

calcium nitrate	→	calcium oxide	+	nitrogen dioxide	+	oxygen
$Ca(NO_3)_2$ (s)	→	$CaO(s)$	+	$2NO_2$ (g)	+	$O_2(g)$

Note: Group I metal nitrates break down into the metal nitrite and oxygen when heated.

An industrial example is the manufacture of calcium oxide (quicklime) from calcium carbonate.

calcium carbonate	→	calcium oxide	+	carbon dioxide
$CaCO_3(s)$	→	$CaO(s)$	+	$CO_2(g)$

Cracking

Cracking is a special case of thermal decomposition. Cracking occurs when hydrocarbons are heated. They break down into a mixture of **alkanes** and **alkenes**.

propane	→	ethene	+	methane
$C_3H_8(g)$	→	$C_2H_4(g)$	+	$CH_4(g)$

THERMAL DISSOCIATION

Thermal dissociation reactions as compared with **thermal decomposition** reactions are **reversible**. When a compound is heated it breaks down into simpler substances. The products formed recombine on cooling.

Some examples of thermal dissociation are:

ammonium chloride	⇌	ammonia	+	hydrogen chloride
$NH_4Cl(s)$	⇌	$NH_3(g)$	+	$HCl(g)$
phosphorus(V) chloride	⇌	phosphorus(III) chloride	+	chlorine
$PCl_5(s)$	⇌	$PCl_3(l)$	+	$Cl_2(g)$

THERMOSETTING PLASTICS

Thermosetting plastics can be moulded when first formed into the required shape when they are hot. They become hard and brittle when they are cold. Thermosetting plastics cannot be melted once they have been formed. Examples of thermosetting plastics are **Bakelite** and melamine.

USES

These plastics are used to make heat proof containers and electrical fittings such as light bulb holders or sauce pan holders. Thermosetting plastics cannot be recycled.

THERMOSOFTENING PLASTICS

Thermosoftening plastics can be heated to soften and then shaped; this process can be repeated. Examples of thermosoftening plastics are Perspex, polythene, nylon and Terylene. If collected clean, they can be recycled.

THOMSON, SIR JOSEPH JOHN (1856–1940)

Thomson was the discoverer of **electrons** in 1896. He also showed that electrons were to be found in all atoms.

TIN, Sn

The symbol is derived from the Latin name for the metal; *stannum*. Tin has been known since prehistoric times. It occurs in the ore tinstone or cassiterite which is mainly tin(IV) oxide SnO_2.

Tin is in Group IV of the **periodic table**.

Tin is a soft, silvery white metal; it has a low melting point. It is very low in the **reactivity series** (just above hydrogen) and is therefore relatively unreactive.

USES

It is used to plate iron which prevents the iron from corroding. Thus, tin cans are made of iron coated with a thin layer of tin, called *tin plate*.

Tin forms a number of alloys. (See Table T.1.)

Alloy	*Composition*	*Use*
pewter	75% Sn, 25% Pb	drinking vessels
solder	50% Sn, 50% Pb	joining metal pipes
type-metal	10% Sn, 75% Pb, 15% Sb	printing

Table T.1 Tin alloys

TITANIUM, Ti

Titanium was discovered in 1795 by M.H.Klaproth. It is one of the **transition metals**. It is the seventh most common element in the earth's crust. It has the typical physical properties of a metal. However, it is relatively unreactive and is used as the anode in processes where chlorine gas is given off e.g. Castner-Kellner process.

Uses

Titanium is extremely hard but has a relatively low density. Hence it is also used in the construction of aircraft skins, nuclear submarines and jet engines.

TITANIUM(IV) OXIDE, TiO_2

It is used as a white pigment in manufacture of paint, white rubbers (erasers) and paper.

TITRATION

Titration is a technique for investigating the volumes of solutions that react together. One solution is placed in a **burette** and slowly added to a fixed volume of another solution, usually measured with a **pipette**, until the end- point of the reaction is shown using an **indicator**. (See Fig. T.1.)

Salts can be made by this method by repeating the titration between an acid and alkali using previously measured quantities without using the indicator.

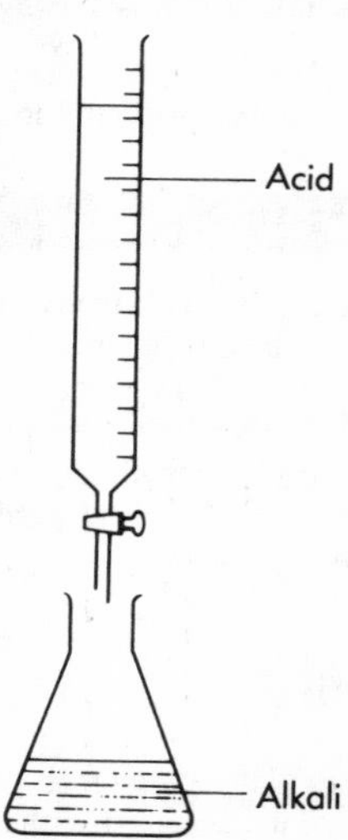

Fig. T.1 Titration of acid and alkali

TRANSITION METALS

If you look at the **periodic table** you will find the transition metals are the elements with atomic numbers 21 to 30. They are called transition metals (sometimes 'heavy metals') because they go across a period. (See Table T.2.)

Metal	*Symbol*	*Atomic number*	*Atomic mass*	*Melting point °C*	*Boiling point °C*	*Density g/cm³*
scandium	Sc	21	45	1540	2730	2.99
titanium	Ti	22	48	1675	3260	4.54
vanadium	V	23	51	1900	3000	6.11
chromium	Cr	24	52	1890	2482	7.19
manganese	Mn	25	55	1240	2100	7.42
iron	Fe	26	56	1535	3000	7.86
cobalt	Co	27	59	1492	2900	8.90
nickel	Ni	28	59	1453	2730	8.90
copper	Cu	29	64	1083	2595	8.94
zinc	Zn	30	65	420	907	7.13

Table T.2 Transition metals

PROPERTIES

Transition metals have similar properties:

- They are all typical **metals.**
- They have high densities (they all sink in water).
- They have high melting points and boiling points.
- Many of these elements or their compounds are **catalysts**, e.g., iron in the **Haber process** for the manufacture of ammonia and vanadium (V) oxide in the **Contact process** for the manufacture of sulphuric acid.
- They show variable valencies or oxidation state, e.g., iron forms iron(II) and iron(III) compounds and copper forms copper(I) and copper(II) compounds.
- You will have noticed coloured solutions in your school laboratory: these usually contain the compounds of one of these metals dissolved in water, e.g., iron(II) sulphate – sulphate is green and copper(II) sulphate solution is blue. (See Table T.3.)

Ion	*Colour of ion in aqueous solution*
Sc^{3+}	colourless
Ti^{3+}	purple
V^{3+}	green
Mn^{2+}	pink
Mn^{3+}	violet
Fe^{2+}	green
Fe^{3+}	yellow
Co^{2+}	pink
Ni^{2+}	green
Cu^{2+}	blue
Zn^{2+}	colourless

Table T.3 Colours of ions

You will notice that scandium and zinc are not true transistion metals.

Note: Transition metals are not a group in the periodic table.

TRENDS IN THE PERIODIC TABLE

The periodic table brought order into the study of elements. This order can also be seen in the following tables which summarise various properties of elements in Period 3. (See Tables T.4 and T.5.)

Property	*Sodium*	*Magnesium*	*Aluminium*	*Silicon*	*Phosphorus*	*Sulphur*	*Chlorine*
state	solid	solid	solid	solid	solid	solid	gas
structure	giant metallic	giant metallic	giant metallic	giant atomic	molecular	molecular	molecu-lar
M.pt °C	98	650	660	1410	44	113	−101
B.pt °C	890	1110	2470	2360	280	444	−35
density (g/cm^3)	0.97	1.74	2.70	2.33	1.82	2.07	2.99 g/dm^3
relative atomic mass	23.0	24.3	27.0	28.1	31.0	32.1	35.5

Table T.4 Physical properties of elements in Period 3

Property	*Sodium*	*Magnesium*	*Aluminium*	*Silicon*	*Phosphorus*	*Sulphur*	*Chlorine*
	metal	metal	metal	non-metal	non-metal	non-metal	non-metal
electronic structure	2,8,1	2,8,2	2,8,3	2,8,4	2,8,5	2,8,6	2,8,7
valency	1	2	3	4	3,5	2,4,6	1
formula of oxides	Na_2O	MgO	Al_2O_3	SiO_2	P_2O_3	SO_2	Cl_2O
	basic	basic	amphoteric	acidic	acidic	acidic	acidic
structure	giant ionic	giant ionic	giant ionic/covalent	giant molecul-ar	molecular	molecular	molecu-lar
formula of chloride	$NaCl$	$MgCl_2$	$AlCl_3$	$SiCl_4$.	PCl_3	S_2Cl_2	Cl_2
structure	giant ionic	giant ionic	molecular	molecul-ar	molecular	molecular	molecu-lar
formula of hydride	NaH	MgH_2	AlH_3	SiH_4	PH_3	H_2S	HCl

Table T.5 Chemical properties of elements in Period 3

TRIANGLE OF FIRE

◀ Fire triangle ▶

1,1,1 – TRICHLOROETHANE

This compound is a solvent and is used to dissolve the white plastic found in some correcting fluids. It is harmful.

TRICHLOROMETHANE, $CHCl_3$

This compound is also commonly known as chloroform. It was at one time used as an anaesthetic. It is sometimes used as a solvent for covalent compounds.

TRITIUM

Tritium is an **isotope** of hydrogen. Its nucleus contains 1 proton and two neutrons.

TUNGSTEN, W

It was discovered by J.J.de Elhuyar and F. de Elhuyar in 1783. It is named from the Swedish words; *tung sten* meaning 'heavy stone'.

USES

It is used to make the filaments of light bulbs because it has a very high melting point. The alloy tungsten steel is used as a cutting tool in high drills because the edge stays sharp at high speeds and high temperatures.

TYPICAL ACID

Hydrochloric acid is a typical acid. A typical acid has the following properties:

- sour taste
- changes the colour of indicator paper:
  methyl orange – orange to red
  phenolphthalein – remains colourless
  litmus – blue to red
- reacts with metals above hydrogen in the reactivity series to give hydrogen and a salt

magnesium	+	hydrochloric acid	→	magnesium chloride	+	hydrogen
Mg(s)	+	2HCl(aq)	→	$MgCl_2$(aq)	+	H_2(g)

- reacts with a base to give a salt plus water

copper(II) oxide	+	hydrochloric acid	→	copper(II) chloride	+	water
$CuO(s)$	+	$2HCl(aq)$	→	$CuCl_2(aq)$	+	$H_2O(l)$

- reacts with a carbonate to give carbon dioxide, a salt plus water

sodium carbonate	+	hydrochloric acid	→	sodium chloride	+	water	+	carbon dioxide
$Na_2CO_3(s)$	+	$2HCl(aq)$	→	$2NaCl(aq)$	+	H_2O	+	CO_2

UNIVERSAL INDICATOR

Universal indicator (U.I.) is a mixture of synthetic dyes, blended to produce a visibly distinct colour for each **pH** value. The colour change for pH 1 to 14 is that of the visible spectrum. (See Table U.1)

Table U.1 Universal indicators

pH	*Colour*
4	red
5	orange
6	yellow
7	green
8	blue
9	dark blue
10	violet

UNSATURATED FATTY ACIDS

Fatty acids are organic acids found in animal oils and fats or vegetable oils. They are also called **carboxylic acids.** Unsaturated fatty acids have the general formula $C_nH_{2n}CO_2H$. They have one or more carbon-carbon double bonds. Examples of this type of acid are oleic acid and linoleic acid. Polyunsaturated acids reduce the cholesterol levels in the body and help to prevent heart disease.

UNSATURATION

Compounds containing carbon-carbon double bonds or carbon-carbon triple bonds are said to be unsaturated because they do not contain the maximum number of atoms per molecule that the electrons available for bonding would allow. There is spare bonding and molecules can undergo **addition reactions.**

Ethene is an example of an unsaturated compound containing a carbon-carbon double bond.

ethene + bromine → 1,2−dibromethane

$$\begin{array}{c} \mathrm{H}\quad\mathrm{H} \\ |\quad\;\; | \\ \mathrm{C} = \mathrm{C} \\ |\quad\;\; | \\ \mathrm{H}\quad\mathrm{H} \end{array} + Br_2 \rightarrow \mathrm{H}-\begin{array}{c} \mathrm{Br}\quad\mathrm{Br} \\ |\qquad | \\ \mathrm{C}-\mathrm{C} \\ |\qquad | \\ \mathrm{H}\quad\;\mathrm{H} \end{array}-\mathrm{H}$$

Ethyne is an example of an unsaturated compound containing a carbon-carbon triple bond.

ethyne + hydrogen → ethane

$$H-C\equiv C-H \quad + \quad 2H_2 \quad \rightarrow \quad H-\overset{\displaystyle H}{\underset{\displaystyle H}{\overset{|}{\underset{|}{C}}}}-\overset{\displaystyle H}{\underset{\displaystyle H}{\overset{|}{\underset{|}{C}}}}-H$$

Unsaturated hydrocarbons are more reactive than saturated hydrocarbons.

Test for unsaturated hydrocarbons

There are two important tests for unsaturated hydrocarbons:

- add bromine dissolved in water; the brown colour disappears
- add potassium manganate(VII) dissolved in dilute sodium carbonate solution; the purple colour turns to a dirty brown.

◀ Alkenes ▶

URANIUM, U

Uranium was discovered in 1789 by M.H. Klaproth. It is named after the planet Uranus which was discovered in 1781. Uranium has two main isotopes U−235 and U−238. In 1939 it was observed that when U−235 was bombarded with neutrons, the uranium atom split into two parts and released three more neutrons. These neutrons could split more U−235, thus starting a chain reaction. This is an example of **nuclear fission** – matter is destroyed and a large amount of energy is set free. This chain reaction can be controlled in nuclear power stations and the energy released is used to convert water into steam. The steam is used to drive generators to produce electricity.

UREA, $(NH_2)_2CO$

The systematic name of urea is carbamide. Urea is excreted in urine. It was the first organic compound that was synthesised. The experiment was carried out by **Wohler** in 1828. He allowed a solution of ammonium cyanate to evaporate to dryness – the product was urea:

ammonium cyanate	→	urea
$NH_4CNO(s)$	→	$(NH_2)_2CO(s)$

MANUFACTURE

Urea is manufactured from ammonia and carbon dioxide:

ammonia	+	carbon dioxide	→	urea	+	water
$2NH_3(g)$	+	$CO_2(g)$	→	$(NH_2)_2CO(s)$	+	$H_2O(l)$

Uses

Urea is used in the manufacture of plastics, barbiturate drugs and as a fertiliser.

VALENCY

The valency of an element is a number which shows its combining power.

Ionic compounds

In ionic compounds, the charge on the ions of the element is equal to its valency, e.g., NaCl-the valency of both sodium and chlorine is 1. In Al_2O_3 the valency of aluminum is 3 and that of oxygen is 2.

Covalent compounds

In covalent compounds it gives the number of **covalent bonds** an element can form. In ammonia NH_3, the valency of hydrogen is 1 and that of nitrogen is 3 and in carbon dioxide, the valency of carbon is 4 and oxygen is 2.

$$O = C = O$$

Carbon dioxide

$$\begin{array}{ccc} & & H \\ & & | \\ & & N \\ & \diagup & | \\ H & & H \end{array}$$

Ammonia

VANADIUM, V

Vanadium was discovered by N.G.Sefstrom in 1830. Its name derives from *Vanadis,* a Scandinavian goddess. Vanadium is a **transition metal**. It is used for making alloys for use in high speed drills and car exhaust valves.

VANADIUM(V) OXIDE

Vanadium(V) oxide is used as the **catalyst** in the **Contact process** for the manufacture of sulphuric acid.

VAPOUR

At its boiling point the particles in a liquid are moving fast enough to escape. When they have escaped they will be great distances apart and there will be little attraction between them; in other words they will have formed a gas. This gas is the vapour of the liquid. When the vapour is cooled it returns to the liquid state. The word vapour is often used instead of the word gas. A vapour is gas that can be compressed into a liquid without cooling.

◄ Gases ►

VINEGAR

The name vinegar is derived from the French; *vinaigre* – *vin* (wine) and *aigre* (sour). Vinegar is about a 5% solution of **ethanoic acid** in water. It was made by allowing wine or cider to oxidise, but nowadays it is almost entirely made by the oxidation of fermented malt liquor which is the liquid that is used to make beer (but it contains no hops).

VOLATILE

Liquids which easily turn to **vapour** are volatile. They have low boiling points. Many organic liquids such as ether are volatile.

VOLTA, ALESSANDRO (1745–1827)

Volta made the first electric **battery** by constructing a pile of copper discs and zinc discs separated by moist pasteboard; this was the first source of a continuous supply of electricity.

VON LIEBIG, JUSTUS (1803–1873)

Von Liebig was the inventor of the familiar **Liebig condenser**. He was also one of the pioneers in the use of artificial **fertilisers**.

VULCANISING

This word is used to describe the hardening of rubber using **sulphur** to make it suitable for use as tyres. The process was discovered by Charles Goodyear (1800–1860).

WASHING SODA, $Na_2CO_3.10H_2O$

Washing soda is hydrated sodium carbonate crystals. It is added to water before washing clothes to soften the water. It removes the calcium ions as insoluble calcium carbonate.

WATER, H_2O

Water is the most abundant compound. It is the best **solvent** and so it never occurs pure in nature.

TYPES OF WATER

Water is found as:

Rain-water

which contains dissolved gases from the air - this is usually carbon dioxide, but if the air is polluted it can contain other gases such as sulphur dioxide

River water

contains different dissolved chemicals depending on where it flows – often river water nowadays contains pollutants such as **fertilisers** and it can also contain sewage and factory waste

Spring water

contains few impurities – as rain water passes through the earth it is slowly filtered to remove solids and bacteria, it contains some dissolved solids

Sea-water

contains a large amount of dissolved substances, including gold; if 100 g of sea-water were evaporated, about 36 g of solids would be left and about 26 g of this residue would be **sodium chloride.**

Mineral water

contains various salts and gases that are said to make them suitable as medicines – there are many famous spas at places such as Bath, Vichy or Wiesbaden, all are renowned for their mineral water.

Water which will form a lather easily with soap is called **soft water** and water which will not lather easily with soap is called **hard water**.

TEST FOR WATER

Water can be detected by using anhydrous copper(II) sulphate which changes from white to blue when water is added. Cobalt(II) chloride paper is often used, it changes from blue to pink when water is added.

PROPERTIES

At normal atmospheric pressure water melts at 0°C and boils at 100°C. If a substance melts and boils at this temperature then it is pure water. Water is a covalent molecular compound.

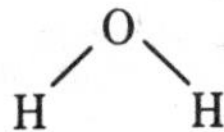

Water reacts vigorously with metals in Group 1 (e.g;. sodium and potassium) and with the metals calcium, strontium and barium in Group 2.

Water does not react with copper, silver and aluminium.

USES

Water is used in the home for cooking, drinking and washing. Water in the form of steam is used to generate electricity. It is used to extract oil, sulphur and sodium chloride from the earth and in the manufacture of ammonia, nitric acid, sodium carbonate and sulphuric acid.

WATER GAS

Water gas, a mixture of carbon monoxide and hydrogen, is made by passing steam over white hot coke; the process is **endothermic**. It is a very good fuel because both products burn. It has been replaced by **North Sea Gas** as a fuel for domestic use because the carbon monoxide in water gas is very poisonous. Water gas is usually made together with **producer gas**.

WATER GLASS, Na_2SiO_3

Water glass is sodium silicate. It is soluble in water. When metal salts are added to sodium silicate solution, fern-like growths of insoluble metal silicates are formed. **Transition metals** form highly coloured silicates and the effect produced is often referred to as a 'chemical garden'.

Uses

Sodium silicate is used both for preserving eggs (the pores on the egg shell become filled with calcium silicate) and as an adhesive.

WATER OF CRYSTALLISATION

Many salts form dry crystals containing molecules of water. This water which does not wet the crystals is known as water of crystallisation. The salts containing water of crystallisation are known as **hydrated salts** or 'hydrates'. Examples of hydrated salts are hydrated copper(II) sulphate $CuSO_45H_2O$ and hydrated magnesium sulphate $MgSO_4.7H_2O$. When these salts are heated gently, they lose their water of crystallisation. Salts containing water of crystallisation cannot be dried by heating them even gently. They have to be dried between pieces of filter paper or blotting paper or in a stream of air.

WATER TREATMENT

◄ Filtration, disinfection, chlorine, ozone ►

WATSON, JAMES DEWEY (1928–)

James Watson, together with Francis Crick, in 1954 managed to work out the structure of DNA (deoxyribose nucleic acid), a substance present in all living cells.

WEAK ACIDS

◄ Acids ►

WEAK ALKALIS

◄ Alkalis ►

WHITEWASH

This is a thick **suspension** of **calcium hydroxide** in **water**. It is used to brush on walls and to make the white lines on sports fields. The water evaporates and the calcium hydroxide slowly absorbs carbon dioxide from the air changing to calcium carbonate.

WOHLER, FRIEDRICH (1800–1882)

Wohler, in 1828, discovered that **urea** which is found in the urine of mammals and birds, could be synthesised from ammonium cyanate. He also discovered the metal, **aluminium**, in 1825, and worked on the theory of **fertilisers** with **von Liebig**.

WROUGHT IRON

If all the carbon is removed from **pig iron**, wrought iron is formed. This is pure iron and it is easily bent. It is mainly used for ornamental ironworks such as gates and scrolls.

XANTHOPHYLL

This is the yellow pigment found in green living vegetation such as grass, nettles and spinach. It becomes more obvious in autumn as the chlorophyll disappears from the leaves.

XENON, Xe

Xenon is one of the **noble gases**. It was discovered in 1898 by Ramsay and Travers. The name xenon is derived from the greek word; *xenos* meaning 'stranger'.

USES

It is used in bulbs for lighthouses because bulbs containing this gas give a very intense light from a small bulb. Xenon prevents the filament of the bulb from vaporising. It is also used in photographic electronic flash units.

XYLENE

This is an organic liquid that is used as a **solvent** for many molecular compounds. It is also used as a solvent for sulphur and the glue 'Evo-stick'.

YEAST

Yeast is used in the manufacture of **ethanol** by a process known as **fermentation**. Yeast contains biological **catalysts** known as **enzymes**. Yeast is also used in bread making.

ZEOLITE

Zeolite is an **ion-exchange** resin used in the softening of water. Zeolite can be considered as sodium aluminium silicate.

Process

When **hard water** passes through the zeolite, calcium ions are exchanged for sodium ions thus softening the water.

sodium aluminium silicate + calcium ions → calcium aluminium silicate + sodium ions

When all the zeolite is used up it can be regenerated by running a concentrated solution of sodium chloride through it and the reverse reaction to that described above takes place. The zeolite is then ready for use again.

Uses

It is frequently used to soften water in the home particularly in dishwashers and washing machines. Synthetic zeolite is also used in purifiers and filters in the water industry.

ZINC, Zn

Zinc was discovered in 1746 by A.S.Marggraf. It is the last element of the **transition metals** but it is not a true transition metal. It is a white, shiny, fairly reactive metal.

Zinc occurs in ores such as zinc blende, ZnS, and calamine, $ZnCO_3$. It is extracted by heating zinc blende in air to form zinc oxide. Zinc oxide is reduced by heating it with carbon. (See Fig. Z.1.)

It can also be made by **electrolysis** of zinc sulphate solution.

Zinc is an amphoteric metal; it reacts with acids to form hydrogen and a salt. This reaction is used in the laboratory for the preparation of **hydrogen**. Zinc is reacted with dilute sulphuric acid using copper(II) sulphate as a **catalyst**.

Zinc also reacts with alkalis to form hydrogen and a salt.

Uses

Zinc is used for galvanising steel to protect it against corrosion, for outer

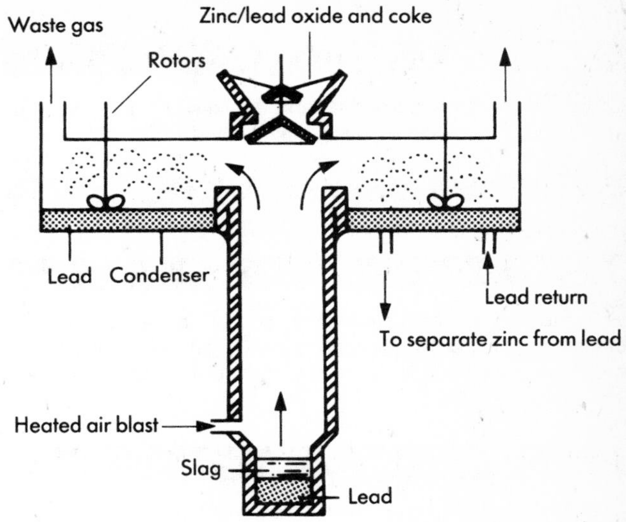

Fig. Z.1 Zinc smelting

casings of batteries and for making **brass**. Brass is an alloy of copper and zinc, the % of zinc varies between 20% and 35%. Zinc castings are common in motor car parts. (See Fig. Z.2.)

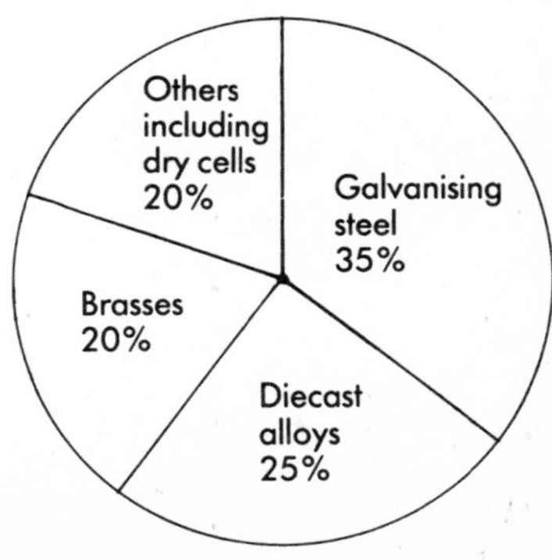

Fig. Z.2 The uses of zinc

ZINC CARBONATE, $ZnCO_3$

Zinc carbonate is the main ingredient in 'calamine lotion' which is used to relieve the discomfort of sunburn and insect bites. The other ingredients in calamine lotion are glycerol, lime-water, water and zinc oxide.

ZINC CHLORIDE, $ZnCl_2$

Zinc chloride dissolves zinc oxide, and the liquid obtained sets to a hard solid which is used in dentistry for filling holes in teeth. Zinc chloride is also used as a flux in soldering. The zinc chloride reacts with, and removes, any metal oxide that forms on the surface of the hot metal producing a clean surface for soldering.

ZINC OXIDE, ZnO

This is used as a white pigment in paints, in various medicines such as ointments, dusting powders and, together with zinc carbonate, in calamine lotion. It is also used in cosmetic powders, creams and white rubbers (erasers).

ZINC SULPHIDE, ZnS

Zinc sulphide is used to make fluorescent paints that are used to coat screens as in the cathode ray tube in television screens.